Operations Analysis in the U.S. Army Eighth Air Force in World War II

Operations Analysis in the U.S. Army Eighth Air Force in World War II

Charles W. McArthur

HISTORY OF MATHEMATICS

Volume 4

AMERICAN MATHEMATICAL SOCIETY
LONDON MATHEMATICAL SOCIETY

1980 *Mathematics Subject Classification* (1985 *Revision*). Primary 01A60.

Library of Congress Cataloging-in-Publication Data

McArthur, Charles W., 1921–
    Operations analysis in the United States Army Eighth Air Force in World War II/Charles
W. McArthur.
        p. cm.—(History of mathematics, ISSN 0899-2428; v. 4)
        ISBN 0-8218-0158-9
        1. World War, 1939–1945—Aerial operations, America.   2. United States.   Army Air
Forces. Air Force, 8th—History.   3. Strategy.   I. Title.   II. Series.
D790.M226   1990   90-829
940.54′4973—dc20   CIP

From *Europe: From Argument to V-E Day, January 1944 to May 1945*, vol. 3 of *The Army Air Forces in World War II*. Copyright ©1951. Reprinted by permission of The University of Chicago Press.

A General's Life, An Autobiography. Copyright ©1983 by the Estate of General of the Army Omar N. Bradley and Clay Blair. Reprinted by permission of Simon & Schuster, Inc.

My Three Years with Eisenhower. Copyright ©1946 by Harry C. Butcher, renewed ©1973 by Harry C. Butcher. Reprinted by permission of Simon & Schuster, Inc.

From *The First and the Last* by Adolf Galland. Copyright 1954, ©1982 by Holt, Rinehart and Winston. Reprinted by permission of Henry Holt and Company, Inc.

From *Brave Men* by Ernie Pyle. Copyright ©1943, 1944 by Scripps-Howard Newspaper Alliance. Copyright ©1944 by Henry Holt and Co., Inc., copyright ©1971, 1972 by Holt, Rinehart and Winston. Reprinted by permission of Henry Holt and Co., Inc.

This book is dedicated
to the two operations analysts I know best,

William Larkin Duren, Jr.,

and

Griffith Baley Price.

Dr. Duren was my mentor and the chairman
of the mathematics department at Tulane University
where I obtained my doctorate.
He and Dr. Price have given me
much inspiration and encouragement
during the writing of this book.

Contents

Foreword

As the clouds of war began to gather over Europe in the mid-1930s, scientists in the United Kingdom began to help with the urgent preparations for defense. Initially they worked on weapons and other military devices, but, as equipment emerged in deployable form, how to use it to best advantage in operations became an urgent question.

In particular, as radar was developed as a means for detecting and tracking aircraft, experiments were undertaken to explore how to use it effectively in cooperation with fighter-plane defenses. During this work the scientists and military men worked closely together; there emerged an effective form of military/scientific cooperation. In the summer of 1938 the scientists gave their part in this work the name operational research.

The success of the early cooperative military/scientific analyses of operating problems led the British Royal Air Force to incorporate operational research sections into its operating units. By the time the United States became involved in the war, these sections were a standard feature of British military operating staffs, and their successful work led British military and scientific leaders to recommend this arrangement to their American counterparts.

By this time, too, American scientists were mobilizing to help with the U.S. war effort, so it was natural for them to respond positively to the concept of helping with operations as well as weapon and device development. The first U.S. operations research group was established by the U.S. Navy, but, as Professor McArthur brings out in this book, the U.S. Army Air Forces were not far behind. Professor W. Barton Leach led this effort; he not only recruited the first operations analysis section and took it to the Eighth Air Force in England, but also later established sections in all of the other AAF commands.

In addition to being the first operations analysis section in the AAF, the one in the Eighth Air Force also became the largest—and arguably the most important. Its successful work—as brought out in this book—helped spread the concept throughout the AAF. Thus, it is particularly interesting and useful to have this comprehensive account of the relations of the Eighth Air

Force section's work to the operations of this important military unit in the European war.

During the two and a half years of existence of the Eighth Air Force section, forty-eight persons with scientific and technical training were involved, representing more than a dozen specialties; mathematicians were the largest subgroup, with fifteen persons, thirteen of whom stayed with the section for six months or more.

All of these specialists were plunged into an unfamiliar context as part of a staff dealing with the phenomena arising from military operations. To the scientists these phenomena were completely new, so a great deal of attention was paid to finding ways to observe them and produce records of the observations that were accurate enough to be a reasonable basis for analysis. Once the observations yielded clues as to what was going on, the analysts could develop theories (or, as operations researchers later came to call them, models) to represent the phenomena. Deductions from these models could then be made the basis for findings and recommendations related to tactics and plans. If tactical changes were adopted, the new operations could be used to check the validity of the theoretical constructs. Thus, the analysts were involved in the usual scientific processes related to their novel environment.

Since the models were relatively simple and made use of standard mathematical and statistical tools, postwar observers have credited much of the success of the work to the high scientific craft skills that the analysts brought to their work. In particular, it should be noted that the mathematicians were functioning, not just in a mathematical role, but as scientists developing theories about actual phenomena and applying them to problems of operations, policy, and plans.

Since the Eighth Air Force's primary mission was bombing, much of the attention of its operations analysis section was paid to the tactics of bombing operations and the results they achieved. While it would be both unfair and inaccurate to attribute improved operating results to any one element in a complicated cooperative situation, it is fair to say that the bombing accuracy analyses were influential in producing tactical changes leading to substantial increases in the efficiency and effectiveness of the bombing operations. For example, in 1942 less than 15 percent of the bombs dropped fell within one thousand feet of the aiming point, but this figure showed steady growth until two years later it was 60 percent.

The wartime knowledge developed by the Eighth Air Force operations analysis section was not lost. To mention just one example, after the war one of the analysts who had been active in this section assembled a comprehensive and systematic account of what had been learned about choosing bombs and fuzes and estimating force requirements. In addition to being used extensively in the Korean war, it became the basis for the U.S. Air Force standard manual on planning and carrying out conventional bombing operations.

By now the influence of the successful operations research work during the war has spread very widely. After the war the U.S. military services established operations research activities as part of their peacetime staffs, and the concept of such work in civilian contexts is now widespread. Indeed, by 1990, operations research activity extended to most of the world: over forty national and international operations research societies adhere to the International Federation of Operational Research Societies, and an international abstracting journal for operations research tracks the literature of thirty-one primary journals in this field and a much larger number of other supplementary and specialist journals. It is difficult to estimate with any precision how many operations research workers are active in the world, but the number is by now in the tens of thousands. Their work has yielded not only a great many new and valuable solutions to operating, policy, and planning problems but also much new and challenging mathematical theory. The operations research work of World War II—of which that of the Eighth Air Force operations analysis section was an important part—planted the seeds from which this large and diverse activity sprang.

Thus, it is particularly valuable to have this conscientious account of how one important segment of the wartime work interacted with the operations that it analyzed. The operations research community is indebted to Professor McArthur for his meticulous effort to set forth a systematic and realistic view of this seminal experience; others will be inspired by this insight into the beginnings of a new science. Too, the fascinating story of this early experience in which scientists faced totally new challenges offers hope that there remain other new frontiers to be explored, to the end that complicated phenomena and problems of society can be brought under the disciplined understandings of science, together with the supporting new mathematical theories that will be needed.

Hugh J. Miser

Preface

As a bombardier in the 493d Bomb Group of the Eighth Air Force in World War II, I was part of the operations that the operational analysts were studying. At that time, I was totally unaware of them. The analysts and I traveled in different circles. Most of them were stationed at Eighth Bomber Command Headquarters at Wycombe Abbey School, High Wycombe, England, about thirty miles northwest of London, whereas I was flying missions to Normandy and Germany from a base near the coast in Suffolk, England. The operational analysts had lots of dealings with lead crews, but I was not part of a lead crew.

As I progressed in my postwar career as a mathematician, I became aware that some of my teachers and older colleagues in mathematics had been operational analysts. The first of these was Dr. William L. Duren, Jr., chairman of the mathematics department at Tulane University, where I obtained a doctorate in mathematics. He had been an operations research man with the Second Air Force. He later became president of the Mathematical Association of America.

The mathematicians who served as operational analysts with the United States Army Eighth Air Force were: Dr. James W. Alexander, Dr. William L. Ayers, Mr. Blair M. Bennett, Dr. Harry C. Carver, Dr. James A. Clarkson, Dr. Robert P. Dilworth, Dr. Ray E. Gilman, Dr. Edwin Hewitt, Dr. Forrest R. Immer, Dr. Ralph D. James, Dr. George W. Mackey, Dr. John W. Odle, Dr. G. Baley Price, Dr. H. P. Robertson, Mr. Frank M. Stewart, Dr. Angus E. Taylor, Dr. W. John Youden, and Dr. J. W. T. Youngs.

In the operational analysis section of the Eighth Air Force, in addition to the eighteen mathematicians (including three who were not analysts), there were nine lawyers, thirteen physicists and engineers, an architect (Bissell Alderman), a newsman (Porter Henry), an economist (Dr. Richard G. Gettell), two business analysts (William J. Pilat and George P. Shettle), and several unclassified people. It was a highly talented group. Several of them later became members of the National Academy of Sciences. One of them, Dr. Richard Gettell, became president of Mount Holyoke College. Another, Dr. Angus E. Taylor, became the university provost, University of California

System. A number of these men held high offices in their professional societies. G. Baley Price, for example, became president of the Mathematical Association of America, and George Mackey became vice-president of the American Mathematical Society. One, John Marshall Harlan, became an associate justice of the United States Supreme Court. Leslie Arps became a founder and senior partner of a powerful law firm with main offices in New York City and branches in several other cities.

The operational analysis section of Eighth Fighter Command began with six analysts: Dr. Alva E. Brandt (mathematician), Dr. Ralph P. Johnson (physicist), Roland W. Larson (electrical engineer), Dr. Horace W. Norton (meteorologist), Theodore Tannenwald, Jr. (lawyer), Dr. Lauriston S. Taylor (physicist). Theodore Tannenwald, Jr., later became chief judge of the United States Tax Court in Washington, D.C. The first chief of this section was the distinguished physicist Lauriston S. Taylor.

I especially thank the following analysts for the use of their unpublished memoirs or their letters: Bissell Alderman, Leslie H. Arps, William L. Duren, Jr., J. Porter Henry, Jr., Edwin Hewitt, G. Baley Price, Theodore Tannenwald, Jr., Angus E. Taylor, and Lauriston S. Taylor.

My wife, Bert (Bertha) Moffit McArthur, was a faithful companion and assistant while I gathered the material for this book and while I wrote it. She helped to edit and proofread each chapter.

The American Mathematical Society has provided strong editorial support for the book. Mary Lane, the director of publication, assigned Caroline B. Tucker to work directly with me. She has worked cheerfully and efficiently.

Finally, Professor Hugh Miser, himself a mathematician and World War II operations analyst, gave the book a thorough reading. His experience as an analyst at the Pentagon gave him the interest and knowledge which, with his insight, enabled him to make many helpful suggestions for improving and enriching the book.

I am deeply grateful to each of them.

Much of the material on which this history is based was found in the archives of the Simpson Historical Research Center at Maxwell Air Force Base, Montgomery, Alabama. I spent six weeks there in the summer of 1981.

This history documents the very large role that mathematicians played in operations research in World War II.

Charles W. McArthur
Tallahassee, Florida
29 January 1990

Introduction

My purpose in writing this history was to document the important role played by civilian analysts in operations research in the United States Eighth Air Force in World War II, especially the mathematicians. Of the forty-seven analysts, eighteen were mathematicians.

Eighteen of the analysts, fifteen of them mathematicians, were teaching university classes when they were persuaded to become operations analysts. These men, most of whom had never been near a military airplane, were soon advising the air force on the dropping of bombs on German factories and the firing of machine guns at the planes of the Luftwaffe.

Their story is told chronologically, beginning in October of 1942 with the arrival of the nucleus of the Operational Research Section in England and ending with the end of hostilities in the spring of 1945. It emphasizes the men themselves rather than the technicalities they struggled with. I was an Eighth Air Force bombardier, not an operations analyst, so I have included a few personal recollections, such as of the time my bomb group leader was shot down near Leipzig.

The book tells how the analysts evaluated the month-by-month strategic bombing of the Eighth Air Force. Recurring themes are visual and radar bombing accuracy, damage assessment of targets, loss and battle damage to the bombers themselves, and radio countermeasures to enemy radar.

Against the backdrop of the recurring activity was the section's work to combat the Luftwaffe, to combat the V-weapons, to prepare for D day and the other bomber attacks on German lines, and to assist in the various campaigns, such as those against aircraft factories, railroads, and oil.

The reader will learn about the history of the strategic air war against Germany in World War II as seen by the pioneer Eighth Air Force and a bombardier.

The Eighth Air Force operational analysts helped the Air Force learn its bombing capabilities so that its future operations could be better planned. Furthermore, they discovered the variables that affected the accuracy of formation bombing, thus enabling the air force to improve its bombing.

Top generals of the Eighth Air Force, Generals H. H. Arnold, Carl Spaatz, Ira C. Eaker, James H. Doolittle, W. E. Kepner, Curtis E. LeMay, and F. L.

Anderson, all wrote letters commending the Eighth Air Force analysts. In particular, two mathematician–operational analysts, Dr. James A. Clarkson and Dr. W. J. Youden, were given the Medal of Freedom, and a third, Dr. Edwin Hewitt, was awarded the Air Medal for flying combat missions. Members of each of the subsections of the operational analysis section were likewise awarded high honors. For example, Bissell Alderman, an architect, was given the Medal of Freedom.

The history of the Eighth Air Force operations analysts and their efforts and achievements is intended to honor these men whose story has not been told before.

1

The Beginning of Operations Analysis in the Eighth Air Force

INTRODUCTION

Operations research as an organized scientific activity with its own professional societies, journals, and academic programs in universities grew out of World War II. Early in the war the Bomber, Fighter, and Coastal Commands of the British Royal Air Force (RAF) began using groups of scientists and other skilled civilians in the application of scientific method to military operations, such as early warning systems, bombing, gunnery, and antisubmarine warfare. The British called this activity operational research. Later, the same activity in the United States Army Air Force (USAAF) was called operations analysis, except in the Eighth Air Force stationed in England where it was called operational research.

Adding groups of civilian analysts to the staffs of commanding generals, to serve as field advisors in the USAAF, was just a small, though very significant, part of the greatest mobilization of science for war up to that time.

THE MOBILIZATION OF SCIENCE IN WORLD WAR II

World War II began on 1 September 1939 when the Germans invaded Poland. Americans were stunned by the quick collapse of most of northern Europe under the German onslaught. Poland was overrun in less than one month. Norway held out for two months. The Netherlands fell in four days and Belgium in eighteen. France signed an armistice on 22 June 1940 after less than six weeks of fighting.

A number of American scientists were deeply concerned that the United States would be drawn into the war, which it would not be prepared to fight because it lacked modern weapons. Four leaders in American science discussed the matter among themselves and enlisted the support of President Roosevelt to improve the situation. They were Vannevar Bush, president of the Carnegie Institution of Washington and an electrical engineer; Karl Taylor Compton, president of Massachusetts Institute of Technology and a physicist; James Bryan Conant, president of Harvard University and a chemist; and Frank Baldwin Jewett, president of the National Academy of Sciences, president of Bell Telephone Laboratories, and an electrical engineer.

Working through Harry Hopkins, advisor to President Roosevelt, Vannevar Bush succeeded in persuading the president of the need to use science to improve weapons. Accordingly, the National Defense Research Committee (NDRC) was created with the approval of President Roosevelt on 27 June 1940, about a year and a half before the United States entered World War II (WWII). The original members of the committee were Dr. Vannevar Bush, chairman; Rear Admiral Harold G. Bowen; Conway Peyton Coe, Commissioner of Patents; Dr. Karl Compton; Dr. James Conant; Dr. Frank Jewett; Brigadier General George V. Strong; and Dr. Richard Chace Tolman, professor of physical chemistry and mathematical physics, California Institute of Technology. Vannevar Bush, chairman, reported directly to President Roosevelt as his science advisor.

On 28 June 1941, a year and a day after the creation of the NDRC, the Office of Scientific Research and Development (OSRD) was created. It included the old NDRC, with James Conant as chairman, and the new Committee on Medical Research. Vannevar Bush, as overall director of the enlarged organization, still reported to the president. The OSRD had broad powers to aid and supplement the experimental and research activities of the War and Navy Departments, and to conduct research for "the creation and improvement of instrumentalities, methods, and materials of warfare." However, it did not do research and development directly. The research and development were done by contract with universities and industrial institutions. It was organized as the National Science Foundation is today. (Indeed, the National Science Foundation was created after the war on Vannevar Bush's recommendation to the president.) The NDRC grew, as needs dictated, to nineteen divisions, two panels, and three committees. For example, there were divisions for: ballistics research, special projectiles, subsurface warfare, fire control, and radar. An applied mathematics panel, with mathematician Warren Weaver as chief and Thornton C. Fry as deputy chief, existed from 9 December 1942 to 5 April 1946. It was established to help the NDRC divisions and the armed forces handle mathematics-related problems, such as air-to-air gunnery. [1]

THE BEGINNING OF OPERATIONS ANALYSIS IN THE UNITED STATES ARMED FORCES

The NDRC played an important role in starting operations research (OR) in the United States armed forces and in nurturing and promoting it until the end of the war.

The secretary of war under Roosevelt during the war years was Henry L. Stimson. His role in ensuring effective cooperation between civilian scientists and the huge organization over which he presided was great. The following extract from "Operations Analysis, Headquarters, Army Air Forces, December, 1942–June, 1950" tells of the part Secretary Stimson and Vannevar Bush played in the origin of operations analysis in the USAAF:

> In the early spring of 1942, Secretary of War Stimson and his Special Assistant, Mr. Harvey H. Bundy, went to the Canal Zone for an on-the-spot investigation of the Canal defenses. In conversations with Major General Andrews, it was concluded that a group of analytically minded civilians, some scientific and technical, with no operational or administrative duties, would be of great assistance in solving the unusual and insistent problems of planning and tactics involved in the defense of the Canal. (The immediate need at Panama was met by appointing Dr. C. M. Jansky, Jr., as a Special Consultant in the Office of the Director of Air Defense, under Colonel Gordon P. Saville. Dr. Jansky sent several men to Panama, notably Mr. Parker and Mr. Tevis, electrical engineers who performed a most valuable service in coordinating the then little known radar equipment into the defenses of the Canal.)
>
> On his return to Washington, Mr. Bundy discussed this matter with Dr. Vannevar Bush of the Office of Scientific Research and Development and found that an activity along these general lines had been conducted for some time in the Royal Air Force under the title of Operational Research. Bundy, as a lawyer, thought naturally in terms of the type of advice on policy matters habitually rendered by a corporation's general counsel. Bush, as a scientist, thought in terms of the type of advice rendered by a director of research. Combining these ideas, they agreed upon an investigation into the matter to be conducted by a lawyer and a scientist. Bush nominated as the scientific partner Dr. Ward S. Davidson, Director of Research at Consolidated Edison. Bundy nominated as the legal partner Major W. B. Leach, a professor at Harvard Law School.
>
> The two got to work on July 7, under a directive from the Joint Committee on New Weapons and Equipment, Joint Chiefs of Staff, of which Dr. Bush was Chairman. During the next six weeks, Leach and Davidson collected information on the RAF system, scoured the War and Navy Departments for activities in the nature of Operational Research (and found a surprising number of close relatives in odd corners) and put their heads together to concoct a workable system for fitting such an organizational oddity as a civilian staff section into Army and Navy regulations and admin-

istrative procedure. About August 15, they submitted a report.

The report was placed in the hands of the Joint Chiefs of Staff, but of these only General Arnold appears to have given it serious consideration. Doubtless impressed by the fact that General Spaatz, then Commanding General of the Eighth Air Force, had requested an operational research section on the RAF model, General Arnold turned the whole problem over to his Advisory Council for study and recommendation. [2]

The advisory council, in consultation with Leach, drafted a letter that General Arnold sent to all commanding generals of air force commands on 24 October 1942. The letter recommended that they include in their staffs "groups of highly qualified civilians, having unusual scientific or analytical attainments, for Operations Analysis (OA), that is, the study of operations within a command for the purpose of improving tactics, equipment, methods of training and methods of supply." Thus, operations analysis was authorized throughout the USAAF.

The Leach-Davidson report contains a section titled "Summary of Existing Projects of Civilian Analysis." With respect to the British experience, it states:

> Operational research is a vital and growing activity in England and with the British Forces. It began as an activity in the RAF and has also extended into other commands until the total personnel numbers approximately 500 and further growth is determined more by the availability of suitable personnel than by any other factor. [3]

The report contains a chart of operations research administration in Great Britain in July 1942. Fighter Command had an operations research group of forty skilled and twenty-five semiskilled people. Bomber Command had nineteen skilled and an unlisted number of semiskilled people. [4] Coastal Command had eleven skilled and three semiskilled people. The chart sheds no light on the composition of these groups. However, in the preface to his book *O. R. in World War 2, Operational Research against the U-boat*, Professor C. H. Waddington says of operational research personnel at Coastal Command:

> The anti-U-boat O. R. effort can claim ... two Nobel Prize winners (Blackett and Kendrew), five fellows of the Royal Society (Blackett, Kendrew, Williams, Waddington, Robertson) and a Fellow of the National Academy of Australia (Rendel).... The oldest of the influential ORS workers at Coastal was Blackett, who was about forty-five at that time; most of the rest were in their thirties or even twenties. [5]

Waddington's preface also lists other workers.

The Leach-Davidson report tells of four operations analysis-type groups already existing in the United States military forces—two in the navy, one in the army air force, and one in the army. The first of these was the Mine-Warfare Operational Research Group (MORG) in the Bureau of Ordnance of the navy:

> This group is under the supervision of Commander L. W. Mc-Keehan (Underwater Ordnance Research). Its roots go back to the magnetic-mine scare of 1940 when the Bureau of Ordnance brought in some civilian scientists; the group has been functioning informally since January, 1942, and on a permanent basis since June. Dr. Francis Bitter, Research Professor of Physics at Massachusetts Institute of Technology, is in active charge of the group. He has assembled a group of about 20 men, of whom 16 are physicists and mathematicians, 3 are other scientists, and 1 is an economist. [6]

The second American group was the Operational Research Group on Anti-submarine Warfare (ORG-ASN) of the navy:

> This group (ORG-ASW) is under the supervision of Captain W. D. Baker, head of the Anti-Submarine Warfare Unit at Cominch (Commander-in-Chief). It has men stationed with Commander Lewis, ASW officer for the Atlantic Fleet, with Commander Hungerford, ASW officer for the Eastern Sea Frontier, and with the operations officers at Miami and San Juan. This group has been operating since April, 1942. Dr. Philip Morse, Professor of Physics at Massachusetts Institute of Technology and member of NDRC Section C-4 supervises the group on a part-time basis. Dr. William Shockley, formerly with the Bell Telephone Laboratories, is the executive head. The personnel numbers 16, divided about equally between mathematicians and physicists. [7]

The third group was in the Canal Zone under Colonel Saville, headed by Mr. C. M. Jansky, Jr. The fourth unit was the Technical Research Group on Radar-Signal Corps, Directorate of Planning:

> This group reports to Colonel Meade, Director of Planning, Army Signal Corps, and to Major Fell of the Radar Division in this Directorate. It deals with engineering problems in the development and use of radar equipment and with the training and selection of personnel to operate the same. Dr. William L. Everitt, Professor of Electrical Engineering at Ohio State University, a consulting engineer, started organizing the group in March, 1942. [8]

It is clear that the U.S. Navy established the first Operations Research Groups (ORG) in the armed forces. The antisubmarine group led by the physicists Morse and Shockley is especially noteworthy for its contributions during WWII and its role in the origins of scientific operations research. Both Morse and Shockley became members of the National Academy of Sciences, and Shockley, a Nobel Prize winner. Philip Morse later became the first president (1952–1953) of the Operations Research Society of America.

An Operational Research Section Is Established in the Eighth Air Force [9]

In October 1942 the Eighth Bomber Command and the Eighth Fighter Command of the United States Air Force were in Great Britain. The Eighth Bomber Command was composed of the First, Second, and Third Bombardment Wings, which each had groups below them. The groups were the operating units, each assigned to an airfield. Later, the bombardment wings were changed to air divisions with combat wings, usually composed of three groups, under them.

In January 1944 the Eighth Bomber Command became the Eighth Air Force, commanded by General James H. Doolittle, who controlled the Eighth Fighter Command, three heavy bombardment air divisions of the former Eighth Bomber Command, and a service command. General Spaatz became commanding general of the United States Strategic Air Forces in Europe, which included the new Eighth Air Force and the Fifteenth Air Force based in Italy.

In the early spring of 1942, Brigadier General Ira C. Eaker, the first commanding general of the Eighth Bomber Command, asked that his headquarters be located within twenty miles of the RAF Bomber Command headquarters just north of High Wycombe, about thirty miles from London. Acceptable accommodations were found at Wycombe Abbey, one of England's top schools for young ladies. Despite angry letters to the *Times*, the first were pushed out, and General Eaker and his staff moved in. General Eaker's proximity to Air Marshal Sir Arthur Harris's headquarters made him aware of the work of the Operational Research Section at RAF Bomber Command.

In April 1942 General Eaker recommended to General Spaatz, commanding general of the Eighth Air Force, that an operational research program be established at his headquarters at Wycombe Abbey. In a letter to General Arnold, General Spaatz requested an operational research section of fifteen analysts. Immediately after the Leach-Davidson report was filed on 1 September 1942, Leach was designated project officer to form the section. Davidson and Leach felt that fifteen analysts were too many to start with, so they recommended an initial section of six. During September and early October, they recruited Dr. James Alexander, mathematician from the Institute of Advanced Study at Princeton; Leslie H. Arps and John M. Harlan, New York lawyers from the firm of Root, Ballantine, Harlan, Bushby, and Palmer: Dr. H. P. Robertson, a physicist from Princeton University; Dr. W. Norris

Tuttle, director of research at General Radio Company; Dr. W. J. Youden, biochemist and statistician; Boyce Thompson, Plant Research Institute. John M. Harlan was appointed chief of this first operations analysis section of the Eighth Air Force.

These operations analysts were men of exceptional ability. Two of them, physicist W. Norris Tuttle and mathematical physicist H. P. Robertson, had served in important positions with the NDRC. Dr. Robertson and Dr. Alexander would soon be members of the National Academy of Sciences. Although W. J. Youden's doctorate was in chemistry, he had spent a year at the Rothamsted Experiment Station with the British statistician R. A. Fisher before the war, so it was natural for him to return to statistical work when he reported to England as part of the first OR group from the United States. After the war Youden became one of the leaders in the field of design of experiments. The chief of the section, John Marshall Harlan, later became an associate justice of the United States Supreme Court. James Alexander, at fifty-four, was the oldest of the group. The others ranged in age from thirty-nine to forty-three. These men were older than later analysts who were in their twenties and thirties.

The new section reported personally to General Eaker on 22 October 1942. It was attached to General Eaker's staff at the Eighth Bomber Command headquarters and quartered on the grounds of Wycombe Abbey, about six miles from British Bomber Command. Dr. B. G. Dickens, chief of the ORS at British Bomber Command, spared no effort to help the new American section. Throughout the war, both sections worked closely, freely exchanging valuable information. [10]

The interest of Vannevar Bush and the Office of Scientific Research and Development (OSRD) in providing operations research services to the American armed forces is shown above by the 'loan' of two top consultants, Tuttle and Robertson, to help make up the team of six operations analysts in the field. A basic source of information on the deep interest and involvement of the OSRD in promoting civilian operations research in WWII is told by James Phinney Baxter III. [11] His chapter, "Operations Research and Field Service," begins with an insightful quotation from Isaac Newton: "If instead of sending the observations of seamen to able mathematicians at land, the land would send mathematicians to sea, it would signify much more to the improvement of navigation and safety of men's lives and estates upon that element." By midsummer 1943 the OSRD had sent hundreds of scientific consultants to the American and British military.

As the war progressed, the need for scientists and engineers to help the army and navy effectively use their weapons increased. The demand led Bush to create a major new subdivision of the OSRD, the Office of Field Service, on 15 October 1943. Dr. Karl T. Compton, president of Massachusetts Institute of Technology and member of the NDRC, was chief, and Dr. Alan T. Waterman, professor of physics at Yale and also in the NDRC, was made deputy chief. In a memorandum dated 14 August 1943, Bush stated:

> Experience has shown that successful use of such personnel...
> requires, (a) that the officer to whom they are detailed definitely
> wants them; (b) that they be allowed access to such information as
> they may need for their work (c) that they be allowed reasonable
> freedom as to the way in which they do their work; (d) that they
> be responsible to the Commanding Officer and make their reports
> and recommendations to him, distribution of such reports within
> and beyond the Command to be subject to his approval.

Furthermore, these operations analysts retained civilian status so they
might talk freely to both the commanding general and the lowest GI, and
so they might be moved more easily if desired. These principles were stated
in the Leach-Davidson report a year earlier. By this time they had been field
tested.

OPERATIONS ANALYSIS
AND THE COMBINED BOMBER OFFENSIVE [12]

By the end of December 1942 the headquarters of Operations Analysis for
the USAAF had been established and was headed by Major (later Colonel)
W. B. Leach. It was part of Air Staff Management Control in Washington,
D.C. Major Leach's immediate superior in the military chain of command
was Colonel (later General) Byron E. Gates, assistant chief of management
control. During December Operations Analysis planned strategic bombing
for the USAAF.

The United States in WWII had the Norden bombsight and two excellent
four-engine bombers—the B-17 and the B-24. With this equipment, visual
precision bombing was possible from an altitude of twenty-five thousand
feet. The Army Air Corps, through activities started in 1932 at the Air Corps
Tactical School at Maxwell Field in Alabama, by General Muir S. Fairchild,
developed the concept of strategic bombing. This concept was that the industrial structure of every nation, if properly analyzed, reveals weaknesses
and bottlenecks. Therefore, targets chosen to exploit these areas should be
attacked with precision to achieve maximum destruction. Amateur strategists could list industries vital during WWII to a nation such as Germany.
Such a list, however, would be of little value to the military planner unless
the industries were reasonable military objectives which might be successfully
attacked with the forces available. Detailed, quantitative information about
German industries, of their suitability as targets, and their vulnerable points,
could only be supplied by experts.

By November 1942 General Fairchild had become the air force member
of the Joint Strategic Survey Committee. The job of this committee was

to make strategy recommendations to the U.S. Joint Chiefs of Staff. After preliminary conferences and drafts by General Fairchild, Colonel Gates, and his assistant, Colonel Guido R. Perera, [13] General Arnold issued a directive to Colonel Gates on 8 December 1942:

> You are directed to have the group of operational analysts under your jurisdiction prepare and submit to me a report analyzing the rate of progressive deterioration that should be anticipated in the German war effort as a result of the increasing air operations we are prepared to employ against its sustaining sources. This study should result in as accurate an estimate as can be arrived at as to the date when this deterioration will have progressed to a point to permit a successful invasion of Europe. [14]

In response, a committee was formed, first called the Advisory Committee on Bombardment, but later called the Committee of Operations Analysts (COA). Military members of the committee were Colonel Byron E. Gates, assistant chief of Air Staff, Management Control, chairman; Colonel Guido R. Perera, Management Control deputy, *de facto* chairman and former lawyer; Brigadier General Edgar P. Sorenson, office of the assistant chief of Air Staff, Intelligence; Lt. Col. Malcolm N. Moss, Air Intelligence, Target Information Section; Lt. Col. Joseph W. Clark, Management Control; Lt. Col. Thomas G. Lanphier, Air Unit, Military Intelligence, War Department, General Staff; Major W. Barton Leach, Operations Analysis Unit, Management Control, former professor, Harvard Law School; and Captain Arthur W. Wood, Management Control. Civilian members of the committee were Dr. Edward S. Mason, Office of Strategic Services and economics professor at Harvard University; Dr. Edward M. Earle, Institute for Advanced Study at Princeton; Mr. Elihu Root, Jr., lawyer, director of American Telegraph Company, and director of Carnegie Foundation; Mr. Fowler Hamilton, chief of the Enemy Branch of the Board of Economic Warfare, former antitrust lawyer in the Department of Justice and later the first chief of the Operations Analysis Section of the USAAF in the India-Burma theater; Mr. Noel Hall, British Ministry of Economic Warfare; and Thomas W. Lamont, senior officer of the J. P. Morgan Company. This was really a steering committee for a small army of analysts.

COA subcommittees were established, one for each of the following industries: petroleum, aircraft production, electric power, transportation, electric equipment, rubber, chemicals, overall Axis economy, coke, nonferrous metals, machine tools and precision instruments, food, motor vehicles, iron and steel, and submarines. Each of these subcommittees had its own expert advisors.

One of the original intentions of the COA was not only to inform the military of the economic validity of a given system of strategic air attacks, but also to calculate approximate size of the force required to accomplish its mission. Thus, to estimate the number and size of bombs required to destroy targets, a subcommittee on probabilities and force was formed on 14 December 1942. It consisted of General Edgar P. Sorenson, chairman; Colonel C. G. Williamson, Directorate of Bombardment; Lt. Col. C. B. Thornton, director of Statistical Control; Major R. E. Foss, A-2; Mr. G. B Dantzig, Office of Director of Statistical Control; Mr. Elihu Root, Jr.; Mr. D. B. Dyer, statistical analyst, A-2; Dr. Heinike, Eglin Field. As a result of a conference with Dr. Vannevar Bush, Dr. John E. Burchard of the OSRD was added to the Probabilities and Force Committee. Dr. Burchard was an architectural engineer from Massachusetts Institute of Technology, and chief of Division Two, Structural Defense and Offense, OSRD. Division Two determined the best means of destroying enemy defenses and industrial targets.

Mathematicians, statisticians, computer scientists, and operations researchers should recognize the name of G. B. Dantzig on the Probabilities and Force Committee. Shortly after the war, Mr. Dantzig completed his doctorate in mathematics at the University of California at Berkeley. He became professor of computer science and operations research at Stanford University and is a member of the National Academy of Sciences and has received the National Medal of Science. Mr. D. B. Dyer, statistical analyst, became a member and eventually chief of the Operations Analysis Section of the Twentieth Bomber Command in the Pacific.

Although the COA had only been organized in the first two weeks of December 1942, its report was needed for the January 1943 Casablanca Conference between President Roosevelt and Prime Minister Churchill. As it was impossible for the COA to complete a full report in time for the Casablanca Conference, two interim reports were submitted, one on bombardment objectives in Axis Europe (Germany, Italy, and their allies), and another on the Western Axis oil industry. The oil memorandum, prepared by the petroleum committee chaired by Mr. Fowler Hamilton, recommended the destruction of twenty-eight German synthetic oil plants plus the oil refineries at Ploesti, Romania. The interim report concluded:

> It is clear that it is better to use a high degree of destruction in a few really essential industries or services than to cause a small degree of destruction in many industries.
>
> It is clear that results are cumulative and that a master plan, once adopted, should be adhered to with relentless determination.
>
> It is clear that our day operations and the night bombing of the Royal Air Force should be correlated so that both may be applied to the same system of targets, each at the point where it is most effective.
>
> It is already clear that with the force available during 1943, concentrated on the right targets, very grave injury can be done to

the Western Axis economic system.

There are substantial grounds for hoping that the study now in hand, if pressed further, may indicate that this injury will critically impair the military strength of the Western Axis. [15]

At the beginning of the war in Europe, RAF Bomber Command attempted daylight attacks on German military targets. However, losses of bombers to German fighters had sometimes reached 50 percent, so daylight raids were abandoned. Instead, Bomber Command shifted to night bombing of industrial cities, known as area bombing.

The USAAF made its first daylight strikes against German-occupied Europe in the summer of 1942. The Americans believed strongly in daylight precision bombing or selective bombing and refused to participate in an Allied night bombing campaign. At the Casablanca Conference the role of the air forces in the war against the Western Axis was defined:

> To conduct a joint U.S.-British air offensive to accomplish the progressive destruction and dislocation of the German industrial and economic systems and the weakening of the morale of the German people to a point where their capacity for armed resistance is fatally reduced. [16]

At Casablanca the decision was made for the Americans to bomb the Romanian oil refineries at Ploesti in a daring daylight raid of B-24s flying from Bengazi, North Africa, and over the target at an altitude of one thousand feet. [17]

The COA's final report on Western Axis industrial systems was approved by General Arnold on 25 March 1943. (Subsequently, separate reports were prepared by the COA on Italy and the Far East.) The report consisted of a general statement and appraisals of each industrial target system. Priority established by the committee was:

1. fighter aircraft
2. ball bearings
3. petroleum
4. abrasives
5. non-ferrous metals
6. rubber and tires
7. submarine construction yards and bases
8. military transport vehicles
9. transportation
10. coking plants
11. iron and steel
12. machine tools
13. electric power
14. electrical equipment
15. optical precision instruments
16. chemicals
17. food
18. nitrogen
19. antiaircraft and antitank artillery [18]

In Great Britain the report was reviewed by a committee of representatives of the Eighth Air Force, the Royal Air Force, the Air Ministry, and the Ministry of Economic Warfare, which formulated a plan for the strategic bombardment of the Western Axis based on the COA report. General Eaker presented the plan to the Combined Chiefs of Staff in Washington who approved it on 18 May 1943. The approved plan, the Combined Bomber Offensive, became the authorized method of fulfilling the mission of air power defined in the Casablanca directive.

Sir Charles Portal, chief of Air Staff of the Royal Air Force, had this to say about the plan:

> As you know, the Eighth Air Force has been engaged with the Air Staff in drawing up a detailed plan for the purpose of discharging the responsibilities laid upon our combined bomber forces at the Casablanca conference.
>
> The plan is now complete. It is based on our combined resources in the matter of intelligence and operational data including the very valuable report of your Operations Analysts and has been drawn up in close consultation with the Ministry of Economic Warfare.
>
> I have carefully examined the plan and discussed it in all its aspects with the Commanding General, Eighth Air Force. I take this opportunity of saying that I believe it to be entirely sound and that it has my full support.
>
> For all these reasons, I earnestly hope that every effort will be made to achieve and if possible to exceed the program.
>
> The plan has been carefully examined by the Commander in Chief, Bomber Command, and he too is convinced of its soundness and importance. [19]

The effectiveness and appropriateness of the strategic bombing of Germany has been questioned and debated both militarily and morally since WWII. The British point of view may be found in Noble Frankland's book, *Bomber Offensive, the Devastation of Europe* [20]. The German Luftwaffe played a major role in preventing the plan from being implemented as intended in 1943. The British switched to night bombing in the first place because losses inflicted on them by the Luftwaffe in daylight raids were intolerable. RAF night bombing, at first, was so inaccurate that selective bombing seemed impossible. Cities, not buildings, became the primary targets. The adoption of the Combined Bomber Offensive (CBO) plan in May 1943 did not alter Great Britain's preference for night area bombing. British Bomber Command under Air Marshal Sir Arthur Harris continued, expanded, and perfected night bombing of German industrial cities, including Hamburg in August 1943. The Americans, however, attempted to adhere to the plan with selective daylight bombing. They learned that, though their bomber formations were heavily armed, they could not penetrate Germany deeply without fighter escort. Unfortunately, British and American fighters did not have the needed range. As late as August and October 1943 the Americans sustained severe losses of men and bombers in unescorted daylight strikes against the ball bearing factories at Schweinfurt. In the 14 October strike against Schweinfurt, the Americans lost sixty of 291 B-17s over enemy territory, five others were abandoned when the crews parachuted over England, and seventeen sustained damage beyond repair. [21] In December the P-51 Mustang fighter, fitted with jettisonable auxiliary fuel tanks, became operational in the Eighth Air Force. The Mustangs could escort the bombers as far as Berlin, enabling daylight offensive and selective bombing to continue.

Despite the combination of British area bombing and American selective bombing, German armament production continued to rise until July 1944. American daylight bombing in the first half of 1944 became a major factor in winning command of the air, not by bombing the places where German planes were produced, but by luring the German fighters into battle. The Germans could replace their planes, but they could not replace their pilots. Their supply of experienced pilots steadily declined.

From May to December 1944 the Eighth and Fifteenth Air Forces and Bomber Command launched a systematic attack on Germany's oil industry. General Adolf Galland of the Luftwaffe Fighter Arm, made this evaluation:

> The most successful operation of the entire Allied strategical air warfare was against the German fuel supply. This was actually the fatal blow for the Luftwaffe. Looking back it is difficult to understand why the Allies started this undertaking so late, after they had suffered such heavy losses in other operations. Right from the start fuel had been the most awkward bottleneck for the German conduct of the War ... .
>
> Again, the operation was based on a detailed plan worked out by specialists, and included 80 different targets of the fuel industry concentrated in the Ruhr, in Silesia, and in the Ploesti area ... .
>
> The raids of the Allied air fleets on the German Petrol supply installations was the most important of the combined factors which brought about the collapse of Germany. The enemy was surprised by the results.
>
> Only after the invasion did the Allies realize the true strategical importance of the German synthetic oil plants. They were now given top priority on the list of targets. [22]

Thus, the Combined Bomber Offensive applied to the oil industry literally caused the German war machine to run out of gas.

Albert Speer, minister for armaments and munitions in Germany, in charge of all war production, has been quoted by both sides of the debate on the effectiveness of the CBO. He discussed how his side narrowly missed catastrophe in the Combined Bomber Offensive against ball bearings. According to

Speer, ball bearings had become a bottleneck in German armament production. Destruction of five or six relatively small targets at Schweinfurt, Berlin-Erkner, Cannstatt, and Steyr would have paralyzed production of thousands of armament plants. The American raid against Schweinfurt on 17 August 1943 reduced production by 38 percent, forcing the Germans to use up reserves stored by their armed forces. Before the second American raid against Schweinfurt two months later, Germany had time to repair the plant. The second raid, however, reduced ball bearing production by 67 percent. The Berlin-Erkner plant was bombed on 23 December 1943. The whole set of targets (Schweinfurt, Berlin-Erkner, Canstatt, Speyr) was bombed in February and March 1944, reducing production to 29 percent of what it had been before the raids. Then in April the Allied raids on the ball bearing industry ceased abruptly. According to Speer, "the Allies threw away success when it was already in their hands." Speer pointed out that, contrary to Allied beliefs, the Germans had not been able to disperse the ball bearing industry as late as August 1944. [23]

On 1 December 1944 Speer told his colleagues at an armament conference that the enemy was following a wise plan of air raids on the German economy. Furthermore, Germany was fortunate that the Allies had only implemented the plan six to nine months earlier. [24] At the time of the conference, Speer later explained, he did not know that the essential concept had been articulated two years earlier on December 9, 1942. Speer's judgment of the CBO was that "the idea was correct, the execution was defective."

In 1945 distinguished American Elihu Root, Jr. was awarded the highest civilian decoration, the Medal for Merit, for his work on the Committee of Operations Analysts. In a letter to Guido Perera, another key member of the committee, he illuminated the work of the committee, its problems, and achievements:

> May 16, 1946.
>
> Col. Guido R. Perera,
> 12 West Cedar Street,
> Boston, Mass.
>
> Dear Guido:
>   Here is the group photograph taken at the presentation of the Medal for Merit.
>   There should have been four medals or none for if four men ever worked in complete and unstratified equality you and Bart [Leach] and Fowler [Hamilton] and I did during our years on the steering committee of the COA.
>   We were given a strange job late in '42—to determine where, within the operating possibilities, bombing would most cripple the

supporting enemy economy. Nobody had ever really tackled that job before. You will remember that on our first trip to England we found to our surprise that while the British had studied the vulnerability of individual plants they had not really considered economic systems of targets. There weren't any rules. There wasn't any preexisting body of doctrine to guide us. We had to start from scratch, and the problem was of major importance. The enemy economy was too large—thousands of times too large—to blast it all. We had to choose vital points where small physical damage would cause great industrial disruption. We had to choose things which would give results within the time limit set, and we had to choose things which were within the operating possibilities. If the choice had not been well made the treasure and effort that went into building the strategic air force and the blood that was shed in operating it would have been wasted.

I think on the whole the job was well done. We made mistakes. In a new field we were bound to make some mistakes. But we developed early a sound philosophy. Certainly we very early came to the sense which the British had not yet come to, that it was better to destroy a great deal of a few things than a little of a great many. We came to the sense that the program should be simple and concentrated and that once laid down it should be adhered to with grim determination and pressed forward with inexorable energy, because there was bound to be a race between destruction on the one hand and repair and evasion on the other. Those doctrines became standard doctrines through the air corps and even the language of the early reports got into the air corps terminology and conditioned people's thinking in Washington and in the field. There was some scattering of effort—a good deal of it. The weather caused some of it and the importunities of enthusiasts overseas caused some of it. But the air corps never lost sight of the fundamentals so that when the attacks on synthetic oil were delivered they afforded an almost perfect example of timing, concentration, rapidity and follow up, and wrecked the enemy's program. And let me say that they also furnished an example of the effect of holding one's fire until the time is ripe, and refusing to start an attack before it can be made effective or to give the enemy advance notice to begin the maneuvers of dispersal and concealment. I think the operations relating to the attack in the Pacific went more smoothly and rapidly, and were technically better than the operations relating to the attack on Germany. Before the end we had gone a long ways toward learning the new art.

A small army of people helped in the work—the FEA, the OSS [Office of Strategic Services], Ground Intelligence, Air Intelligence,

Naval Intelligence, the British economic warfare section and many
others had a hand in it. But you, Guido—and Bart and Fowler—
saw the venture born and gave it always first claim and were still
standing by at the final wind-up. You were its mainspring and an-
imating spirit. I hope you take from it a sense of accomplishment.
I for one am sure that you shortened the war and saved God knows
how much in life and treasure.
Elihu Root, Jr. [25]

The achievements made in operations analysis, or operations research,
owe much to prior British experience in this field. Fortunately, excellent
bibliographies of the relevant literature are given in three overview articles
and a book for anyone who would like to explore further. [26]

REFERENCES

1. Irvin Stewart, *Organizing Scientific Research for War* (Boston: Atlantic Little, Brown, 1948).

2. "Operations Analysis, Headquarters, Army Air Forces, December, 1942–
June, 1950," 143, 504, Archives, Simpson Historical Research Center, Maxwell Air
Force Base, Alabama.

3. "Summary Report on Operations Analysis by Major W. B. Leach and Dr.
Ward S. Davidson," 1 September 1942, 160.811121-1, Archives, Simpson Historical
Research Center, Maxwell Air Force Base, Alabama.

4. Ibid., 18.

5. C. H. Waddington, *O. R. in World War 2, Operational Research against the
U–boat* (London: Elck Science, 1973).

6. "Summary Report on Operations Analysis," 7.

7. Ibid., 7–8. Morse gives a recent account of this work in an autobiography,
"The Beginnings of Operations Research in the United States," *Operations Research* **34**
(1986), 10–17. Morse also tells of his operations work in WWII in his autobiography,
In at the Beginnings: A Physicist's Life, (Cambridge, Massachusetts, and London,
England, MIT Press, 1977, 172–212.

8. Ibid., 9.

9. "Eighth Air Force, History of Operations Analysis Section, October, 1942–
June, 1945," Leslie H. Arps, 520.303-3, Archives, Simpson Historical Research Center, Maxwell Air Force Base, Alabama. This is an excellent, very readable history
covering the whole life of the section.

10. Headquarters, Eighth Air Force, "The Operational Research Section at the
Eighth Air Force, 20 March 1943–17 July 1944," John M. Harlan, 520.303-1, Archives, Simpson Historical Research Center, Maxwell Air Force Base, Alabama. This
gives the history of the beginnings of the section and contains some valuable documents of the early history and mission of the section.

11. James Phinney Baxter III, *Scientists against Time* (Boston: Atlantic Little,
Brown, 1946).

12. "History of the Organization and Operations of the Committee of Operations Analysts, 1942–1944," Guido P. Perera, 118:01, Archives, Simpson Historical
Research Center, Maxwell Air Force Base, Alabama. This is the basic source for this
section.

13. "Memoirs, Washington and War Years, 1936–1960," Guido R. Perera, 1973,

168.7042, Archives, Simpson Historical Research Center, Maxwell Air Force Base, Alabama. In the memoirs, Colonel Perera tells of his work on the Committee of Operations Analysts and also his work for the Strategic Bombing Survey.

14. "History of the Organization," 6.

15. Ibid., 16.

16. Ibid., 46.

17. James Dugan and Carroll Stewart, *Ploesti, the Great Ground-Air Battle of August 1, 1943* (New York: Random House, 1962).

18. "History of the Organization," 44.

19. Ibid., 45.

20. Noble Frankland, *Bomber Offensive, the Devastation of Europe* (New York: Ballantine, 1970).

21. Thomas Parrish and S. L. A. Marshall, eds., *The Simon and Schuster Encyclopedia of World War II* (New York, 1978).

22. Adolf Galland, *The First and the Last* (Bantam, 1978).

23. Albert Speer, *Inside the Third Reich* (New York: Collier, 1971).

24. Ibid.

25. "Memoirs, Washington and War Years."

26. For three articles and a book that were not referred to in chapter one but contain excellent bibliographies see the following:

McCloskey, Joseph F. (1987), "The beginnings of operations research, 1934–1941," *Operations Research* 35, 143–151.

McCloskey, Joseph F. (1987), "U.S. Operations Research in World War II," *Operations Research*, **35**, 453–470.

McCloskey, Joseph F. (1987), "U.S. Operations Research in World War II," *Operations Research*, **35**, 910–925.

Air ministry (1963), *The Origins and Development of Operational Research in the Royal Air Force*, Her Majesty's Stationery Office, London, 238 pp.

2

The Pioneer Operations Research Section Organizes
October–December 1942

General Eaker Issues Directives to the New ORS

The original six members of the first Operations Research Section arrived in Great Britain on 15 October 1942. At that time the Eighth Air Force, under the command of General Spaatz, consisted of the Eighth Bomber Command under General Eaker, and the Eighth Fighter Command under General Frank O. Hunter. Each of these organizations had headquarters in a different place, close to London, and close to its RAF counterpart. Eighth Air Force headquarters was in southwest London, Eighth Bomber Command headquarters was at High Wycombe, and Eighth Fighter Command headquarters at Bushey Hall near Watford. The only attacks on the Germans by the Eighth Air Force at that time were by the bombers of the Eighth Bomber Command. After consultations with General Spaatz and General Eaker, the ORS was attached to General Eaker's headquarters at High Wycombe. (In December, General Eaker became commander of the Eighth Air Force, replacing General Spaatz, who went to Africa in November.) The members of the section reported for duty at High Wycombe on 22 October 1942.[1] On 23 October General Eaker issued two directives concerning the section. The first, to the commanding officers of the First, Second, and Third Bombardment Wings, contained these paragraphs:

> 1. A unit to be known as the Operational Research Section is now being established at this Headquarters for the purpose of analyzing bombing operations with a view to finding weak points in our method of attack in bombing and also any weaknesses in the employment of the enemy defense system; to ascertain the cause of casualties with a view to their reduction. To assess and evaluate the effectiveness of bombing attacks and also to investigate various communication problems relating to this command. This section

19

will be independent of all other Staff Sections of this Headquarters
and will operate directly under the Chief of Staff.
2. In order to accomplish the foregoing, it will be necessary for
the members of this section to visit all Headquarters within this
command and have ready access to all facilities therein. This includes contact with air crews, authority to visit operations rooms,
situation rooms, attend briefings of crews and in short all activities
that would aid them in their work. It is desired that all concerned
extend every facility to the members of the Operational Research
Section to enable them properly to perform their functions.
3. Unit Commanders desiring scientific investigation relating to
operation or other matters of a similar nature will forward requests
to this Headquarters for consideration. [2]

General Eaker's second directive was to ORS Chief John M. Harlan. Its
first paragraph listed fourteen studies or tasks for the section, such as compil-
ing damage assessment reports of each target attacked, studying navigational
aids in homing and locating targets, and analyzing the causes of casualties to
develop methods of reducing the percentage.
The second paragraph stated:

2. The forementioned subjects are those which are most pressing
at this time and are the ones which should be undertaken at the
earliest practicable date. Further directives will be furnished you
when conditions so warrant. [3]

In his history of the section, Leslie Arps notes that General Eaker's directive is important because it defined the functions of the ORS, as they were
understood at the time. Interestingly, this was the only directive ever issued
to the ORS. As Leslie Arps explains, "Experience more than anything else
governed the enterprise." [4]
When the ORS six reported for duty in October 1942, the Eighth Air Force
had, on 9 October, flown its largest mission so far—108 heavy bombers attacked a steel works in Lille, Belgium. Indeed, this remained the largest mission for the Eighth Air Force throughout the next six months. More than half
of the thirteen missions—the first was flown on 17 August—were twelve-plane
missions to targets in France or the low countries. All were daylight missions,
usually escorted by fighters, to specific military targets: airfields, marshalling
yards, shipyards, aircraft factories, and submarine bases. [5] By contrast, on
the night of 30 May 1942 the RAF had made its famous thousand-plane raid
on Cologne, Germany.
An explanation of the limited forces available to the Eighth Air Force in
its first year of operation is relevant to the history of operations research in
European and Mediterranean theatres. General Eaker and his staff arrived
in England on 20 February 1942 to begin a build-up of American air power

for a strategic bomber offensive that would precede the invasion of Europe. The American high command wanted to invade the Continent from England by mid-1943 or sooner. Churchill and his advisors, however, opposed such a plan. General Rommel's success placed the British in extreme crisis in North Africa. Rather than invade Europe, the United States and Great Britain planned a November 1942 invasion of Northwest Africa, known as Operation Torch, instead.

For this invasion two new American air forces were created. The first, created in July 1942, was the Middle East Air Force, renamed the Ninth Air Force on 12 November under the command of General Lewis H. Brereton. The second, established on 20 August in Washington, D.C., was the Twelfth Air Force, commanded by General James Doolittle. Forces for the North Africa invasion assembled in Great Britain. The Eighth Air Force, in furnishing a nucleus for the American striking force, sent much of its personnel and equipment to North Africa. Thus, when the ORS reported for duty to General Eaker, the American strategic bombing force in England was in its infancy, its planned growth delayed for at least six months by the campaign in Africa.

By the middle of November 1942 the section had temporary offices, access to clerical help, and "the first suspicions of the established military sections were somewhat alleviated." [6] The section personnel was increased by the arrival of Captain Philip C. Scott on 14 November 1942. Captain (later, Lieutenant Colonel) Scott, another lawyer of the New York firm Root, Ballantine, Harlan, Bushby, and Palmer, was destined to head the Bombing Accuracy Subsection.

Still in its infancy, the section experienced its most critical period. Leslie Arps described the discouragement.

> Nothing had as yet been produced and a certain feeling of frustration prevailed. Later when the section was grossly overworked and hard put to meet the demands of the Command, it hardly seemed possible that there was a time when for awhile it looked as though there would not be enough to do.
>
> Life in the ORS dormitory was one constant discussion. After dinner and at the end of each day the others would foregather in their room and discuss the problems of the day and speculate on the future. What should an ORS do? What should its objective be? Should it engage in any steady recurring projects? Was there any place in the Section for analysts without scientific training? Was there any place for higher mathematicians? to mention only a few of the innumerable questions. Many diverse points of view were expressed and urged, but from these discussions there gradually emerged the principles the Section followed throughout its entire history.

In addition, many pleasant hours were spent in lighter discussion. The Section was most congenial and by living, eating, and working together a close personal relationship was created. Those of us who lived in the ORS dormitory will long remember the famous limericks of Dr. Alexander and Dr. Robertson. Dr. Youden's famous stories told with a poker face, with just sufficient plausibility to be confusing, and the none too dignified poker games were high lights of this period. [7]

Baley Price, in his memoir "Gremlin Hunting in the Eighth Air Force European Theatre of Operations" recounted one of "Dr. Youden's famous stories" that also captures the camaraderie of the ORS.

Dr. Youden was invited to a dinner party with friends in London on New Year's Eve (December 31, 1943). He was delayed in leaving Pinetree (Code name for Headquarters at High Wycombe), and he soon realized that he would be called on to explain an hour's tardiness. The ride to London allowed ample time for preparation.

"Well," Dr. Youden said when the other members of the party attacked him, "I am sorry, but I really could not help it. It was like this: When I got on the train, I observed that the locomotive was on the wrong end and headed in the wrong direction. I was fearful then that the engineer might forget which way he was supposed to go, but I soon forgot the matter. After we had been under way for some time, however, I looked up and we really were going in the wrong direction. I pulled the cord to stop the train, and presently the conductor came back. He was furious and wanted to know what I was up to. I pointed out to him that the train was going in the wrong direction. Now there is a five pound fine for improper pulling of the cord, and the conductor began to examine his book of rules at this point. Traveling in the wrong direction was not one of the reasons listed as a legitimate cause for stopping the train. Ungrateful wretch that he is, he started for the telephone to call the police to have me arrested!" By this time the members of the dinner party had forgotten Dr. Youden's tardiness, and they began to plan his defense. [8]

ORS Produces its First Reports

In December 1942, when General Eaker became commanding general of the Eighth Air Force, General Longfellow succeeded him as commanding general of the Eighth Bomber Command. In the first specific problem put to the section, General Longfellow asked Dr. Robertson to study the vulnerability of submarine pens. Dr. Robertson's report, dated 8 December

1942, was titled "Perforability of German Submarine Pens, Located at Lorient and Elsewhere, by American and British Bombs." He concluded that no bomb available to the Eighth Bomber Command was capable of perforating the roofs of pens from any practicable bombing height. As a result of this well-received report, exposed installations, rather than the pens themselves, were targeted during subsequent attacks on German submarine bases. [9] This became the first report of the Bombs and Fuzes Subsection, soon to be established.

The second report of the ORS, "Some Notes on the Estimation of Bombing Probabilities under Combat Conditions," submitted by Drs. Alexander and Robertson on 16 December 1942, had important consequences for bombing accuracy. With very few exceptions targets were attacked by more than one formation or combat box. Lieutenant Bates, an American officer assigned to the British reconnaissance unit, prepared bomb plots for the Eighth Air Force based on photographs taken by reconnaissance aircraft after an operation. It was impossible to segregate the bomb fall of a particular unit from these. In their report, Alexander and Robertson seriously doubted whether it would be possible to estimate future bombing probabilities with these data. The report clarified the need for a thoroughgoing analysis of bombing accuracy. The newly arrived Captain Scott was assigned to help Robertson and Alexander in this task. [10]

One of the tasks assigned to the section in Eaker's directive of 23 October 1942 was to "make a study of navigational aids used in homing as well as location of targets by radio means." The weather over England and the continent was a great enemy of daylight bombing. Indeed, on 7 October General Spaatz told General Eisenhower that the daylight bombing program that the Eighth Air Force was engaged in had developed only one real weakness, its dependence on good weather. [11] Weather had permitted the B-17s to fly only one mission in the month since 7 September 1942.

> Some hitherto strong supporters of the American policy (of daylight precision bombing) were developing doubts. And some were becoming openly convinced that the Eighth Air Force, or whatever was left of it after the African invasion began, should join the RAF on the night raids which did not require precision. [12]

Dr. Tuttle, one of the original ORS six, was a physicist who had been director of research at General Radio Corporation. His first undertaking was to familiarize himself with British radar equipment which might be useful in heavy bomber operations. His observations about the weather appear in a subsequent report.

> The problem of bombing through overcast appears to be one of the most urgent facing this Command. Studies covering the last eight years show that throughout the year an average of less than six days

per month which will be suitable for high level visual bombing of typical European targets are to be anticipated, and that during the winter months from November to February, inclusive, the expectation for suitable weather averages between two and three days per month. Blind (radar) bombing equipment is thus needed for the many occasions when bad weather is predicted and a mission would not ordinarily be scheduled, even if special planning of the missions is required for its use. [13]

Shortly after their arrival in October, the section members visited the Ninety-seventh Bomb Group, one of the first to go to England.

There, operations were explained by such officers as the intelligence officer, engineering officer, operations officer, armament officer, etc. Prior to this time many of the Section members knew no more about the problems and operating methods of a heavy bombardment group than could be obtained from the newspapers. In fact, this was the first time that many of the Section members had ever seen a B-17." [14]

One of the first programs the newly established ORS decided to undertake was "a study of damage to our aircraft and its cause." In early December 1942 Dr. Youden prepared a form for reporting battle damage to aircraft and secured its approval. Before the form was implemented in February 1943, information about battle damage was gathered informally from engineering officers; in at least one instance Youden and Robertson got information by personally inspecting a damaged bomber. [15]

Fuel consumption studies of the B-17 under combat conditions were requested in early December. Dr. Youden undertook this task and soon found that information on aircraft fuel consumption was inadequate. Consequently, on 27 December 1942 General Longfellow sent a letter to the bombardment wings stating that Dr. Youden would consult with the group navigator, group operations officer, and other personnel as soon as possible after each mission to gather fuel consumption data. This was the first letter to the combat units which outlined a problem the section was working on and requested information and help. Many such letters were to follow in the life of the section in which subordinate units were directed to furnish information to be analyzed by the ORS. [16]

Another task initially undertaken by the section was to compile a complete report of each mission, the Day Raid Report. This job was the responsibility of Leslie Arps. These reports were to serve two purposes: to provide the commanding general and the section with all the available basic information about each Eighth Bomber Command operation in one report, and to gather data from each operation staff section in the command. During the early days when the operations were small and relatively simple, preparing these reports was not too great a burden. Furthermore, they were valuable in making the ORS known, not only at the Eighth Bomber Command, but also at Eighth Air Force headquarters, where they were used extensively. ORS Day Raid Reports Nos. 1 to 22 covering the Eighth Bomber Command operations from its first mission on 17 August 1942, to 23 November 1942, were published on 30 December 1942.[17]

REFERENCES

1. Headquarters, Eighth Air Force, "The Operational Research Section at the Eighth Air Force, 20 March 1943–17 July 1944," John M. Harlan, 520. 303-1, Archives, Simpson Historical Research Center, Maxwell Air Force Base, Alabama, 3.

2. Ibid., appendix II, 1.

3. Ibid., appendix III, 1.

4. Eighth Air Force, History of Operations Analysis Section, October, 1942–June 1945, Leslie H. Arps, 520.303-3, Archives, Simpson Historical Research Center, Maxwell Air Force Base, Alabama, 14.

5. Roger A. Freeman, *A History of the U.S. 8th Army Air Force* (London: Macdonald, 1970), 12–18.

6. "Eighth Air Force," 24.

7. Ibid., 25–26.

8. G. Baley Price, *Gremlin Hunting in the Eighth Air Force, European Theatre of Operations, 1943–1945*, 19–20. This memoir was written by Baley Price at the Pentagon in 1945 while he had access to all needed documents and before he left the service of the air force.

9. "Eighth Air Force," 26.

10. Ibid., 27–28.

11. *My Three Years with Eisenhower, the Personal Diary of Captain Harry C. Butcher, USNR* (New York: Simon and Schuster, 1946), 136.

12. Thomas M. Coffey, *Decision over Schweinfurt, the U.S. 8th Air Force Battle for Daylight Bombing* (New York: David McKay Company, 1977), 145.

13. "Memorandum as to the Use of Blind Bombing Equipment in the Operations of this Command, HQS VIII Bomber Command, Operational Research Section," 11 July 1943, 1.

14. "Eighth Air Force," 16.

15. "History of the Battle Damage Subsection, Operational Analysis Section Hq. Eighth Air Force, Dec. 1943–May 1954," 520.3031, Archives, Simpson Historical Research Center, Maxwell Air Force Base, Alabama, 1, 7.

16. "Eighth Air Force," 28–29.

17. Ibid., 29–30.

3

The Operational Research Section of the Eighth Bomber Command Continues to Organize January–June 1943

A CRISIS WITH PERSONNEL

Nineteen forty-three began in crisis at the ORS. Two of the four scientists in the section at that time left. Arps wrote:

> Matters were further complicated by the fact that two of the Section's personnel felt they could no longer remain with the Section. Dr. [H. P.] Robertson decided that he should return to OSRD and left the Section on January 4, 1943. Dr. [James] Alexander, after a long period of uncertainty, became convinced that he could never function effectively in operations analysis work. After carefully reviewing the problems that had presented themselves and the type of work which seemed likely to develop in the future, Dr. Alexander became convinced that higher mathematics was not involved. It was Dr. Alexander's opinion that the work in the future would entail primarily the accumulation of facts and the application of common sense principles to these facts. He was convinced that he would not be required to employ his specialized knowledge in higher mathematics and since this was his primary interest, he felt he should return to the United States, which he did January 10, 1943. [1]

Such a full explanation by Arps of why Alexander left with none of why Robertson left is curious. In his biography, Massachusetts Institute of Technology physicist Philip Morse gives an account of Robertson's departure. Morse and Shockley, physicists and operations analysts in antisubmarine warfare for the U.S. Navy, visited England in November and December of 1942. They spent many days with Blackett, the distinguished British leader in operations research. They also visited the new ORS at the Eighth Bomber Command. (The ORS staff at the Eighth Bomber Command numbered seven at this time, whereas Morse's group in Washington had thirty members.) Morse recalled that the ORS at the Eighth Bomber Command was headed by a lawyer whom he left nameless (John Marshall Harlan). However, he notes that among the section members was his former colleague and MIT teacher, H. P. (Bob) Robertson. He portrayed Robertson as troubled by plans to bomb German cities. According to Morse, Robertson could show that bombing cities would inevitably destroy more homes than military targets. He thought such a plan would strengthen rather than weaken Germany's will to resist. Robertson, Morse wrote, was unable to convince the leader of his group or the staff of the U.S. bomber force. Furthermore, the lawyer heading the group monopolized the group's contacts with General Spaatz, so Robertson's frustrations were delivered to people who could do nothing about them. [2]

Morse's recollections (thirty-five years later) of Robertson's dissatisfaction are surprising. Indeed, at the time of Morse's visit, RAF Bomber Command was bombing German cities, and its commander, Sir Arthur Harris, was expanding and perfecting night area bombing. On the other hand, the Americans, Arnold, Spaatz, and Eaker, were doing everything in their power to remain uninvolved in the British plan of area bombing of cities. At the very time of Morse's visit and Robertson's dissatisfaction, the group in Washington, which soon became the Committee of Operations Analysts, had already been charged by General Arnold, USAAF commanding general, to draw up a plan for selective precision bombing of industrial targets in the Western Axis. This plan was the antithesis of area bombing of cities.

On 14 December 1982 Leslie Arps, author of the official history of the section, wrote in a personal communication about Robertson's leaving:

> Referring to the departure of Drs. Alexander and Robertson from the Section in early 1943, the only explanation that I can give for not dwelling on Bob Robertson's departure in any great detail was that I didn't know the background developed by Philip Morse.
>
> In fact I am by no means certain of Dr. Morse's accuracy. My best recollection is that Robertson felt he could do more for the war effort by returning to OSRD. It was as simple as that. So far as I know, or can recall, Robertson's departure was friendly.

A recent communication from Professor Hugh Miser gives a different version of Robertson's departure, which Bart Leach told him shortly after the war.

> Leach accompanied the first operations analysis section to England and stayed with it for a time while it settled in. At some time during this period, when the RAF officers and analysts were being particularly hospitable to the somewhat cold and uncomfortable Americans, the whole group was invited to a reception at an RAF officers' mess.

Now, the RAF cultivates among its officers an attitude of vigorous play, with much physical contact and apparent conflict, and it is often indulged in on the formal nights at which the staff dines in the mess with great ceremony. But this rowdyism does not cross the lines of respect and authority: rather, those in authority are usually the leaders.

On the evening of the reception, the host was an RAF Group Captain (the equivalent of a US Colonel, but in those days much rarer and more important a person)—and, like any good host, he made ample provision for warming up the chilled Americans (have you ever stayed in an unheated hut in England in the fall?) In sum, there was plenty of Scotch (of which there had been a very scarce supply).

It did not take long for the party to get somewhat uproarious in the way only RAF parties can get, and, of course, the Americans did their best to join in fully.

Robertson, in the course of the evening, managed to give the group captain, who was standing at the end of the table, a hot foot.

Bart [Leach] did not offer the details of what followed, but it was clear that the Group Captain was not amused; indeed, he was sufficiently outraged that the matter came to the attention of the Commanding General of the Eighth Air Force. Thus, Bart's first interview with this man was not, as he had devoutly hoped, to report some important and constructive research finding, but to explain why his distinguished scientist had given the Group Captain a hot foot—and to apologize therefore.

This incident made Robertson *persona non grata* among the UK opposite numbers—and certainly to Leach. Robertson's departure ensued fairly soon (I dare say delayed by the availability of transport).

A sad but cautionary tale.[3]

The departure of Alexander and Robertson left Captain Scott, a lawyer, as the only analyst working on bombing accuracy. Dr. Youden was soon assigned to study bombing accuracy also. His work eventually established a good reputation for himself, as well as for the section.[4]

HARLAN IS AUTHORIZED TO RECRUIT

Before the departure of Alexander and Robertson, the section chief, John Harlan, was aware that the section was not adequately staffed to complete the jobs it had begun, bombing accuracy, radar and radio countermeasures, the Day Raid Reports, and miscellaneous tasks such as fuel consumption studies.

The section, knowing it needed experts to determine force requirements for missions, created a bombs and fuzes subsection. Clearly, analysts were also needed to study loss and damage of aircraft on missions. No evidence exists to suggest that the section, for reasons discussed later, realized it needed analysts to specialize in gunnery.

Harlan conferred with Generals Longfellow and Eaker about the status and future of the section. On 7 January 1943, Harlan recommended that he and Leslie Arps, the section deputy, be commissioned, that a Table of Organization consisting of six officers and ten enlisted men be established, and that he be authorized to return to the United States to secure additional analysts and a Table of Organization. On 10 January, General Eaker wrote to General McClelland in Washington about Harlan's proposals and recommended that Harlan be sent to Washington to work out the program. As a result, Harlan was sent to Washington on 10 February, and did not return until 26 April 1943. [5]

The loss of Robertson and Alexander in early January was alleviated on 17 January when two analysts arrived, Dr. James A. Clarkson, mathematician, and Mr. Louis Lusky, lawyer. Dr. Clarkson was first assigned to help Dr. Tuttle with radar matters. Mr. Lusky prepared the ORS Day Raid Reports. [6]

THE BOMBING ACCURACY SUBSECTION MAKES FUNDAMENTAL ADVANCES

By the beginning of January 1943, the Eighth Bomber Command had flown approximately thirty missions since 17 August 1942. All were to German-occupied countries, but none were to Germany. Daylight precision bombing of industrial and military targets—the mission of the Eighth Air Force—was on trial before it started. British Prime Minister Churchill, Air Chief Marshal Sir Charles Portal, Air Chief Marshal Sir Arthur Harris, and others did not expect daylight selective bombing to succeed. Instead, they wanted the Americans to join them in the night area bombing of German cities. It was only a matter of time, they thought, until the Americans realized their error and did so. [7]

Accuracy was at the heart of strategic bombing, as conceived by American planners. Consistent accuracy had been achieved from high altitudes on practice missions in the United States. However, these crews bombed targets on well-established ranges under conditions very different from combat. Locating a target one had never seen before was not a problem on the U.S. bombing ranges. Moreover, targets at home did not shoot back, and the bombers were not under attack on their way to the target and the bomb run.

The first thirty combat missions of the Eighth Bomber Command were judged to range from bad to good. At first, losses due to fighter attacks were small. However, in December 1942, 8.8 percent of attacking bombers fell to enemy fighters.[8] Each time a bomber went down its crew of ten went down with it. Interest in the effectiveness of missions was intense throughout the war because the cost was high in terms of men and planes. Helping to improve visual bombing accuracy became one of the great achievements for the ORS.

The ORS's first and most fundamental contribution to bombing accuracy was to identify and gather reliable data. Since the earliest mission of the Eighth Air Force, attacks were made by bombers flying in formation. Attacks on a single target were made by more than one unit. Each unit, or combat box, consisted of several aircraft flying in formation. The number of combat boxes varied from target to target, but typically there was more than one and sometimes many.

As its first important step in analyzing bombing accuracy, the section instituted procedures to identify, or segregate, the bomb fall of each combat box at each target. The means for doing this were already at hand. In each combat box several aircraft carried automatic cameras that took photographs at short intervals, from before a bomb was released, until after it hit the ground. On the face of these strike photographs appeared the name of the target, the date of the attack, the unit, the altitude, and the number of photographs in the series. The section assembled them into bomb plots which recorded the bomb fall of each attacking unit. To measure and classify, circles of 500 feet, 1,000 feet, and 2,000 feet were drawn around the aiming point, and the bombs were plotted within these circles. This method of segregating each combat box's bomb fall opened up the whole field of bombing accuracy analysis. It was now possible to estimate bombing probabilities, and determine what methods of bombing were most effective. By the middle of February 1943 a substantial number of bomb plots were prepared, and the first tangible results became apparent.[9]

To appreciate the next advance made in bombing accuracy, a brief description of one phase of the bombing procedure is needed. Formation flying and attacking in combat boxes necessarily meant that the lead aircraft in each combat box controlled the direction or path that the formation took towards the target, a procedure known as deflection sighting. The operation which controlled whether the bombs would fall on, over, or short of the target was called sighting for range, which was done by the bombardier in each plane.

A participant in the next development in bombing accuracy was Colonel (later General) Curtis E. LeMay. His group, the 305th Bomb Group, flew its first mission on 17 November 1942. By December German fighter opposition to the American attacks stiffened. Colonel LeMay experimented to find the best formation for staving off fighter attacks. One-level formation (combat box) did not offer adequate bomber protection. In practice flights, LeMay worked out the first version of the multi-level box formation. It consisted of staggered three-plane elements within each squadron and staggered squadrons within each group to provide a compact, maneuverable box formation. Such a formation could not be maintained on the bomb run, however, if each plane maneuvered for accurate range sighting. LeMay decided this problem could be avoided if each plane maintained its position in formation and dropped its bombs on a signal from the leading plane in the aircraft box. Thus, the leader of the combat box aimed for deflection and range for his entire box. [10]

The first 1943 mission, on 3 January, was to the well-defended submarine base at St. Nazaire (Flak City). The mission of eighty-five bombers was led by Colonel LeMay's 305th Bomb Group. General Hansell went along to observe LeMay's new tactics. This mission was the first to use the "bombing-on-leader" technique developed by LeMay. [11]

The Eighth Air Force's adoption of "bombing-on-leader" as standard operation policy is described by Arps in his section history:

> The Bombing Accuracy Subsection became convinced that greater accuracy would be achieved if the lead aircraft in the formation was the only one performing a sighting operation—at that time a very startling conclusion indeed. It had been the well-settled practice, not only in peace time but on operations, that each aircraft in the formation should sight for range. Some groups notably the 305 [Colonel LeMay's group] however, had employed the technique of having the lead formation sight for both range and deflection.
>
> As soon as sufficient data was assembled to present, in a convincing manner, the results of this analysis, a conference was arranged with Brigadier General Hansell, then Acting Commanding General of VIII Bomber Command during General Longfellow's temporary absence. The results of this conference, while interesting, were not very conclusive and General Hansell recommended that the matter be brought up again on General Longfellow's return. This was done and a conference was held with General Longfellow; Colonel Bubb, the Chief of Staff; Colonel Wallace, the A-3; and Colonel Garland, a bombing expert who had been sent over on temporary duty to VIII Bomber Command. At this conference General Longfellow was shown tables and charts demonstrating the advantages which group leader sighting had over individual sightings for range. In addition, individual group bomb plots had been prepared which, in a striking manner, showed the advantages that sighting on the leader had over individual range sightings. The General and other officers present, although surprised at the results, became firmly convinced of the soundness of the sighting on the leader technique. General Longfellow requested that the analysis be written up so that it could be forwarded to Eighth Air Force Headquarters and from there to Washington.

Several days later, on March 17, Colonel Garland asked Colonel Scott and Dr. Clarkson to go to the 1st Division to see General Hansell. The results of this expedition were exceptionally gratifying. General Hansell agreed wholeheartedly that sighting on the leader was the best technique to be used and assured the men that he would use his best efforts to see that it was adopted by the combat groups. The groups were contacted on that day, and on the next day an attack was made on Vegesack [Germany]. This was the first attack in the history of the VIII Bomber Command where all the groups were instructed to drop on the leader. The results were phenomenally successful. As a matter of human interest, just prior to the Vegesack raid Scott and Youden were informed that on this operation all groups would drop on the leader. The Section felt that its entire reputation and future were at stake and awaited the outcome of the attack with considerable intrepidations [*sic.* trepidation]. ... Needless to say, the Section was very much elated when the pictures showed the story. [12]

After the Vegesack mission the Bombing Accuracy Subsection prepared a report dated 20 March 1943 entitled "Advantage of Dropping on the Leader over Sighting Individually for Range when Bombing in Formation." The report made these recommendations:

(1) All groups should be instructed that the bombardiers in each combat box should release their bombs when the bombardier of the lead ship of the combat box releases his, i.e., "bomb-on-the-leader."
(2) The aiming point for the lead ship should be selected to place the formation pattern most effectively over the target area.
(3) Every effort commensurate with defensive needs should be made to reduce the length of the bomb pattern. [13]

The first recommendation was adopted immediately. Within two or three weeks sighting on the leader was the only technique used during all Eighth Air Force missions in the European theater. The second recommendation, simply a logical consequence of the first, was also adopted. Of course it modified the whole concept of aiming point selection. The lead bombardier was now aiming a pattern, not just his own bombs. This introduced a new term into bombing vocabulary, Mean Point of Impact (MPI). Previously, headquarters specified aiming points for attack. It now specified MPIs instead, and left the selection of aiming points to the groups. The third recommendation, shorter bombing patterns, vital though it was, took longer to become understood and accepted throughout the command. Nevertheless, this set of recommendations laid the groundwork for very significant improvements in bombing accuracy. Dr. Clarkson helped write the report, and because of his interest, was permanently attached to the Bombing Accuracy Subsection in late March 1943.

"Permanent" quarters for ORS. On 23 February 1943 the section moved into "permanent quarters" built especially for it. At first they consisted of a large Nissen hut, three smaller Nissen huts, and an outside latrine. The large hut housed ten offices, and the smaller huts were living quarters. The buildings were located in a wooded area on the grounds of Wycombe Abbey, an attractive spot "sufficiently off the beaten path so that the Section was never bothered by casual visitors."

As the section expanded during the war, more office space and living huts were added. Still some of the personnel had to be quartered elsewhere. By the end of the war, forty-nine civilian analysts had served at one time or another with the section. Also at the end of the war twenty-five officers and forty-five enlisted personnel—men and women—were working for the section. [14]

Women helped from the beginning.   From the beginning, the headquarters personnel of the Eighth Bomber Command included women. When General Eaker moved into his headquarters at Wycombe Abbey in March 1942, Air Marshal Harris of the RAF Bomber Command provided him with two dozen WAAFs (Women's Auxiliary Air Force) on temporary assignment for his office force. Harris told Eaker the women were more dedicated. He said he even used them to keep his secret files, because they didn't get drunk at the club on Saturday night and tell everything they knew. [15]

When General Arnold visited the Eighth Bomber Command headquarters at Wycombe Abbey in May 1942, he inquired about the WAAFs working there. Eaker explained that they were loaned by the RAF. Eaker asked Arnold for a company of American WACs (Women's Army Corps.). Later, Arnold talked to General Chaney, commander of American forces in England. Chaney, he learned, was opposed to having WACs in his theater.

However, by the middle of June 1942 Dwight Eisenhower became the United States Army's European theater commander. Under his command women and black American personnel were utilized wherever possible. [16] It was not, however, until July 1943 that the ORS got its first WAC, Sgt. Eileen Hazelton, assigned to the Bombing Accuracy Subsection. By the end of the war thirteen WACs were working for the section. [17]

Predictions of bombing accuracy.   Early in April 1943 Eighth Air Force headquarters asked the section to help prepare a report for Washington outlining their future aircraft and crew requirements. Specifically, the section was asked to project a rate of mission failures, and to estimate bombing accuracy probabilities, that is, the percentage of bombs expected to fall within standard distances from the aiming point. Given the circular probable error and the expected size of the bomb plot, Scott, Youden, and Arps were able to determine the percent of bombs falling within any other specified distance from the aiming point. Thus they produced the probabilities requested using bomb plot data. After that, all requests from Washington or elsewhere for information on bombing accuracy or bombing probabilities of the Eighth Air Force were referred to the section. [18]

More from the bomb plots. The bomb plot studies yielded a surprising fact about bombing accuracy. Though the two lead groups faced flak and enemy fighters, their bombing was consistently more accurate than that of subsequent groups. After the first two groups dropped their bombs, smoke and debris usually obscured the aiming point, accounting for the less accurate bombing of subsequent groups. On 2 May the ORS sent a memorandum to the commanding general which concluded:

> The foregoing suggests the best bombing results will be achieved by having not more than two groups attack the same target at the same time. However, before this suggestion should be acted upon, careful consideration must be given to the effect that this course would have upon defensive tactics presently used and whether it would increase present hazards. [19]

Subsequently, numerous reports were written on the relationship between the size of the attacking force and bombing accuracy. However, the best size of force for bombing accuracy might be too small to destroy the target, or too small to provide protection for the bombers against German fighters. Thus, the mission planners at headquarters had to balance several factors, including bombing accuracy, in structuring each mission.

EIGHTH FIGHTER COMMAND WANTS AN ORS

The Eighth Fighter Command had experienced the same growth problems as Eighth Bomber Command. On 20 October 1942 there were eight American fighter groups in the United Kingdom composed of Spitfires, P-38s, and P-39s. Most of these were Twelfth Air Force groups bound for Africa, and by November 1942 all but one of them had left to participate in TORCH, the North African invasion. Only the Fourth Fighter Group, an American Spitfire group, remained. [20] By Christmas the Eighth Fighter Command had received its first P-47 airplane and it began to develop into a fighter command of P-47s. Compared with its competitors, the British Spitfire and the German Me-109, the P-47 was massive. It weighed twice what the others did and looked more like a fighter-bomber than a fighter. By 1 March 1943 the Fourth Fighter Group became operational. Two other P-47 fighter groups became operational later in March.

The mission of the Eighth Fighter Command was to protect the bombers of the Eighth Bomber Command during missions. General Hunter had requested an operational research section for his Eighth Fighter Command.

On 6 March 1943 Harlan, then in the United States, sent a cable to the ORS of the Eighth Bomber Command instructing Arps and Tuttle to ask General Hunter how many men his ORS would need. They returned a cable to Harlan requesting one radar expert, an assistant, three physicists, and two mathematicians. [21]

Harlan's recruits.   The first of Harlan's recruits, Dr. Richard G. Gettell, arrived from the States on 14 April 1943 to head the Loss and Battle Damage Subsection. On 26 April Harlan returned with Mr. Bissell Alderman and Mr. Charles Kring for the Bombs and Fuzes Subsection, Mr. Kenneth Norton for the Radar and Radio Countermeasures Subsection, and Dr. Edwin Hewitt and Mr. Frank M. Stewart, both mathematicians, for the General Missions Analysis Subsection. In May, Mr. George P. Shettle arrived for the Loss and Battle Damage Subsection. These men, together with those already present, constituted the core of what became the largest ORS in the USAAF. [22]

The history of the headquarters office of operations analysis in Washington sheds some light on how operations analysts were recruited.

> Operations Analysis can be no better than the men who perform it. It is no magic formula, but only a means of putting qualified men in a position to see and solve pressing problems. Hence the primary task of the Operations Analysis Division in Washington was to get the right men.
>
> Initially analysts were individually selected by the Washington office, but this was definitely a mistake. Any Operations Analysis Section inevitably faces tasks and conditions of such difficulty as to put its members under serious strains and pressures. This requires a cohesion in the unit which cannot be expected of groups of men who have to be introduced at the time they board a plane for an overseas station. It later became an established practice to select a Section Chief and place upon him the responsibility of selecting analysts for that section. There was thus created a personal bond between each analyst and the Chief, and a sense of responsibility on the part of the Chief for the men whom he had chosen. The Washington office had certain sources of personnel and placed these sources at the disposal of the Section Chiefs but left the matter of selection—subject to a veto power rarely exercised—to the Chiefs themselves. The organizations within the OSRD provided a constant flow of capable personnel within two specialist categories. The Princeton Station of the NDRC, Division 2, under the successive leadership of Professor John E. Burchard and Professor H. L. Beckwith, established in 1943 a course of training designed to indoctrinate architects and construction engineers in analysis of weapons and targets. The selections of personnel for this course by Division 2 were nothing less than brilliant. Gradu-

ates of the Princeton Station were high in the councils of all Air Forces in matters concerning the selection and fuzing of weapons for their targets. The Applied Mathematics Panel under the leadership of Dr. Warren S. Weaver and the Applied Mathematics Group of Columbia University under the leadership of Professor E. J. Moulton undertook to recruit a series of mathematicians and to indoctrinate them in gunnery, partly in New York City and partly in various gunnery schools of the AAF. These men not only made a distinguished contribution to the improvement of aerial gunnery but, when the fighter menace became so slight that gunnery problems receded in importance, they adapted their mathematical skills to a wide variety of other problems.

Apart from these two regular sources of personnel, the selection of analysts was a matter of heart-breaking slowness and numerous disappointments—particularly in the field of radio and radar. It was discovered over a considerable period that it took about a week of full-time effort of one officer or a Section Chief to recruit a single analyst. For any post it was SOP (standard operating procedure) to have the first choice decline to serve, the second unable to get a release from his employer, the third unable to pass the physical examination and the fourth refuse out of pique at having the others consulted before he was. Under these circumstances the temptation was to take fifth and sixth choices; and it required great determination to recommence by establishing a new slate of first-class men. [23]

THE BEGINNING
OF THE LOSS AND BATTLE DAMAGE SUBSECTION

On 19 February 1943 the reporting scheme for battle damage on the bombers worked out in December by Dr. Youden was finally implemented. Group engineering officers were responsible for completing the forms and forwarding them to the ORS. The form, which included a simplified diagram of the aircraft, was used to record the location of any hits received, the direction from which each hit came, the type of missile causing the damage, the severity of the damage, its effect on the handling of the aircraft, the crew position of any casualties incurred, and a description of any damage to interior parts of the aircraft. Photographs of the damage, if available, were included. [24]

Dr. Richard G. Gettell, who reported for duty as head of the Loss and Battle Damage Subsection on 14 April 1943, earned his Ph.D. at the University of California, Berkeley, in economics in 1940. Before he came to the ORS he had been director of the Miscellaneous Products Rationing Division of the Office of Price Administration in Washington, D.C. Also, he had been an operations analyst to General Eubanks, Director of Bombing of the AAF. He had left his assistant professorship in economics at Yale to participate in these war activities. (In 1957, Gettell became president of Mount Holyoke College in Massachusetts.) George P. Shettle, who arrived on 21 May 1943 to work with Gettell in the Loss and Battle Damage Subsection, had been an investment analyst in New York City. [25]

By the time Gettell arrived two months of battle damage reports had accumulated. They revealed that a surprising number of aircraft received damage inflicted by their own guns or by stray shots from friendly aircraft. Most of this self-inflicted damage was caused by waist gunners who accidentally fired into the tail sections of their own planes while firing at attacking fighters. Thus, the first report of the Loss and Battle Damage Subsection, dated 5 June 1943, was titled "Analysis of Battle Damage Caused by Machine Gun Fire, Missions 37–60, February–May 31, 1943 (Self-Inflicted Damage)." Their second report, dated 23 June 1943, was less embarrassing. It was titled "Loss and Damage from Enemy Fighters as Related to Size of the Missions and Order Over the Target." [26]

Obviously minimizing battle damage and loss was important. Losses, as well as the time necessary for repairing planes, seriously limited air force striking power. The basic function of the ORS Loss and Battle Damage Subsection was to apply analytical methods to the problem of loss and damage by

> ... collecting and analyzing information regarding our defensive experience, not merely as a historical record of the cost incurred on past missions, but as operational data on the basis of which to calculate risks for future missions, to plan for the most efficient use of the striking force, and to discover, from experience, remedial measures, both tactical and engineering, by which loss and battle damage can be reduced. [27]

In the six months from November 1942 through April 1943 the Eighth Air Force conducted its day bomber offensive from England with four B-17 groups and two B-24 groups. However, because of diversions and detachments, rarely were more than a score of B-24s available for bombing missions. The command had a potential strength of about 140 B-17s. Fewer than two thirds of these planes could be used for any one mission because the remaining one third were undergoing repairs or being serviced. [28]

During February 1943 twenty-two bombers had been lost. The number of planes out of service due to battle damage was about equal to the number lost. Crews were lost faster than they could be replaced. Twenty-five combat missions had been set as the number each crewman would fly. Approximately one-fourth of the crewmen survived twenty-five missions at that time. [29]

THE BOMBS AND FUZES SUBSECTION GETS UNDERWAY

In March 1943 John Harlan visited the Princeton University Station of Division 2 of the National Defense Research Committee (NDRC), where Professor John Burchard was director. Burchard, an architectural engineer, and his division studied the theoretical and experimental effects of explosive waves in air, earth, and water, and the effects of explosions and projectiles on targets. [30] Since December 1942 Burchard had been on the Probabilities and Force Subcommittee of the COA, which drew up the systems of German industrial targets for the Combined Bomber Offensive. The Princeton Station was indoctrinating architects and construction engineers in weapons and target analysis. Two "students" were Bissell Alderman, assistant professor of architecture at MIT and Charles U. Kring, a structural engineer who had worked with Bermuda Architects-Engineers, Army Air Base, Bermuda. [31] According to G. Baley Price, [32] they were learning to reverse their peacetime practices and use their knowledge to destroy buildings rather than build them. After completing the two-month course at Princeton, Alderman and Kring reported for duty at the ORS in England with Harlan on 26 April 1943.

Although the need had been established for bomb and fuze specialists to look objectively at the effectiveness of the Eighth Air Force bombing, the method had not been established. A first suggestion was to station one of the two new American specialists at the nearby British Ministry of Home Security (MHS). The MHS was at that time planning raid assessment reports which would assess bomb damage, estimate production loss, and estimate the date when the target would be repaired and ready for another attack. Although Alderman and Kring cooperated with this project, they both remained stationed at the ORS. The MHS was within easy reach of ORS headquarters should the need for meetings arise. [33]

At first Alderman and Kring studied the weapons currently in use (bombs), and made damage assessments from the strike photographs of missions. Alderman said:

> We followed closely the work of the Bombing Accuracy Subsections and referred occasionally to their bomb plots which they were making from the strike photographs. We were consulted frequently on accuracy matters and were interested in their work. They were always eager to be as helpful as possible in presenting their data in the form which would be most useful to us. From the very beginning it was this section which concerned us most directly; Dr. Youden, Dr. Clarkson, and Major Scott, the charter members of that section, called us 'Bomb Damage Assessment', a name which stuck for some time, even though we were not chiefly concerned with assessment as such.
>
> Our bomb damage analysis studies were concerned primarily

with more recent missions. At that time there had not been many
famous attacks, but we studied the damage to Meaulte, Vegesack,
Renault, and other targets. The areas of damage seemed in many
cases discouragingly small. The 1000-lb. G. P. [general purpose]
bombs were being used almost exclusively without regard for the
type of target being attacked. The Chief of Operations at that time
was General Longfellow, and it appeared that he and other top staff
members including Col. Bubb, Col. Wallace, and Col. Cleveland
(perhaps for lack of any information on bomb effectiveness) were
Big Bomb enthusiasts. All bombs and fuzes were being selected
by the chiefs in A-3, and there was a general awareness elsewhere
in the Command that weapon selection was not being given the
proper attention. The Ordnance Section which had been consulted
at one time was no longer represented in the Ops [Operations]
Conference. [34]

Alderman and Kring studied the damage of German raids to English cities
and industrial targets in many reports. They also visited many of the blitzed
areas, and studied information available on RAF raids on the Continent.
Alderman explained their conclusions:

In these surveys one of the first items which attracted our attention
were the very large areas of damage to British single-story steel-
frame industrial structures caused by German bombs or mines
which detonated at roof level. Further research led us to our
recommendations of fuzing (.01 second delay tail) which would
cause our bombs to detonate close to the roof structural members.
We believed that damage to the machinery and contents of industrial buildings by fragmentation effect was important and that
it could be achieved most effectively by the airburst of a General Purpose bomb. (The .025 second delay fuze then in use
caused bombs to crater or detonate close to floor level.) We knew
that the fragmentation effect on bombs which cratered was negligible and that fragments from bombs detonating close to the floor
was less effective than the fragmentation effect of bombs detonating higher where the shielding effect of blast walls or other
machines was reduced to a minimum. In addition, it seemed
to us that on certain targets a great deal of the energy of the
bombs fuzed .025 was wasted in forming craters. We selected the
500 lb. G. P. bomb fuzed .01 tail (and .1 nose) because we believed
it to be the smallest bomb which could most effectively destroy the
structural framework of our single story steel-frame industrial target buildings. The Ministry of Home Security did not agree at first
with this rather revolutionary fuzing recommendation; the RAF

after all were using .025 largely (never .01), and the Army manual TC50 had recommended .025. [35]

In their efforts to gain influence in the selection of bombs and fuzes for each mission, Alderman and Kring had the support of Lieutenant Colonel Sims, Ordnance Officer. Colonel Sims arranged for them to meet with Colonel Bubb, who agreed they should play a more important role in selecting weapons. In selecting bombs and fuzes, he explained, the Army manual TC50 was relied upon entirely. (Alderman and Kring had observed that in some instances bombs heavier than those specified in TC 50 had been used.) Colonel Bubb seemed interested in one suggestion: namely, that they prepare a new set of bomb and fuze recommendations for attacks on industrial targets, which they did.

> We were well acquainted with TC 50, disagreed with many of its recommendations, and decided to proceed immediately with a report on Bombs and Fuzes for Attacks on Industrial Targets, for submittal to the Commanding General. We included in this report recommendations for bombs and fuzes for Light Industrial structures, Heavy Industrial types, Submarine Building Yards, Power Stations and so forth. We presented our reasons in detail for each bomb and each fuze selection.
>
> Mr. Harlan felt that the report should not only acknowledge TC 50 but should explain why our recommendations differed. Kring and I felt that it should contain no reference to TC 50 but should present only our reasons for our selections. The result was that it became cluttered with references to TC 50 which at that moment may have been timely but very soon lost all significance.
>
> We discovered later that this report was widely circulated in the U.K., in other theaters of operations and in the States. [36]

The report was first issued 8 July 1943.

General Mission Analysis Subsection

The original purpose of the General Mission Analysis Subsection was to engage in nonrecurring projects. In practice the subsection undertook only two projects. One was producing the Day Raid Reports. This job, first done by Leslie Arps, was turned over to Mr. Lusky shortly after he arrived in December 1942. On 26 April 1943 Lusky was joined by Dr. Edwin Hewitt and Mr. Frank Stewart who had been recruited by Harlan. Both men had been mathematics instructors at Harvard. Both completed doctorates at Harvard, Hewitt before the war, Stewart after the war. Both later became well-known mathematicians and professors, Hewitt at the University of Washington, Stewart at Brown University.

One of Mr. Lusky's first tasks and contributions was, with the help of the Statistical Control Unit, to prepare a model form for each group commander to use to report group operations. After each operation, the ORS received a comprehensive report from each group commander. These reports became a basic source of information for the various subsections. [37]

Another task assigned to this subsection was to study fuel consumption. The problem of bombers not having enough fuel to return to base after missions would come up again and again throughout the war. I was the bombardier of a B-17 crew which made an emergency landing at a U.S. fighter field near Charleroi, Belgium, in October 1944, because the plane did not have enough gasoline to get back to England after a mission deep into Germany. Predicting fuel consumption for combat missions precisely was difficult.

Though Youden had begun work on this problem in December, he gave it up to work on bombing accuracy. After the arrival of Hewitt and Stewart, the subsection was able to complete three reports, "Preliminary Memorandum on Fuel Consumption of the B-17F" on 7 April 1943, a memorandum on "Gasoline Consumption of the B-24D" on 16 May 1943, and a "Memorandum Concerning a Formula for Determining the Operational Ranges of the B-17F in Combat Formation Flying" on 11 July 1943. [38]

RADAR AND RADIO COUNTERMEASURES

The many uses for radar discovered during WWII had a great effect on the war. Radar, a contraction of *ra*dio *d*etection *a*nd *r*ange, detects distant objects by determining their position, velocity, and other characteristics by analyzing very high frequency radio waves reflected from their surfaces.

Radar was used by all of the combatants in WWII. The superiority of British and American radar was an important factor in winning the war. In 1938 the British established a chain of radar stations along the English Channel to detect and locate approaching enemy aircraft. This early warning system played a big role in the winning of the Battle of Britain—Germany's first major defeat. All of the combatants were soon using radar early warning systems and radar controlled antiaircraft guns.

In order to carry the air war to Germany, the British resorted to night bombing early in the war. To guide their bombers to their targets in the darkness, they had developed various radar devices. When the Americans realized that bad weather was perhaps the greatest enemy of daylight bombing, they relied on British experience to help them develop blind (radar) bombing through clouds.

Two aspects of radar of great concern to the ORS were the blind bombing operations of the Eighth Air Force and thwarting the early warning system and radar controlled antiaircraft guns of the enemy. Accordingly, when Mr. Kenneth A. Norton arrived on 23 April 1943, the Radar and Radio Countermeasures Subsection was divided into two independent subdivisions. The first, the Radar Division, headed by Dr. Tuttle, gradually narrowed activities and eventually confined work primarily to Gee-H and Micro-H blind bombing activities. The second, Radio Countermeasures, was headed by Mr. Norton.[39]

Dr. Tuttle studied Great Britain's use of radar equipment to see how it might be useful to bombing operations of the Eighth Air Force. He became "the best informed man in the Command on British radar equipment." His first report, dated 9 February 1943, was entitled "Review of British Experience with 'Gee' with Comments on Possible Operational Uses by Eighth Bomber Command." This was followed by a comprehensive memorandum dated 11 July 1943 in which he reviewed these blind bombing devices: Oboe, SCR-297, Gee-H (short range devices), H2S, H2X, Eagle (in developmental stage), and Oboe with repeater (also in developmental stage). The last four had either unlimited range, or a range of 550 to 700 miles.[40]

Gee was a navigational aid put into operational use by the British in March 1942. This system employed paired master and slave stations in the United Kingdom, and an airborne receiver that converted radio signals into pulses which were visible on a cathode ray tube. The navigator used a special chart to plot the time interval between signals from the paired stations to calculate his position relative to them.

Oboe, which became operational in December 1942, was more accurate than Gee. A control station in England broadcast a directional beam for the Oboe-equipped bomber and tracked the plane on radar. The controller was able to guide the bomber to its target. Because the radar wave did not conform to the curvature of the earth, Oboe's range was limited.

H2S, introduced in January 1943, was an airborne radar installed in the bomber itself. A rotating H2S transmitter scanned the ground and a receiver picked up the radar return, displaying it on a cathode tube. Land, urban areas, and water gave distinct images on a screen which enabled the navigator to establish his position. Although H2S had unlimited range, the clarity of targets on the screen did not permit precise bombing. Thus, the Radiation Laboratory of the Massachusetts Institute of Technology developed an improved version of H2S, called H2X, which gave clearer pictures on its screen. It was first used in November 1943 by the Eighth Air Force in an attack on the port of Wilhelmshaven.[41]

Tuttle's report of 11 July 1943 recommended Oboe equipment for short range and a modified form of H2S, until H2X became available, for unlimited range. The British, however, did not use the Oboe equipment for daylight operations for security reasons. Thus, Dr. Tuttle urged that Gee-H be used. With Gee-H, a variant of Oboe, the crew, rather than ground station personnel, measured distance and computed the plane's position.[42]

Tuttle's report of 11 July 1943 presents an interesting analysis of visual bombing accuracy during the first five months of the Eighth Air Force's operations in 1943. Visual bombing accuracy steadily improved as the war progressed.

> It is presumed that accuracy requirements should be such, ideally, as to permit our present operations to be carried out when the target is obscured, without substantial loss of effectiveness. Although this may not be possible, an understanding of the factors limiting accuracy in operations where visual bombing is employed is necessary to determine the reasonable requirements of blind-bombing equipment.
>
> In operations of this Command covering the first five months of 1943, of all individual aircraft attacks on the target 26 percent were unsuccessful because they were part of missions which were failures as a whole (almost invariably because of unexpected bad weather). An additional 24 percent were on successful missions but part of unsuccessful group attacks. These latter cases are sometimes due to borderline weather conditions when several of the groups get a glimpse of the target through broken cloud while others do not, but may also be due to traffic problems at the target, smoke obscuration from preceding attacks, disturbance by fighters or flak, or to gross error from other causes on the part of the navigator or bombardier. Part of these group failures are thus due to weather or to other factors in the operation not related to the method of bombsighting or release. Some of the failures, however, are almost surely due to the difficulties in adjusting the bombsight or to the relatively long time, about 40 seconds, required for the operation.
>
> In the half of the attacks remaining after the mission and group failures are discarded, 51 percent of the bombs fell within 2000 feet of the aiming point. Thus, we have what might be termed a "visual reliability factor" of 50 percent, giving the percentage of actual attacks in which it was possible to use the bombing equipment as intended, and the further figure of 51 percent of bombs within 2000 feet, which represents the performance of the equipment in the cases when it is used. The two factors must be considered together in making any comparison between visual and radio bombing. The percent of failures of radio equipment may well prove less than the 50 percent figure of failures experienced with visual sighting. [43]

Such was the hope of Tuttle at this early stage of the game.

Mr. Kenneth A. Norton arrived on 23 April 1943 to begin a program of radio countermeasures (RCM) in the ORS. He arrived none too soon.

German flak was the best in the world and remained so until the summer of 1944 when the Americans unveiled a triple threat: the SCR-584 radar, the M9 director, and the proximity fuze against the buzz bombs.

> Flak (and fighters) inflicted such severe losses on the 8th Air Force in 1943 that day bombing might have had to be suspended if we had not found a way to blind the eyes of the German fire-control radars... Something had to be done quickly about the small Wurzburgs (radars) which controlled the German flak so accurately. [44]

Mr. Norton was well acquainted with the development of RCM equipment in the United States. He had been assistant director of the Propagation Unit, Operational Research Staff, Office Chief Signal Officer, Washington, D.C., so he was exceptionally well qualified to get the RCM program started with little delay. [45]

In a letter dated 10 May to Colonel Stanford, Command signal officer, Norton recommended various countermeasures against German radar installations. In a 31 May memorandum he recommended other things:

> (1) installation in each bomber of a jamming transmitter called 'carpet';
> (2) installation in each bomber of a small receiver called "boozer" to warn the pilot when his aircraft was under enemy radar observation;
> (3) consideration of the feasibility of modifying tactics in such a way as to reduce the effectiveness of the enemy's early warning radar system;
> (4) destruction of the enemy fighter aircraft, communication and navigational control system 'Benito' by means of direct attacks on the ground stations;
> (5) obtaining British cooperation for programs involving the use of 'Ground Mandrel' and 'Moonshine'; and
> (6) monitoring enemy reaction to the proposed program so as to evaluate its success.

In addition to making these recommendations, Mr. Norton designed an effective jammer to the German Wurzburg radar system. His recommendations and design were submitted to the commanding general of the Eighth Bomber Command, who promptly forwarded the plan to the Eighth Air Force headquarters with a request for speedy implementation. In this way, the Eighth Air Force RCM got under way. [46] However, it was not until October 1943 that Carpet was used during a raid against Bremen. [47]

References

1. "Eighth Air Force, History of Operations Analysis Section, October 1943–June 1945," Leslie H. Arps, 520.303-3, Archives, Simpson Historical Research Center, Maxwell Air Force Base, Alabama, 31–32.

2. Philip M. Morse, *In at the Beginnings: A Physicist's Life* (Cambridge, Mass., and London: MIT Press), 191–94.

3. Professor Hugh Miser, personal communication, March 1990.

4. "Eighth Air Force," 32.

5. Ibid., 32–33.

6. Ibid., 33.

7. Thomas M. Coffey, *Decision over Schweinfurt, The U.S. 8th Air Force Battle for Daylight Bombing* (New York: David McKay, 1977), chapter 9, especially p. 141 and p. 150.

8. Roger A. Freeman, *The Mighty Eighth, A History of the U.S. 8th Army Air Force* (London: Macdonald, 1970), 24.

9. "Eighth Air Force," 40–43.

10. *The Mighty Eighth*, 22–23.

11. Ibid.

12. "Eighth Air Force," 44–46.

13. Ibid., 46–48.

14. Ibid., 35–36.

15. *Decision over Schweinfurt*, 98.

16. Ibid., 117.

17. "Eighth Air Force," 120.

18. Ibid., 49.

19. Ibid., 51–52.

20. *The Mighty Eighth*, 9.

21. "Eighth Air Force," 27.

22. Ibid., 38.

23. "Operations Analysis, Headquarters, Army Air Forces, December 1943–June 1950," 143.504, Simpson Historical Research Center, Maxwell Air Force Base, Alabama, 8–10.

24. "History of the Battle Damage Subsection, Operational Analysis Section, Hq. Eighth Air Force, Dec. 1943–May 1945," 520.303-1, Simpson Historical Research Center, Maxwell Air Force Base, Alabama, 7–9.

25. "Operational Analysis in World War II, United States Army Air Forces, 15 October 1942–August 1945," LeRoy A. Brothers, 143.504, Simpson Historical Research Center, Maxwell Air Force Base, Alabama, 11.

26. "History of the Battle Damage Subsection," 11, and "Eighth Air Force," 129.

27. "History of the Battle Damage Subsection," 3.

28. *The Mighty Eighth*, 20.

29. Ibid., 31.

30. Irvin Stewart, *Organizing Scientific Research for War* (Boston: Little Brown, 1948), 85.

31. "Operational Analysis in World War II," 10.

32. "A Mathematician Describes His Work as Operations Analyst with the Eighth Air Force, 1945–46," G. Baley Price, 520.310, Simpson Historical Research Center, Maxwell Air Force Base, Alabama, 2.

33. "Report for Colonel W. B. Leach on the History and Development of the Bombs and Fuzes Subsection of the Operational Analysis Section, Hq. Eighth Air

Force, March 1943–April 1945," Simpson Historical Research Center, Maxwell Air Force Base, Alabama, 3.

34. Ibid., 4–5.

35. Ibid., 5.

36. Ibid., 6.

37. "Eighth Air Force," 81.

38. Ibid., 148.

39. Ibid., 94.

40. Ibid., 95.

41. James Phinney Baxter III, *Scientists against Time* (Boston: Little Brown, 1946), 95–96.

42. "Eighth Air Force," 95–96.

43. "Memorandum as to a Suggested Program for the Use of Blind Bombing Equipment in the Operations of this Command, Hq. VIII Bomber Command," 523.02 B, Simpson Historical Research Center, Maxwell Air Force Base, Alabama, 1–2.

44. *Scientists against Time*, 92–93.

45. "Operational Analysis in World War II," 11.

46. "Eighth Air Force," 104–5.

47. *Scientists against Time*, 94.

4

Operations Research in the Eighth Bomber Command June–December 1943

EIGHTH BOMBER COMMAND LEARNS ITS TRADE

By the beginning of June 1943, after ten months of operations, the Eighth Bomber Command began to grow in size and strength. As recently as April it still had only six operational groups of heavies—four groups of B-17s and two of B-24s. The demands of the war in the Pacific and in North Africa had made the planned buildup of the Eighth Bomber Command impossible in the early months of 1943. It was not until the end of May that the Eighth Bomber Command began to build the strength needed for its assigned mission. By the end of May it had twelve groups of heavies. The largest number of heavies to attack targets on a given day (Bremen on 17 April) in the months from January to April was 107, whereas on 29 May, 238 planes attacked targets in France. [1]

The German U-boats were such a menace to Allied shipping in 1942 and the first part of 1943 that submarine facilities in France and Germany were made the primary targets for the Eighth Bomber Command. In the first quarter of 1943, 63 percent of the tonnage of bombs dropped by the Eighth Bomber Command was directed toward submarine facilities; in the second quarter, 52 percent. About 15 percent of their bombs were dropped on aircraft installations, and close to another 15 percent on transportation sites—especially railroad marshalling yards.

A report edited by Wesley Frank Craven and James Lea Cate contains an analysis of damage done by this bombing. It concluded that operations of the Eighth Bomber Command in the first half of 1943 were significant not because they damaged the German war machine, but because they prepared the Eighth Bomber Command for future big blows against the German Air Force (GAF) and German industry. This period is described as a time when, "the day bombers were still learning their trade." [2]

Recall, for example, that in March the Operational Research Section of the

Eighth Bomber Command recommended that, when bombing in formation, bombs should be dropped on the leader rather than by individual sighting for range. It was also in March that lead bombardiers began to use the automatic flight-control equipment (AFCE) on bomb runs. With the "autopilot" equipment, the lead bombardier, with the controls of the bombsight, controlled the lateral motion of the airplane on the bomb run. Bombsighting and pilotage were synchronized by the autopilot with mechanical precision and provided a steadier bombing run than could be achieved by even the most experienced pilots.[3]

Bombing accuracy improved markedly in the Eighth Bomber Command during the first half of 1943 because better bombing techniques were discovered. In January and February a group's bombing was above average if 20 percent of bombs identifiable by photographic reconnaisance fell within 1,000 feet of the aiming point. By March and April it was common for groups to report that 30 to 40 percent of their bombs fell within 1,000 feet of the aiming point. In a number of instances, bombing was above the 50 percent mark.[4]

From January through May weather was the worst enemy of the daylight bombing program. There had been only thirty-four days in this period on which missions could be flown, an average of just under seven days each month. Need was intense for radar bombing techniques which would enable the Eighth Bomber Command to bomb through clouds and make the program less dependent on weather.

By April Germany had increased fighter plane production and moved units out of Russia and the Mediterranean. German fighter strength in the West had increased. The German Air Force (GAF) was preparing to defend Germany from the expected onslaught of the bomber offensive which had already begun, especially with the RAF night bombing over Germany. From January to May, the Eighth Bomber Command had flown twenty-one missions to targets in France and the Low Countries and thirteen to targets in Germany. The German targets were U-boat yards, U-boat bases, and industrial areas at Wilhelmshaven, Emden, Bremen, Kiel, Flensburg, Vegesack, and Hamm.[5] All of these targets except Hamm could be approached from the sea. The Eighth Bomber Command had not yet tried to bomb targets deep in Germany.

From January to May 1943 the Eighth Bomber Command lost 6.4 percent of the planes that actually attacked targets, or 5.6 percent of all planes which entered enemy-defended areas, whether they attacked or not. These figures include both those bombers lost in action and those damaged beyond repair. On the first four missions to targets in Germany (Wilhelmshaven-Emden, Emden, Wilhelmshaven, and Hamm) approximately 11 percent of the attacking planes were lost. Most of these losses resulted from German fighter attacks.

Of the bombers missing in action in the period from January to May, over half were lost to enemy aircraft. Some planes listed as lost to unknown causes doubtless met a similar fate. Flak, on the other hand, was credited with destroying slightly over 14 percent of those lost.

The battle damage reports of February-March, instituted by the ORS, reveal that 29 percent of all sorties resulted in reparable damage; only one in five suffered major damage. Of the damaged aircraft, however, approximately 59 percent were hit by flak. Flak damage no doubt enabled enemy fighters on many occasions to destroy the bomber. Though flak caused relatively few bomber losses during this stage of the war, it was a major source of damage. Because a plane damaged by flak became a straggler, flak proved an important indirect cause of losses. [6]

The experience of the Eighth Bomber Command in its first ten months of battle up through May 1943 showed that the GAF posed the gravest threat to the daylight strategic bombing offensive. USAAF commanders and planners believed that daylight bombing was tactically feasible, but they knew the GAF must be destroyed before the bomber offensive could achieve its purpose. [7]

Thus, on 10 June 1943 a new phase of the bomber offensive began. On that date the Combined Chiefs of Staff issued a directive marking the official beginning of the Combined Bomber Offensive (CBO). In general terms it set forth the objectives of the campaign which was to prepare the way for an invasion of Europe in May of 1944. It was to be a combined effort of the RAF and USAAF strategic air forces; the RAF would bomb strategic city areas at night, and the American force would strike "pinpoint" targets by day. [8]

From June 1943 until the spring of 1944 the CBO was to direct its effort against the GAF, a threat to both the strategic bomber offensive and a planned cross-channel invasion. In the second half of 1943 the bombers would destroy the German aircraft industry wherever it existed. This meant flying deep into Germany, beyond the range of Allied fighter escort. [9] The bombers bristling with their machine guns and flying in formation would have to defend themselves against German fighters. The time was ripe to analyze defensive flexible gunnery operations.

GUNNERY IN THE EIGHTH BOMBER COMMAND

The first three missions of the Eighth Bomber Command in June lost many planes. On 11 June at Wilhelmshaven-Cuxhaven eight out of 218 attacking planes were lost. At Bremen-Kiel on 13 June twenty-six out of 182 planes were lost. Twenty out of 222 attacking planes were lost during the 22 June attack on Huls-Antwerp. These were losses of 3.7, 14, and 9 percent respectively. As usual, most were lost during fighter attacks. The command recognized a potential "gunnery problem." In a personal communication, Professor Hugh Miser, an operations analyst in WWII, expresses the problem in these words:

The nub of it was that the sort of instinct one would use in aiming a gun from a fixed position at a traveling target is not valid when the gun is itself traveling at a high rate of speed. For example, from a fixed firing position, every hunter knows that you lead the bird with your shot; however, when the firing platform is itself moving at high speed, there are some situations in which you fire *behind* the bird, since the vector from the gun's velocity will carry it forward to the bird!

The ORS of the Eighth Bomber Command became involved with this problem in the person of Edwin Hewitt. Hewitt describes what happened.

> I was brought into contact with the gunnery problem in heavy bombardment operations through a visit to the Eighth Bomber Command by Captain Bright, an S-2 officer from the 91st Bomb Group. Capt. Bright had observed that there were enormous difficulties involved in hitting fighter airplanes from B-17's, and he had a notion that it might be possible to work out rules of some sort which would give specific deflections for gunners to take when firing. Colonel John M. Harlan, Chief of the Section, assigned me the problem of studying Capt. Bright's suggestion and trying to determine what simple rules, if any, could be devised for gunners to use. This occurred late in June 1943. [10]

When Dr. Hewitt began his work on gunnery, the command realized that gunnery had not been receiving the attention it deserved. Every other crew position was covered by well-regulated programs, though for gunners no such thing existed. Thus, there were provisions for division and air force bombardiers and navigators, but no comparable provisions at the Eighth Bomber Command headquarters for gunners. Gunnery training and gunnery development received no organized supervision from either the air force or air division levels. Because each group decided how much attention was directed to gunners and their problems, the extent and quality varied from group to group. The groups did not exchange information. It is safe to say that interest in gunnery was exceedingly low. [11] Hewitt played a major role in changing all this.

A further description of the state of affairs in gunnery in June 1943 appears in the history of the Gunnery Subsection by Dr. W. L. Ayres, who later succeeded Hewitt as its head. [12]

> At this time gunnery in the 8th Air Force was in urgent need of development. Many of the gunners were flying combat with little or no previous training in gunnery. Some were attempting to aim by the difficult apparent motion system. Most however were using the "by guess and by God" method. There were no gunnery offi-

cers who were trained as such. The existing gunnery officers were trained as armament officers, pilots or navigators, and gunnery was assigned usually as an additional duty. Frequently whatever knowledge they possessed of gunnery was obtained subsequent to their appointment as gunnery officer.

Edwin Hewitt was a mathematician who earned his Ph.D. from Harvard University in 1942. He and his colleague, Frank M. Stewart, were recruited out of their Harvard mathematics classrooms as operations analysts by John Harlan early in 1943. They taught their last classes on 12 March 1943. Aside from two weeks of indoctrination into operations research activities at the Army Air Force School of Advanced Tactics (AAFSAT) in Orlando, Florida, they were given no courses of instruction before going to the United Kingdom. They left the United States with Colonel Harlan and some other OR recruits, and flew the Bermuda-Azores-Lisbon route to Ireland and on to Bristol.

Hewitt knew nothing about gunnery when he arrived in England. Thus, when he was assigned to study aiming problems by Colonel Harlan, he had to start at the beginning. He spent the first couple of weeks reading available USAAF and U.S. Army documents on aerial gunnery and exterior ballistics. These were of no help to him. He did get "vigorous encouragement" from Captain George R. Weinbrenner, who was at the Eighth Bomber Command headquarters. Furthermore, Weinbrenner loaned him a "formidable" German treatise on ballistics, as well as a small RAF publication on the zone system of firing. Hewitt says: [13]

> The RAF manual, although I did not know it at the time, contained the solution to all of my difficulties, inasmuch as the zone system of aiming, or its very close relative, position firing, is undeniably the only practical system of deflection shooting for a gunner without a computing sight to use.

As Hewitt began to understand the mathematics of the gunnery problem he knew he needed tables giving time of flight of the bullet as a function of range and muzzle velocity. He also found that no such tables were available from American sources in the United Kingdom. His efforts to extrapolate such information from the sketchy RAF tables were unsuccessful. Furthermore, he was unable to find ballistic tables for .50 caliber ammunition.

On 20 July Hewitt went to London, where he met with an ordnance expert at the U.S. embassy who was unable to give him the information he needed. He also conferred with the gunnery experts at the British Ministry of Aircraft Production. Hewitt recalls:

> These gentlemen did not tell me very much about deflection shooting but did produce some elegant ballistic charts, from which it was

possible to compute time of flight and bullet drop for .50 caliber ammunition.[14]

It was not long until Hewitt himself uncovered the theoretical basis of the RAF's system of zone firing.

> After computing time of flight tables and considering the gunnery problem at some length, I found myself able to compute the deflection necessary to hit a fighter attacking the bomber, under the assumption that the fighter's path is rectilinear during the time of flight of the bullet. The computation was made much easier by the use of a formula produced by George Dowker [actually Clifford Dowker], of the IX Bomber Command Operational Research Section. Having computed the bomber's deflections for ordinary B-17 and B-24 altitudes and airspeeds, for several fighter speeds, and representative ranges and angles off, I observed that the principal variable to consider was angle off. It is this fact that the RAF used in devising the zone system of firing, which system I concluded was the best one to use.[15]

In June and July of 1943 the Operations Analysis Section (OAS) of the Ninth Bomber Command at Bengasi, North Africa, had already discovered the validity of the RAF zone system. Clifford Dowker, the mathematician (topologist), had verified its mathematical basis. George Taylor, Roger Haywood, and George Barwell (British gunnery officer) played major roles in implementing it there. The OAS of the Ninth Bomber Command had produced a report, "Defensive Aerial Gunnery," by Clifford Dowker dated 23 July 1943. It contained the formula referred to by Hewitt. Although liaison between operations analysis sections was poor, reverberations of work of the OAS of the Ninth Bomber Command reached the States and the Eighth Bomber Command. This happened because three of the five groups of B-24s in the Ninth Bomber Command in July were Eighth Bomber Command groups which had been temporarily assigned to the great ground-level raid on the Ploesti, Romania, oil refineries on 1 August 1943.

On 25 July 1943 Hewitt enrolled in the gunnery school at Bovingdon. The course was good on mechanics and maintenance of the caliber .50 machine gun but Hewitt observes:

> It gave absolutely no information on deflection shooting. Gunners, bombardiers, and navigators were going into combat without any knowledge whatever of how to aim their guns so as to hit attacking fighters.[16]

At that time only four (those in the Sperry upper and ball turrets) of the thirteen guns on the B-17 computed deflections automatically. Hewitt explains that: "The rest of the defense of the B-17, and all the defense of the

B-24D rested upon gunners who had to put in their own deflections." [17]

In the last week of July, 839 Eighth Bomber Command bombers attacked targets in Germany. Of these planes, ninety-seven were lost—over 11 percent of those attacking. Clearly German fighter resistance was stiffening. Hewitt says:

> I developed a feeling of extreme urgency about the gunnery problem, as fighter oppostion was growing more and more severe, and I at once considered steps to work the zone system into a form so that all gunners, even the least intelligent, could understand it and apply it readily. My first effort in this direction took the form of dividing each gunner's field of fire into zones, which were distinguished by reference marks on the bomber itself, in each of which zones the gunners were to keep a constant deflection. Explicit rules were written down for each gunner in terms of the particular sight he was using and for each of the zones encountered in shooting from his position. These rules, with explanatory diagrams, were set down on 'poop sheets' and were distributed literally to thousands of gunners. [18]

Hewitt's aiming instructions for the B-17 were dated 30 August. There were four sets of aiming instructions, for waist gunners, nose gunners, radioman gunners, and tail gunners.

The Schweinfurt-Regensburg missions were flown on 17 August. The great air battle which ensued between the Eighth Bomber Command and the GAF and the heavy losses on this mission soon became legendary. Subsequently, Hewitt found receptive audiences at his lectures on the zone system of aiming in defensive flexible gunnery. He first lectured to gunners of the 303d Bomb Group. Then, at the invitation of group commands, he lectured to gunners of the 384th and 351st Bomb Groups. He also lectured on the zone system to all officers in the command.

Encouraged by the good reception his work was receiving, Hewitt returned to Eighth Bomber Command headquarters, where he and John Harlan discussed the matter and agreed that the zone system should be "promulgated throughout the Command" as quickly as possible. Colonel Harlan then arranged an interview between General Fred L. Anderson, commanding general of the Eighth Bomber Command, Hewitt, and himself. [19] Twenty-three-year-old Hewitt, new mathematics Ph.D. from Harvard and neophyte gunnery expert—he had learned all he knew about gunnery in the last two months—was in the position to tell the commanding general of the Eighth Bomber Command how the gunners should have been aiming their guns for the past year. If he needed an advocate he had a good one in his chief, John Harlan, who, after the war, would be a U.S. Supreme Court justice. General Anderson, who strongly supported their proposal, sent Hewitt out to explain the zone system of aiming to the three division commanders, General Robert B. Williams of the First Division, General Hodges of the Second Division, and General Curtis LeMay of the Third Division. All three agreed that the zone system should be taught to all the air crews. [20]

Hewitt undertook the responsibility for implementing the zone system throughout the Eighth Bomber Command. In the first part of September he spent five days lecturing to the bomb groups of the Third Division. Capt. John S. Stark and Major Leon W. Blythe helped him. During this time he also prepared "poop sheets" describing the zone system of aiming for the gun positions on B-24 airplanes. These were similar, of course, to those he had previously prepared for the B-17. Then, in the middle of September, he began lecturing the groups of the Second Division, which was composed of B-24s. [21]

Teaching the zone system of aiming to the personnel of the Eighth Bomber Command was a huge task. Hewitt had to move quickly with the work in order not to lose ground. When he began gunnery studies in June, the Eighth Bomber Command had twelve groups of heavies. By the end of the year the force had more than doubled to twenty-six groups. Furthermore, as crews were lost or sent home after finishing their allotted number of missions, twenty-five at that time, they were replaced by new crews from the States who had not yet heard of the zone system. Hewitt made periodic visits to each group, lecturing to the gunners. These lectures involved tremendous effort. Each bomb group had its own base, and the bases were scattered over southeast England. Furthermore, traveling conditions were not good, and living conditions at the groups were austere. Hewitt came to know gunners and their problems more than any man in the air force. [22]

Hewitt describes some of his lecture techniques:

> After giving my lecture on deflection shooting about fifty times, as I had at the end of September 1943, I developed a definite form for it. I found that a certain amount of obscene humor was useful in holding the attention of my audience and it also appeared useful to try to make the boys realize that the German pilots were out for blood. A large majority of the gunners I met had very little aggressive spirit, and I tried to foster a spirit of aggression in them by describing typical Luftwaffe pilots' attitudes and by trying to make them understand that aerial combat is really in earnest. Curiously, very few gunners seemed to understand the seriousness of their situation until they had actually been under fighter attack. I capitalized on my civilian status by pointing out to the men that they could make any comments, however impolite, without fear of retribution from me, but I tried also to impress upon them the urgent necessity of their learning how to shoot and of remembering what I said. This lecturing continued with only a few variations

as the Air Force grew to its full size. [23]

The technique of using obscene humor in military lectures to the perpetually sex-starved troops (usually all men) seemed practically obligatory and was often effective. General Patton was, for example, an acknowledged master of the "art." [24]

Hewitt needed help with his work, and in October T/Sgt. Jillson (later to be 1st Lt.), one of Hewitt's former students at Harvard, became the second member of the Gunnery Subsection. Jillson had been with the 303d Bomb Group and had flown twenty missions as radio operator and gunner. He was able to take over a large part of the computing work as well as administrative detail. [25]

During October and November of 1943, Hewitt wrote, published, and had distributed throughout the command two pamphlets for gunners bearing the name "You Can't Miss It," one for B-17 airplanes and one for B-24 airplanes. The booklets were illustrated with excellent cartoons drawn by Sergeants Sweeney and Bosch of USAAF Headquarters in London. My version of "You Can't Miss It" bears the acknowledgment "Prepared by the O.R.S. Eighth Bomber Command with liberal borrowings from O.R.S. Ninth Bomber Command, Air Ministry and numerous other sources—drawn and drafted by Sgt. Sweeney and Sgt. Bosch."

The commanding general of Eighth Bomber Command, Fred L. Anderson, wrote the following foreword to the booklet:

> Since August 17, 1942, the Eighth Bomber Command has been at death grips with the Germans in the air. We have been destroying their factories, shipbuilding yards, U-boat bases and aircraft repair facilities. We have been destroying them at the cost of many bombers. With more accurate gunnery, many of these bombers might have been saved. We have the proper type of formations; we have the best guns in the world; we have the best men to handle these guns. The time may come not so far distant when we must dig in and slug it out with the Hun day after day. When that time comes, the men who handle these guns must shoot straight—straighter than they have ever shot before. The manual tells you how to do this. All gunners should read it carefully and should practice the lessons outlined continuously. If you do this, the Focke-Wulfs and Messerschmitts will soon learn that it is suicide to attack our heavy bombardment formations. [26]

When General Anderson wrote this foreword, the Eighth Bomber Command was experiencing a crisis due to high losses inflicted by the GAF. The battle between the Eighth Air Force and the GAF for air supremacy over Germany in 1943 was at a critical stage. General Anderson knew that the time "when we must dig in and slug it out with the Hun day after day" had already arrived. His foreword is an example of all-out backing of an ORS report by a commanding general.

Bombing Accuracy Subsection, June–December 1943

ORS becomes scorekeeper for the groups. A development which would help improve bombing accuracy began in May while General Longfellow still commanded the Eighth Bomber Command. In accordance with General Longfellow's instructions, bomb plots and summaries were prepared for each operation, beginning 1 May, 1943. Summaries of each operation showed the group, number of attacking aircraft, total bombs dropped, total bombs identified, number of bombs within 1,000 feet of aiming point, percent dropped within this distance, number of bombs within 2,000 feet of aiming point, percent dropped and percent identified within this distance, order of group over the target, and the target identification. The bombfalls of each group plotted were attached to the summary. The plots for May were sent to the commanding general of the First Bombardment Wing, who in a letter to ORS dated 11 June made the following request:

> I have just received a copy of your group bomb plots and summaries for the month of May. I find this an exceedingly interesting document which will be carefully analyzed within the Wing, and I should like very much to have any future documents of a similar nature which you produce.

Thereafter, requests began to come from the individual groups for the bombing accuracy reports, and copies were sent out upon request.

On 2 August General Anderson, who had succeeded General Longfellow as commanding general of the Eighth Bomber Command, requested the section to make a report of the bombing of all groups during July. When this was submitted to General Anderson he directed that a copy be sent to each bombardment wing commander. From then until the end of operations in 1945, monthly statements of Eighth Air Force visual bombing accuracy were prepared and sent to each subordinate unit of the command, including individual groups. [27]

The section, realizing that publication of these reports would place it in the position of an official scorer, was apprehensive. Arps says,

> The apprehensions experienced prior to the publication of the bombing accuracy plots and monthly statements were more than fully realized. The groups became interested to an extraordinary degree in the reports of their individual performances. [28]

After publication of the results of each operation and the monthly report, the Bombing Accuracy Subsection received innumerable inquiries. The groups, combat wings, and divisions soon began to make their own photographic analyses. If they believed the ORS made an error, a correction was requested. Each request or complaint was carefully studied, and if an error was made, which seldom happened, it was corrected and published promptly. Unquestionably, the monthly statements and the bomb plots and summaries stimulated interest in good bombing. They also served to bring the section to the attention of the field units. From the time of publication through the end of the war, a constant stream of group commanders, bombardiers, and operating personnel visited the subsection. The steady flow of visitors served as a useful medium for exchanging information, and enabled the subsection to use fresh ideas from the field.

Publishing the bombing accuracy summaries and monthly reports made the Bombing Accuracy Subsection a very effective force in the improvement of Eighth Air Force bombing. On the other hand, it substantially increased the subsection's work. Indeed, as more groups were added and attacks became more frequent, the subsection found it increasingly difficult to carry on this phase of its work. Because the volume of work increased so much, in August 1944 the subsection discontinued publication of the bomb plots, but not the monthly statement. Arps said it was his firm conviction that "the Subsection would never have played the role that it did had it not published the bombing accuracy figures."

The need to secure additional personnel for the Bombing Accuracy Subsection became acute. In June 1943 T/Sgt. Ray J. Thompson (Torkowsky) and S/Sgt. Carl J. Boria joined the subsection. S/Sgt. Eileen Hazelton, WAC, came in July, and Major Charles R. Darwin, a photo interpreter, was added to the subsection in September.[29] Also in September negotations were in progress back in the States to persuade G. Baley Price to become an operations analyst.

The recruitment of G. Baley Price.   Griffith Baley Price earned his A.B. degree from Mississippi College in 1925 and his M.A. and Ph.D. degrees from Harvard University in 1928 and 1932 respectively. In September 1943 he was a professor of mathematics at the University at Kansas at Lawrence. Price's own account of his recruitment gives a glimpse of the university scene during the war. It also shows techniques Bart Leach used and difficulties he experienced in recruiting civilian scientists for operations analysis work. Price discussed Leach's reliance on the "scientific establishment," represented by mathematicians Warren Weaver of the Applied Mathematics Panel and R. G. D. Richardson of Brown University. Price wrote in a memoir of 1945:

> As a result of the Army Specialized Training (AST) Programs and the V-12 programs of the Navy, the summer of 1943 was a nightmare for any mathematician still in an academic position. As for myself, I was in charge of the mathematics courses for approximately 750 men in an AST Program at the University of Kansas.

By September the work was under control, but it had been a struggle; one of my instructors was the Head of the Voice Department, and another was the Head of the Botany Department.

When I came from a class one Monday morning about the middle of September, I was told that the Chancellor wanted to see me in his office. It was very unusual for me to be called to the Chancellor's Office, so of course I was immediately curious. On reporting, I was told that there had been a telephone call from Washington saying that the Army Air Forces wanted me for some special work. What was the work and where? There was no indication of the nature of the work, but it was hinted that it would be in the general area of the Pacific. I was asked to consider the proposition and to reply by telephone that afternoon.

Of course, the situation was an impossible one: you cannot consider a proposition about which you know nothing. I discussed the call with my wife at noon, and the only conclusion forthcoming was that we needed more information.

I talked to Chancellor Malott again that afternoon and asked whether it would be possible to go to Washington to find out about the work. I was told no funds were available for such travel. The Chancellor obviously was not anxious to have me accept, and he proposed that we telephone Washington and give the names of three other mathematicians that could do the work as well or better than I could. But Colonel Leach's office replied that these men had been tried already, and that I could get full information from Capt. Hammonds, who would be in Lawrence on Thursday of the same week.

Capt. Hammonds, when he arrived, did in fact give me a lot of information. I was wanted in the South Pacific. (I was never quite told whether I was being considered for a place with the Fifth Air Force or the Thirteenth Air Force, but I always thought I would go to New Caledonia with the Thirteenth.) I was told that Dr. James A. Clarkson had been doing similar work with the Eighth Air Force for about nine months, and some of the problems he had worked on were described to me. Finally, I was told that Dr. Warren Weaver had recommended me for the work. (I learned later that I was recommended to him by Dean R. G. D. Richardson of Brown.)

I had now learned enough to convince me that I should give serious consideration to the request. Eventually I wrote Dean Richardson, whom I often called on for advice, and he suggested that this was probably my niche in the war effort, and that I should accept it.

All this time I had been reading about the South Pacific, preparing myself at least mentally for a life in the tropics—in hot and humid jungles where uncontrolled insects and diseases abounded—and in less civilized parts of the world. With this background I telephoned Colonel Leach's office to say that I would accept the assignment. They were pleased that I would go; but imagine my surprise when I was told that the group going to the South Pacific had been filled, and that I would be sent to England instead!...(this experience was) my first lesson in the ways of the Army, from which I eventually learned patience and an unquestioning acceptance of what the day brought forth. [30]

These events took place in the last half of September 1943. On Friday, 8 October, Price received a telephone call from Colonel Leach's office saying that he should be in Washington on Monday morning, 18 October. On Saturday morning, 9 October, Baley Price met his last class,

> ...a fine class of about fifty Army men. I well remember the shocked hush that fell on the group when I told them that henceforth Miss Babcock would meet them in my place—that I was going overseas immediately for the Army Air Forces. Such are the contradictions of modern war; the men in the Army stayed at home to go to college, and I, who had never had any connection or experience with an army, went overseas to fight the war. [31]

A few words about Deane W. Malott, chancellor of the University of Kansas at the time Price left, are relevant. He, in fact, had divided loyalties at the time he essentially advised Price not to leave. Unknown to Price, since 10 July 1943 Malott had been an educational adviser to the Army Air Forces Technical Training Command. In fact, at the very time Price was leaving, Malott became the first chief of the OAS of the Second Air Force. [32]

Price begins his apprenticeship.   Baley Price and William J. Pilat, who was to be a member of the Loss and Battle Damage Subsection, reported for duty together to Colonel Harlan at the Eighth Bomber Command headquarters at Wycombe Abbey on Thanksgiving Day, 1943. Harlan lectured them on security, introduced them to the other consultants, and left Price at the Nissen hut occupied by Bombing Accuracy. There he met Dr. Youden and Colonel Scott. Dr. Clarkson was away on sick leave. After a discussion which lasted an hour or more, Price was handed the Bombing Accuracy reports with the suggestion that he study them. His apprenticeship had begun. He said,

> At this time and for many months to come I contributed little to the work of the Section, but I was studying and preparing for work that would come later. I read reports, training manuals of all kinds; manuals on bombs, meteorology, navigation and even technical orders. I listened to the discussions that went on in the

office constantly when visitors came or that arose in the course of
settling the day's work. Slowly I began to understand what was
going on. [33]

Informal interaction with lead bombardiers. Much of the section's best work
was done informally through discussions with group bombardiers and their
crews. Because the subsection found itself in a scorekeeping role, delegations
frequently came in to discuss their results on a particular mission. Price
describes such a session.

> A typical delegation would consist of a Wing Bombardier and two
> or three of his Group Bombardiers. They were always warmly
> greeted—they were usually known from previous visits. After
> coats had been laid aside, cigarettes lighted, and hands warmed by
> the stove, the delegation would launch into the subject of bombing.
>   Dr. Youden usually took over the discussion at this time. The re-
> cent record—and especially improvement—of the Air Force called
> for comment. Soon Dr. Youden was sitting on the corner of his
> desk lecturing the group in a stentorian voice. And sooner or later
> he came around to his favorite topic, small patterns.
>   "Make your patterns small," he would say, and then he would
> go over the record that was kept on a large chart on the wall. This
> chart showed the relation between aiming errors, pattern size, and
> the percentage of bombs within one thousand feet of the aiming
> point.
>   "Hit the Hun with the clinched fist—not with the open hand,"
> he would add in ringing phrases. "Make sure the toggle-eers in the
> wing ships get their bombs away quick. You might get still better
> results if you salvoed your bombs."
>   Eventually some question would arise about a particular bomb-
> fall, and Colonel Scott would take over. With a remarkable mem-
> ory, it seemed that he could recall the date, target, and every detail
> of every operation conducted by the Air Force. Before the discus-
> sion was over, Colonel Scott usually took them to the other end
> of the hut, laid out the photographs of the bombfalls in question,
> and convinced them that he knew the facts—even though *they* may
> have been on the mission and thought they had seen something
> very different.
>   The group would finally leave with many apologies for taking so
> much of our time but with our insisting that it was our business
> to talk with them, that we hoped they would come again. [34]

Through these informal contacts the subsection was able to learn many
things which were never disclosed in official reports. It was also able to give

the lead crews hints and suggestions which they were able to develop and incorporate in new and improved practices.

Bombing accuracy takes some flak. The Bombing Accuracy Subsection's role of scorekeeping created some very difficult situations that required all of its skill and tact. For example, Colonel Preston, commanding officer of the 379th Group, forwarded through channels an extensive memorandum, documented with photographs, in which he challenged the treatment and disposition by Bombing Accuracy of a number of his group's bombfalls. Colonel Scott, viewing the memorandum as a serious challenge to the accuracy and integrity of the section's work, proceeded to prepare his reply with the same care that he would have used in preparing his case in a million-dollar lawsuit. He reviewed the photographs again and finally wrote a reply in which he discredited Colonel Preston's objections one by one. Then, instead of forwarding it through channels, he and Dr. Youden delivered it in person. After Colonel Preston spent an evening examining the reply, he admitted his complete defeat. Thereafter, he was one of the strongest friends and supporters that Bombing Accuracy had. [35]

The work of the subsection as reflected in its reports. Between June and December 1943 Eighth Bomber Command had grown from twelve to twenty-six groups. This more than doubled the work of the Bombing Accuracy Subsection. In spite of this, reports were written on "Effect of Spacing between Combat Wings on Bombing Accuracy" dated 11 September 1943, "Analysis of Certain Practice Bombing Bombfall Patterns" dated 7 October 1943, "Analysis of the Eighth Bomber Command Operations from the Point of View of Bombing Accuracy—1 January 1943–15 October 1943" dated 31 October 1943, and "Effect of Altitude on Bombing Accuracy" dated 24 November 1943. There were also seven memoranda on bombing accuracy, most written to the commanding general on topics like "Position of Lead Bombardier's Bombfall in the Group Pattern" and "Effect of Size of Attacking Force on Bombing Efficiency." The subsection was working at full capacity.

Preliminary action in the battle against the buzz bombs. On Christmas Eve 1943 Baley Price noticed heavy bombers returning from missions flying low over High Wycombe in formations of six planes. This was unusual. Formations returning from missions seldom returned at low altitude over High Wycombe and at that time the typical number of planes in a formation was eighteen or twenty-one. Something unusual was up.

On Christmas Day work began at the usual hour; clearly the operations of the preceding day had been on a large scale, and they involved something significantly different. Little was said at the time, and most of that was whispered, but the fact was that the Eighth Air Force had conducted its first large scale operation against the sites the Germans were constructing in the Pas-de-Calais region of France for launching the V-1 secret weapon against

Great Britain. Baley Price gave an excellent verbal picture of the subsection at work at this time:

> The Bombing Accuracy hut was a scene of great activity. Colonel Scott was busy with yards of teletyped field orders which specified the targets, the forces on each, the bomb loadings and so on. It was necessary to make an abstract of these orders before the work of analyzing the photographs could begin. Sergeant Torkowsky (Thompson) had the strike photographs, and he began as soon as possible the long task of segregating the bombfalls and determining the formations that had dropped them. Colonel Scott assisted with this work, and it was from this intimate contact with the photographs that he gained his detailed knowledge of the operations. Major Darwin was busy assembling target data needed for assessing the accuracy of the large number of "Crossbow" or "Noball" targets [V-1 and V-2 launching sites] that had been attacked for the first time the preceding day.
>
> As the analysis proceeded, Corporal Boria and Major Darwin prepared "spot photographs." Corporal Hazelton transferred these to the books in which the bombfalls for the various Groups were kept, and at the same time obtained a carbon impression which Boria inked and otherwise drafted to get the master hectograph copy for printing the bomb plots. Miss Hazelton did the necessary typing.
>
> This particular report called for a lot of careful planning. Because the Air Force had bombed with sixes and nines the preceding day, there were approximately seventy-five bombfalls to be plotted. Formerly the reports had contained one bombfall on each page, but now it was necessary to make changes in order to keep the amount of printing within reasonable limits. Such matters were always decided by discussions among all the consultants in Bombing Accuracy. In this case a scheme was worked out whereby three bombfalls were shown on each page. Even so the printing job was a big one: Bombing Accuracy produced in its own hut and with its own personnel some 60 or 70 copies of a multicolored hectographed report of about 25 pages to cover the operations of December 24 alone! [36]

THE BOMBS AND FUZES SELECTION SUBSECTION

The proper selection of bombs and fuze settings for each target was at the heart of effective bombing. Occasionally bombers fought their way to the target against enemy opposition, dropped their bombs with accuracy, and later learned that the mission had not succeeded because the settings were improper, or bombs inappropriate for the target, or even because bombs were duds. Selecting bombs and fuzes went hand in glove with assessing bomb damage. Both tasks became the primary work of the Bombs and Fuzes Selection Subsection.

The three civilian analysts who constituted the subsection were well qualified for their work by virtue of education and experience. Bissell Alderman, who had begun work on 31 March 1943, had been an assistant professor of architecture at MIT, whereas Charles Kring, who came at the same time, was a civil engineer who had been working as a structural engineer with an architect-engineering firm. The third member, Alfred Hedefine, arrived 21 July 1943. He too was a civil engineer employed by an engineering firm in New York City. [37]

Incendiary bombs. Alderman discovered that the Eighth Bomber Command was not using available incendiary bombs. He investigated the three bombs available and found that each had serious defects. For example, the M-50, a four-pound magnesium bomb in 100- and 500-pound quick-opening clusters was not sufficiently aimable. Furthermore, its quick-opening clusters endangered other aircraft in the formation. The M-47, a 100-pound gasoline jell-filled bomb, could not be carried in economical loads in either the B-17 or the B-24, and it had too much trail to be set into the bombsight with the bombing tables then available. (Trail is the lagging of the bomb behind the plane, caused by the resistance of the air.) The M-69, a six-pound oil bomb in 500-pound, quick-opening clusters had the same disadvantages as the M-50 and also lacked adequate striking velocity. Alderman wrote a memorandum to Harlan about the incendiary bomb problem.

The subsection believed that the effectiveness of bombing could be increased by using incendiaries on suitable targets. The M-47, for example, if it could be made aimable in the Norden bombsight, would be more effective on some targets, even though the total weight of a bombload of M-47s was substantially lower than a load of larger general purpose bombs. Kring and Hedefine worked out a set of tables whereby a false disc speed could be set into the bombsight to overcome the trail deficiency. These tables were tested, distributed, and used occasionally on operations. At first the crews and even the operations officers at headquarters opposed the use of incendiaries. They believed that the best way to destroy a target was with heavy high explosive bombs. Consequently, the subsection spent considerable time convincing people of the effectiveness of incendiary bombs. After 1 July 1943, however, when General Fred Anderson became commanding general of the Eighth Bomber Command, incendiaries began to be used extensively. In fact, on some occasions the supply was inadequate for the demand.

In the early days of the subsection the analysts became thoroughly familiar with the bombsight, the bomb release mechanisms, and the bomb bay loading facilities. They worked with the Ordnance and Chemical Warfare Sections to devise ways of loading the bombs to achieve maximum loads. In particular, the subsection succeeded in increasing the loads of the M-47 incendiaries. With little help from the States, the Eighth Bomber Command, particularly the Chemical Warfare Section, developed and had manufactured its own equipment for increasing the loads of the M-47s by clustering the bombs on their racks. [38]

Operational experimentation with bombs and fuzes. From June through October 1943 the subsection issued a series of reports on selected attacks on certain targets. These were titled "Report on the Effectiveness of Bombs and Fuzes." Each report focused primarily on the effectiveness of the weapon used, usually a single high explosive weapon. The studies isolated and analyzed the areas damaged by single direct hits in order to estimate the effectiveness of a given weapon and compare it with others.

For these analyses and most later ones, damage was separated into two categories: *structural* damage, including the destruction of trusses, beams, columns, and so forth; and *superficial* damage, including the stripping of roof cover and skylights, and damage to secondary structural members such as roof purlins.

The first two reports, written jointly by Alderman and Kring, concerned the damage to the aircraft engine factories at LeMans and Nantes on 4 July 1943. Alderman and Kring, challenging the conventional .025-second-delay fuze settings, recommended .01 fuze settings instead. They argued that the bombs with the longer delay of .025 seconds caused little fragmentation and used most of their force to form craters. A .01-second-delay setting, however, would cause the bombs to detonate close to the roof structural members, causing a great deal of destructive fragmentation. Their predictions were proved true. On the Nantes target, 500-pound general purpose bombs fuzed .025 were used. At LeMans, 500-pound general purpose bombs fuzed .01 were used. The structural damage at LeMans was twice that at Nantes.

Since doubt still lingered among some operations officers, the experiment was repeated twice in attacks on the aircraft engine works at Villacoublay on 14 July and 24 August and similar targets. The reports, Villacoublay I and Villacoublay II, each showed that the .01 fuzing results in twice as much damage as the .025.

Reports on the Schweinfurt, Frankfurt-Heddernsheim, and Anklam missions in August and September dealt primarily with damage caused by the M-47 incendiary. At each target it was possible to identify with reasonable accuracy the areas of high explosive and incendiary damage, but it was not possible to determine how many incendiaries caused the fire damage. However, on each target, the M-47s were many times more effective than the high explosive bomb in causing structural damage. After the circulation of these reports *all* objections to incendiaries ceased.

A report on the Marienburg, Poland, raid of 9 October was prepared by Hedefine. For that attack, a mixture of 500-pound general purpose bombs fuzed .01 and M-47 incendiaries was used. This raid, one of the most accurate and damaging of the Eighth Bomber Command, completely destroyed over 35 percent of the important building area of the factories. The bomb damage report was not circulated, however, because the areas of damage of the M-47 and high explosive bombs could not be accurately separated.

The destructivity of three high explosive bombs used in the Paris area on comparable targets in the period April to December 1943 was carefully analyzed. All of the targets were single-story steel-framed buildings. The analysis revealed that on such targets one ton of 500-pound general purpose bombs fuzed .025 caused the same damage, approximately 6,400 square feet, as one ton of 1,000-pound general purpose bombs. Furthermore, one ton of 500-pound general purpose bombs fuzed .01 did approximately 16,000 square feet of effective damage. [39]

The amount of damage a bombing caused depended upon many things, including bombing accuracy, the bomb's size, fuzing, the type of bomb (high explosive, fragmentation, or incendiary), the number of bombs, and the nature of the target. Because the selection of bombs and fuzes resulted in such different degrees of effectiveness, the job was clearly of great importance and complexity. According to these statistics, half as many missions were required to destroy a target of one-story steel-framed buildings if 500-pound general purpose bombs fuzed .01 were used instead of 500- or 1,000-pound general purpose bombs fuzed .025.

Attendance at the OPS conferences. Although Alderman, Kring, and Hedefine were ideally fitted by education and professional experience to select the bombs and fuze settings for each target, recognition and acceptance of this was not immediate.

Alderman and Kring were summoned to their first operations (OPS) conference to advise on weapon selection for the 13 June attack on U-boat building yards at Kiel and Flensburg. They recommended their "new weapon," the 500-pound general purpose bomb fuzed .01 tail and .1 nose, because the majority of the important buildings were single-story steel-frame buildings. Also, it was believed the .01 fuze would detonate the bomb inside the submarine hull before it had a chance to pass through the hull.

Beginning about 1 July, Alderman and Kring were requested to be available for regular consultation at the OPS conferences. At first they were expected to be on duty in their office awaiting a summons. Because this system did not work well, their chief, Colonel Harlan, helped arrange for one of them to attend the OPS conferences each day. The added duty of attending the daily conferences was relieved when Hedefine became trained and began to take his turn. The OPS conferences became their most important work. Alderman says of the work of the OPS conference:

> We concentrated all our energies on it.
> Much of our work in the conference was taken up with

constant educating of the new (and old) controllers. The turnover of controllers was very high, and it was our job to brief them on the more recent developments in bomb damage and bomb effectiveness. Whenever the Commanding Officer changed, or whenever a new deputy chief took over the OPS conferences, the educational program had to begin all over again. Very few of the newcomers had ever been indoctrinated in the scientific approach to the selection of bombs and fuzes. Some of them were Big Bomb enthusiasts; they had to see large areas of damage even though fewer in number. One controller always wanted to use fragmentation bombs on all German targets just "to kill the bastards." There were many conceptions about bomb size, bomb fuzing, penetration, fragmentation effect and so on. Their feelings could never be brushed off but had to be reckoned with patiently and carefully in each case. It was not always easy, but it was a part of the job that had to be done. [40]

Blind bombing.   In June 1943 the Radar and Radio Countermeasures Subsection consisted of Dr. Tuttle, one of the original six members of the section, Major Warren E. Bales, a Gee-H specialist, and Kenneth A. Norton, a specialist in Radio Countermeasures (RCM).

In the fall of 1942 experiments in blind bombing had been conducted by the Eighth Bomber Command in the use of Gee, a type of radar navigational device which depended on beams transmitted from ground stations. By January 1943 General Eaker had eight B-24s equipped with Gee. That month several flights of these planes, either singly or in groups of four, were made to enemy objectives for the purpose of alerting and harassing air raid defenses that might otherwise have relaxed under the protecting blanket of cloud. These intruder or "moling" missions were not successful. The equipment was too valuable to be risked on missions of such small intrinsic value except under ideal protective cloud conditions. The weather, though too bad for visual bombing, could often clear suddenly and sufficiently to make a "moling" mission too hazardous. The "moling" experiment was therefore abandoned in March 1943.

A more promising British blind bombing device was Oboe. However, the British used Oboe only in their fast night-flying Mosquitoes and would not let it be used by the Eighth Bomber Command for daylight bombing for fear a radar set might be captured. [41]

In a memorandum dated 11 July, "Memorandum as to a Suggested Program for the Use of Blind Bombing Equipment in the Operations of this Command," Dr. Tuttle recommended the use of the British H2S and the improved American version, H2X, as quickly as possible. H2S (and its American counterpart, H2X) was a self-contained set carried in the plane which transmitted a beam that scanned the ground below and produced a map-like picture of the terrain on a cathode ray tube. Tuttle also recommended the use of the British Gee-H, provided that its operational range proved to be 350 miles. Later, on 17 August, he urged the command to proceed with Gee-H. His proposals were adopted by the command, and the Gee-H program was initiated.

Successful Gee-H operations involved several distinct steps including 1) training the crews, 2) preparing lattice charts, computing data for use by combat crews on operations, coordinating RAF beacon operators, and other operational planning, 3) supervising Gee-H maintenance, and 4) analyzing Gee-H operations to improve the use of Gee-H equipment.

In every phase the subsection played an important role. Dr. Tuttle and Major Bales frequently visited the operating groups to furnish guidance and assistance during crew training. Dr. Tuttle also was instrumental in arranging for trained crews to use British trial bombing ranges to practice bombing with Gee-H. In addition, the subsection did all the calculation work needed to make the practice bombing effective. Despite these efforts the Eighth Bomber Command did not fly its first Gee-H mission until 28 January 1944. [42]

The use of H2S and H2X began sooner. Plans for a radar bombing program using H2S and H2X to begin in the fall of 1943 had received priority consideration. By 20 September 1943 the Radiation Laboratory had built and installed twelve H2X sets in B-17 aircraft, and twelve navigators had been trained in their operation. Meanwhile, H2S installations were also being built. Four RAF-trained operators began teaching other navigators. In September General Eaker was able to operate a Pathfinder group, the 482d, composed of three squadrons, one equipped with British radars, mostly H2S, and the other two with American radars, mostly H2X. It was the function of these specially manned and equipped bombers to fly with formations of bombers in the position of group or wing leader. The H2S planes led their first combat mission on 27 September 1943.

The first two large blind bombing missions were both to Emden, Germany. Emden was selected because it was an important small seaport (one mile in diameter). Furthermore, because it was on the coast, it would stand out better on radar scopes than an inland target would. The missions are described in an ORS report, "Memorandum on Blind Bombing Aspects of Missions of September 27 and October 2, 1943 (Emden)," dated 27 October 1943. [43,44]

On 27 September, 305 B-17s of the First and Second Bombardment Divisions were dispatched to Emden with H2S planes acting as guides. Each division, acting as a separate task force, was assigned two Pathfinder planes. By the time the target area was reached, however, equipment failure had left only one H2S set operating in each task force. Each force flew in three combat wings with the Pathfinder leading the first wing. All bombers of the first wing were to bomb on signal from the Pathfinder, which would drop marker bombs to guide the following wings. Should the cloud cover break, the wings were to bomb visually. As it turned out, the second wing of the first force bombed on the marker. The second wing of the second force found a break in the 9/10 cloud cover and attempted to bomb visually. By the time each of the third wings arrived in the vicinity of their targets no evidence of the markers could be found, so they attacked targets of opportunity in the neighborhood. Both of the divisions were escorted by P-47s equipped with belly tanks. This enabled the Thunderbolts to escort the bombers for the first time all the way to a German target. Although stiff enemy opposition was encountered, only seven of the 244 bombers which attacked Emden or targets of opportunity were lost, and only two P-47s were lost.

On 2 October the Eighth Bomber Command sent out an even bigger Pathfinder-led force to Emden—349 bombers. As before, there were two divisions of three wings each. The first wing of each division was led by a Pathfinder. This time 339 planes attacked the target; only two bombers were lost.

An analysis of the bombing accuracy concluded that three of the four leading wings of the twelve wings in both missions that bombed on the H2S planes achieved an average circular error of half to one mile. This is reasonably small. The average circular error is the circle centered at the aiming point within which one half of the bombs fell. The fourth wing had an average circular error of two to three miles. Although one of the leading combat wings caused considerable damage, none of the other bomb falls damaged the assigned target. Confusion at the initial point on the first mission and a high wind during the second, blowing marker smoke rapidly from the target area, helped explain an average circular error of more than five miles.

Though these results were disappointing, H2S and H2X bombing accuracy could and would be improved. Clearly, the wings bombing on the Pathfinders performed the best. Assigning a Pathfinder to each wing, or better yet, a Pathfinder to each group was one way to improve accuracy. Mastering the tactics and techniques of radar bombing was another way to achieve better accuracy. Radar bombing was also safer than visual bombing. Flak was less accurate, and enemy fighters, since they had to intercept through the overcast, were at a disadvantage. [45]

No further radar bombing missions were flown by the Eighth Bomber Command in October. However, on 3 November, 539 B-17s and B-24s led by eleven Pathfinders attacked the port of Wilhelmshaven, Germany. Nine of the Pathfinders used the American H2X for the first time. The remaining two used the British H2S. As with Emden a month earlier, Wilhelmshaven was chosen because it provided the kind of target best picked up by the H2X radar screens at that time. Though no bombing analysis of this mission appears among ORS reports and memoranda of the Eighth Air Force ORS, "Combat Chronology" notes that the aiming point was destroyed. [46]

Fifteen of the twenty-one missions flown in November and December used Pathfinders. Blind bombing had made its debut. The ORS, however, could not write reliable accuracy reports of the blind bombing. Techniques for identifying the bombfalls had yet to be developed, and personnel had yet to be obtained and trained. Nevertheless it was clear to the command that H2X blind bombing was not precision bombing. However, it promised to free the daylight bombing program from the absolute limitations imposed by overcast skies. It was now possible to strike strategic industrial centers even when the prospects for visual bombing seemed poor.

There were those in the air force who believed that a frankly stated program of area bombardment should be added to the CBO plan, at least for winter, which would resemble and supplement the RAF area bombing campaign. [47]

In a report the ORS Loss and Battle Damage Subsection evaluated the blind bombing program as of the end of December 1943:

> Blind bombing seems to offer strong defensive advantages. Our record thus far with this type of operation suggests that restricted visibility not only diminishes enemy fighter opposition (either by keeping his fighters on the ground or by rendering their ability to intercept more difficult), but also may render his flak less effective. Such advantages as these, however, may well be outweighed by the limited offensive effectiveness of this type of operation. Even when we shall have mastered its technique, it remains an alternative to precision bombing which permits us to mount our offensive more frequently, but it is appropriate only for occasions when the more accurate alternative is not feasible. [48]

Radio Countermeasures—Carpet, Window, and Chaff

Kenneth A. Norton had been the RCM expert of the section since his arrival on 23 April. He recommended to the commanding general on 31 May that each bomber carry a transmitter called 'Carpet' to jam Germany's gun-laying radar. He included with his recommendation the design of a jammer for the German Wurzburgs.

The Eighth Bomber Command used Carpet for the first time on 8 October 1943, during a mission to Bremen and Vegesack. Forty planes in the leading wing of the Third Division carried Carpet equipment; no planes of the First Division carried Carpet equipment. Of 399 bombers dispatched, 357 bombed targets in Bremen and Vegesack. Opposition from both enemy aircraft and antiaircraft was very strong. Thirty American bombers were lost and twenty-six others received major damage. The GAF, by their records, had thirty-three of its fighters destroyed and fifteen damaged. The Carpet-protected Third Division had 60 percent of its planes damaged by flak. By comparison, the First Division, without the Carpet jammers, suffered 75 percent flak damage. This degree of flak damage shows why the air force began to pay very careful attention to radio countermeasures. Carpet was used on all of the remaining missions in October. It became standard equipment in the Eighth Air Force. Norton wrote one report, "The Operational Effectiveness of the Radio Countermeasure 'Carpet'" dated 7 November 1943. He also cooperated with the Loss and Battle Damage Subsection in producing another report, "A Comparison of Losses and Flak Damage between Carpet Protected Groups and Other Groups Going to the Same Target on Ten Carpet Operations."[49,50,51]

Window, another effective jamming tactic for blinding the German gun-laying radar, was pioneered by the British. Fourteen-by-twenty-one-inch sheets of metal-coated paper, dropped from the planes, produced echoes on German radar receivers which imitated echoes produced by Allied bombers. Great Britain's use of Window in mid-1943 was a dramatic success. The British chose the 728-bomber night attack on Hamburg on 24 July 1943 for Window's first use. The Americans followed this with day raids on Hamburg U-boat yards without Window. On 25 July sixty-eight bombers attacked; fifty-four attacked the following day.

On 27 July 722 British bombers using Window conducted a second major night area bombing raid against Hamburg. Similar raids were carried out by the British on Hamburg on the nights of 29 July and 2 August. These massive raids produced fire storms which devastated the city and people of Hamburg. The RAF suffered very low bomber loss. Because Window "blinded" German radar equipment so effectively, the Americans, as quickly as possible, adopted their version, called Chaff.[52]

Norton wrote a "Preliminary Memorandum as to Possible Uses of Window in the Operations of the Eighth Bomber Command" dated 19 September 1943. He also wrote a "Supplementary Memorandum Relative to the Use of Window for the Confusion of the Enemy Gunlaying Radar Sets in the Immediate Vicinity of the Target" dated 30 October 1943.[53]

Window was modified by the Eighth Bomber Command in the fall of 1943 for use in large formations of bombers. This new form, Chaff, consisted of foil strips about 1/16 of an inch wide and eleven inches long. Two thousand strips, dropped in the target area by the bombers, were estimated to be electrically equivalent for radar confusion purposes to a B-17 bomber.[54] Chaff was used for the first time on 20 December when more than 470 heavy American bombers attacked the port of Bremen.[55]

Germany, after Hamburg, worked frantically on antijamming equipment, beginning a relentless warfare between radar experts on each side. However, none of the German antijamming devices was entirely successful. German sources after the war claimed that under heavy Window or Carpet seldom were more than 10 to 40 percent of their radars effective. They were effective only long enough to take an altitude fix for use in barrage fire.[56]

Because the RAF and the Eighth Air Force viewed the German early warning radar and gun-laying radar as such serious threats, on 28 December the Eighth Bomber Command was charged with forming and training a special organization called the Radio Countermeasures Unit. It was to have twenty-four specially equipped heavy bombers, contributed by both the Eighth Bomber Command and the RAF, to use radio countermeasures against enemy defenses. [57]

The Loss and Battle Damage Subsection through December 1943

Personnel. Dr. G. R. Gettell, a former professor of economics at Yale University, had been with the Loss and Battle Damage Subsection since 14 April. George P. Shettle, a former industrial analyst in New York City, had been with the subsection since 21 May 1943. William J. Pilat, previously an advertising executive, professor of business administration, and rationer with the Office of Price Administration (OPA), had reported for duty on 26 November. Other civilian consultants came later. Since Gettell had arrived in April, the Eighth Bomber Command had grown from six bomb groups to twenty-six by December 1943. In the second half of 1943, the Eighth Bomber Command flew four times as many sorties as it did in the first half. The subsection grew accordingly. The command backed up the subsection by assigning an exceptionally competent staff of enlisted personnel to process the growing volume of loss and damage reports that were received in an ever-increasing flow and to do spade work on a large number of special projects.

TSgt. William Weintraub served with the subsection from 25 June 1943 until the section was disbanded in June 1945. A practicing lawyer for seven years, Weintraub was invaluable to the subsection. He administered the work of the enlisted personnel and the flow of reports through the subsection, issued routine daily and monthly battle damage summaries, and handled many of the subsection's contacts with headquarters and the lower echelons.

Staff Sergeant William T. Parry served with the subsection from 15 July 1943 until it disbanded. He was usually assigned to the more difficult special studies because his doctorate degree and position as assistant in philosophy at Harvard, together with his knowledge of statistics, suited him admirably for such work.

Sergeant Shirley E. Emhoff served with the subsection from 15 September 1943 until 11 May 1945. Sergeant Emhoff, who had engineering training, was responsible for interrogating the evaders—those airmen who were lost over enemy territory and escaped.

Corporal Richard R. Garrison reported for duty on 10 September 1943, and served until 15 May 1945. He too helped with special studies.

Other enlisted personnel came later. [58]

The significance of loss and damage to the offensive effort. A sobering picture of the cost of the daylight bombing campaign through December 1943 and a summary of the subsection's work up to that time appears in a report, "Reduction of Losses and Battle Damage—A Summary and Analysis of the Defensive Experience of the Eighth Bomber Command 17 August 1942–31 December 1943," dated February 1944. The report, written by Dr. R. G. Gettell, Mr. G. F. Shettle, and Mr. W. J. Pilat, served as a main source for much of what follows. [59]

Combat losses and battle damage were of critical significance for bombardment operations. First, losses of aircraft and crewmen on a particular mission obviously increased the immediate cost of that mission. Second, loss and battle damage reduced the potential striking power for future operations. Every effort was made to minimize these costs without unduly detracting from the offensive effort. Nevertheless, the command was prepared to accept heavy losses during missions to important targets. Damage which did not destroy a plane or its crew was, of course, less costly than total loss. However, damage to a plane often hindered its performance; even when the damage could be repaired it drained materiel, manpower, and time.

The effect losses and battle damage had on the offensive effort is more easily understood when viewed on time scales of at least a month where rates of loss and damage could be established. The subsection enunciated the following three propositions about the significance of rates of loss and damage:

> (a) The *rate* of loss sustained over a series of operations determines the average combat life of an aircraft and crew; small changes in the loss rate make large differences in the number of attacks that can be made by an aircraft before it is lost. For example: If our loss rates should remain at the October level (9.1 percent of the aircraft attacking), the average bomber would be able to attack only 11 times before being lost. If the December loss rate were maintained (3.4 percent of the aircraft attacking), the average bomber would be able to attack almost 30 times before being lost. In terms of bombs dropped on the enemy per aircraft and crews lost to future action, this is increasing the efficiency of our striking power almost three-fold.

> (b) The *rate* of damage is a major determinant of the availability of aircraft for combat; variations in the damage rate affect the number of aircraft which can be dispatched on any particular mission. That is, the availability of aircraft for combat is affected by the damage rate and by the recovery rate, which in turn is a function of the severity of the damage, the repair facilities available, and the time lapse between operations. Every aircraft for which there is an available crew and which is made temporarily nonoperational while battle damage is repaired, is one less aircraft for the striking force throughout the time it is undergoing repair.

(c) Losses and damage, together with replacements, are determinants of our sustained striking power; variations in loss and damage rates have great influence on the weight of bombs that can be dropped on the enemy within a limited period of time. The consequences of simultaneous variations in loss and damage rates to our sustained striking force can be illustrated by the following hypothetical example:

If this Command started a month with a force of 1000 aircraft, and received no replacements during the month, then, if 20 operations were conducted during the month and each aircraft which was battle damaged were made non-operational for one mission, by the end of the month,

If the LOSS RATE were	And if the DAMAGE RATE were	The Number of ATTACKS MADE would be	The Number of AIRCRAFT LOST would be
7%	50%	8831	611
7%	$33\frac{1}{3}$%	9414	661
7%	20%	9981	699
5%	50%	9876	495
5%	$33\frac{1}{3}$%	10692	537
5%	20%	11457	575
3%	50%	11150	338
3%	$33\frac{1}{3}$%	12239	368
3%	20%	13298	397

The extent to which the size of our offensive and the magnitude of our losses are sensitive to variations in the loss and damage rates, as typified by the figures shown above, underlines the importance of constant examination of our defensive experience. [60]

Loss and battle damage suffered by aircraft of the Eighth Bomber Command. [61] From the day of its first operation, 17 August 1942, through 31 December 1943, the Eighth Bomber Command flew 23,205 sorties on which 19,194 aircraft made attacks. Of the aircraft participating, 1,013 were lost; 174 returned, but were so badly damaged that they could not be salvaged; 1,008 suffered major damage that was not reparable by the combat unit; and 5,932 suffered minor damage that was reparable by the combat unit.

Translating these figures into loss and damage *rates*, by expressing them as percentages of sorties (which roughly measures cost relative to exposure to combat risks) or expressing them as percentages of the number of aircraft attacking (which roughly measures cost relative to the weight of bombs dropped on the enemy), results in what appears in Table 4.1.

Table 4.1. Loss and Damage to Aircraft of the Eighth Bomber Command, 17 August 1942–31 December 1943

Item	Number of aircraft	Percentage of sorties	Percentage of attacks
Sorties	23, 305	100%	
Attacks	19, 194	82%	100%
Lost in action	1, 013	4.4%	5.3%
Salvaged	174	.7%	.9%
Lost to future action	$\overline{1, 187}$	$\overline{5.1\%}$	$\overline{6.2\%}$
Suffering major damage	1, 008	4.3%	5.3%
Suffering minor damage	5, 932	25.5%	30.9%
Total damaged			
but reparable	$\overline{6, 940}$	$\overline{29.8\%}$	$\overline{36.2\%}$

Table 4.1 shows the average loss rate for the entire sixteen-and-a-half month period to be about 4.4 percent of the sorties and 5.3 percent of the attacks. When the salvaged planes were also counted those rates climbed to 5.1 percent and 6.2 percent respectively. The reparable damage suffered was 29.8 percent of the sorties and 36.2 percent of the attacks.

According to Table 4.1, one out of every twenty aircraft exposed to combat in the first sixteen and a half months of operations had been lost either during the mission or in the scrap heap. In addition, nearly six out of every twenty were damaged and rendered temporarily nonoperational. One out of every sixteen aircraft which bombed the enemy, whether it hit the target or not, was lost to further action. In addition, nearly six out of sixteen were damaged. The average life to an aircraft throughout this period was sixteen attacks.

Table 4.2 breaks the loss and battle damage statistics into shorter intervals, revealing significant fluctuations in the rates. For example, the high loss rate for October reflects the losses of the second Schweinfurt mission. Similarly, low loss rates of November and December were caused by the introduction of large-scale radar bombing.

ANALYZING THE CAUSES OF LOSS AND BATTLE DAMAGE

Determining the extent of battle damage and its causes on the planes that returned from missions was no problem. Youden had instituted a systematic report form which had been filled out at the groups and sent to the ORS since February 1943 for each damaged plane. These reports were as thorough and objective as one could hope. Furthermore, the crewmen who returned to

Table 4.2. Loss and Damage to Aircraft of
the Eighth Bomber Command, Showing Variations over Time

ITEM	Aug. to Dec. 1942	Jan. to June 1943	July 1943	Aug. 1943	Sept. 1943	Oct. 1943	Nov. 1943	Dec. 1943	Total July to Dec. 1943
Number of aircraft									
Sorties	957	4553	2334	2058	2561	2174	2978	5688	17793
Attacks	780	3794	1609	1653	2088	1926	2545	4799	14620
Lost in action	31	250	109	107	84	176	93	163	732
Salvaged	4	44	19	16	17	22	21	31	126
Lost to future action	35	294	128	123	101	198	114	194	858
Major damaged	40	246	130	93	62	108	88	231	722
Minor damaged	225	1099	876	759	669	770	540	1004	4606
Total damaged	265	1345	1006	852	731	878	628	1235	5330
Percentage of attacks									
Lost in action	4.0	6.6	6.8	6.5	4.0	9.1	3.7	3.4	5.0
Salvaged	.5	1.2	1.2	1.0	0.8	1.2	0.8	0.6	0.9
Lost to future action	4.5	7.8	8.0	7.5	4.8	10.3	4.5	4.0	5.9
Major damaged	5.1	6.5	8.1	6.2	3.0	5.6	3.5	4.8	5.0
Minor damaged	28.9	29.0	54.4	45.3	32.0	40.0	21.2	20.9	31.5
Total damaged	34.0	35.5	62.8	51.5	35.0	45.6	24.7	25.7	36.5

the base with the damaged plane could complete the picture of what had happened.

Determining what had happened to planes that did not return was not only difficult, but often impossible. Some inferences could be made from battle damage suffered by planes that did return. Better, though still unsatisfactory, was information obtained from combat crew members who saw other aircraft go down. Crews returning from combat missions were interviewed in an attempt to piece together the fate of the crews and aircraft that failed to return. Once tabulated, these data produced crude figures showing the number of aircraft lost to flak, fighters, accidents, and unknown causes. These figures, however, were likely to lead to wrong conclusions. They were based on the narratives of witnesses who were otherwise occupied and distant from the circumstances they were describing. Also, they indicated only an external view of what happened to the missing aircraft. Furthermore, such reports typically attributed the loss of the airplane to the last injury suffered, whereas the decisive cause of the loss may have been something else.

The best solution to this problem of fact-finding came in an interesting way. Beginning in October 1943 the Loss and Battle Damage Subsection began interrogating American airmen who were lost over enemy territory and escaped. By 31 December members of the subsection had interviewed 346 crew members on the details of 145 lost aircraft. By September 1944 the number of returning crew members had become so large that interrogation was impractical. Instead, a questionnaire was submitted to all evaders and escapers and also to a number of exchanged prisoners of war and released internees. In all, information on cause of loss was obtained from an estimated 1,600 crew members from about 450 lost aircraft.

The sample of 145 reports of lost aircraft obtained by December 1943 covered about 15 percent of the aircraft lost by the Eighth Bomber Command through 31 December 1943. The sample is representative of the losses in the theater with the following exceptions. It includes very few cases of aircraft lost over Germany itself, and it probably understates the number of aircraft which were hit and destroyed almost immediately, since fewer crewmen escaped to report it.

In the following analysis of causes of loss, nine of the planes which ran out of gas on the Ploesti mission are left out because they were on temporary assignment in North Africa when they were lost. The statistics are based on the remaining 136. [62]

Straggling as a cause of loss.   Of the 136 lost planes in the sample, sixty-five (48 percent) were brought down directly from the formation; the remaining seventy-one (52 percent) were made stragglers first. Of these seventy-one stragglers, twenty-three had been knocked out of formation by flak and nineteen by damage caused by enemy fighters. Of the seventy-one stragglers eighteen lost the formation because of engine trouble. Eleven more lost the formation because of personnel or operational problems such as difficulty at assembly, scattering after bomb run, prop wash, and fuel shortage. Stragglers, flying apart from the formation, were easy targets. Sixty-three were brought down by enemy fighters, six by subsequent flak hits, and two by further engine failure. These statistics indicated three things.

> 1. Flak damage began a sequence of events which ultimately led to the loss of many planes. Minimizing flak damage was important.
> 2. Bombers depended upon other bombers in formation for protection. Engine failure caused a plane to fall behind the others, placing it in danger.
> 3. Single bombers were extremely vulnerable to concentrated attacks by enemy fighters. Enemy tactics for picking off stragglers were successful. [63]

Vulnerability of the power plant.   Losses were also frequently attributed to power plant damage. Because the power plant was so inadequately protected, it was the most vulnerable part of a bomber. Analysis of the circumstances under which 136 aircraft were lost showed that 102 experienced one or more engine failures. In all but nineteen cases the engine trouble was attributable to flak hits or fighter attacks. Of these 102 aircraft, thirty-five lost one engine, thirty-eight lost two engines, nineteen lost three engines, and ten lost four engines.

The subsection recommended more armor protection for the power plant to reduce the chances of engines being damaged by flak or fighters. [64]

Fire as a cause of loss.   Perhaps the greatest single hazard to bombers, and certainly the most frequent single cause for a crew to bail out, was fire. Very few aircraft which caught fire managed to return.

Analysis of the circumstances involved in the loss of 136 aircraft disclosed that eighty-nine of the 136 aircraft suffered 138 fires. Nearly 60 percent of the fires started in the engine nacelles. Not surprisingly, the subsection recommended remedial measures for preventing and extinguishing fires in the engine nacelles, the cockpit, and the wings. [65]

In November 1944 I witnessed an event involving a burning plane that illustrates the ambiguities which confront the aircrew in such a crisis. Our groups of B-17s had just bombed a target at Ludwigshaven. The flak over the target area was intense. First, we saw two planes from our group, apparently hit by the same flak battery, leave formation, roll over, and explode. Then, as we were leaving the target area, our pilot called over the intercom that a plane flying on our right wing was on fire. We could see a column of smoke and flame coming from his number three engine. It looked hopeless. Then our pilot reported that he heard on his radio the pilot of the burning plane tell his crew he was going to stay with the ship and try to put the fire out, but that those who wanted to bail out should do so. Now we had repeatedly observed burning planes pull out or fall out of formation and then explode. This time, as we watched, we saw two crewmen jump out of the ship and open their chutes. Meanwhile, the pilot and copilot worked to maintain course and extinguish the fire simultaneously. As we watched, the column of flame trailing from the engine began to shrink and then disappeared. The fire was out. We looked back in time to see two tiny white chutes flutter down over the outskirts of Ludwigshaven as the plane beside us from which they came headed back to England.

Flak as a major cause of loss.   In their study of the Eighth Bomber Command loss and damage through 31 December 1943, Gettell, Shettle, and Pilat stated, "To the extent that operational decisions involving the balancing of risks have been based on the information hitherto available, it is probable that the importance of flak has been grossly underestimated." In calculating the hazards of a particular mission, and in planning the tactics of operations, it was customary to count flak as a lesser danger. Flak risks were subordinated to the necessity of maintaining a stable platform for the bombing run.

The defensive formations of the combat box and combat wing had been designed to protect against enemy fighters. Formation flying, however, greatly
increased a bomber's vulnerability to flak.

From a group of 102 aircraft lost to enemy action, forty-five were due
to flak hits and fifty-seven to enemy fighters. Among the planes lost to flak
damage, thirteen were en route to the target; thirty were at the target, and
two were on the way back to base.

The subsection concluded that, except when offensive considerations overruled, every possible tactical device should be employed to mitigate the hazards of flak. Although flak hits were unavoidable on the bombing run, the
risk of damage from flak fire could and should be held to a minimum at all
other points on the mission. Furthermore, at the target the flak opposition
should be an important factor in determining the bombing altitude and axis
of attack. The analysts also pointed out that, if other defensive considerations permitted, bombing by squadrons instead of groups or wings would
greatly reduce flak hazards.[66]

Enemy fighters as *the* major cause of loss.   Though flak posed a very serious
threat, the most dangerous opposition the bombers of the Eighth Bomber
Command encountered, and the origin of most losses as of 31 December
1943, continued to be German fighters.

Among the losses of 136 aircraft described by escaped crew members,
sixty-five were brought down from formation. Of those, thirty-eight were
brought down by enemy fighter activity. Of the seventy-one aircraft lost while
straggling, nineteen were made stragglers by enemy fighter activity. Of those
seventy-one, sixty-three were finally brought down by enemy fighter attacks.
In summary, the cause of loss originated with enemy fighters in fifty-seven out
of 136 cases (42 percent), and the final blow which destroyed our bombers
was given by enemy fighters in 101 out of the 136 cases (73 percent).

The subsection drew three conclusions from these data.

> 1. Although enemy fighter attacks were not the main cause of
> straggling, straggling aircraft were extremely vulnerable to enemy
> fighters.
> 2. Enemy fighters shot down more stragglers than planes in for-
> mation. They especially concentrated on withdrawing stragglers.
> 3. Maintaining formation on missions provided a very important
> defense, according to this analysis.[67]

When the losses took place.   On the average, for every 100 lost bombers,
thirty-six were lost on the way to the target, twenty-two were lost in the
target area, and the remaining forty-two were lost during withdrawal from
the target. Though these numbers seem to indicate that the target area was the
safest place for a bomber during a mission, it does not account for time. The
time spent in the target area was very short, compared with the time spent

on the entire mission. Time in the target area was measured in minutes, whereas the time to and from the target area was measured in hours. That only twenty-two planes were lost in the target area is misleading. Of the forty-two brought down on the way back to base after a mission, thirty-five were disabled and became stragglers from damage received in the target area. [68]

Though some crewmen claimed to have napped or read books on the way to or from a target, no such things happened at the target. I remember that, because of the excitement over the target, I would be wringing wet with sweat as our bomber left the target area and would unplug my heated suit until I cooled down. During a mission to a synthetic oil refinery at Merseburg, Germany, a piece of flak caused an explosion in the plane while we were over the target. Our pilot, Stewart R. Reid, first thought he was "shot in the ass" because the explosion seemed to happen under his seat. He could feel blood trickling down the back of his leg. The explosion turned out to be an oxygen bottle exploding when it was punctured by flak, and the blood turned out to be only sweat.

Fuel shortage as a cause of loss. As of 31 December 1943 the subsection had interrogated escaped crewmen from 145 lost bombers. Of those, eighteen suffered a fuel shortage; fuel shortage contributed to 12.4 percent of these losses.

Nine of these eighteen aircraft ran out of fuel because they used too much. Reasons for the excessive fuel consumption included overloading, excessive speed, attempting to stay in the formation on only three engines, consuming too much during assembly or on extra bomb runs, and getting lost.

Another eight of the eighteen ran short of fuel because flak damage caused their tanks or fuel transfer systems to leak. One additional aircraft ran short of fuel because of a tank leak unconnected with battle damage.

Of the eighteen aircraft lost because of fuel shortage, thirteen crash-landed, eight in neutral territory. In the remaining five planes the crews bailed out. These five planes were stragglers under attack by enemy fighters during bail-out. [69]

The need to estimate the fuel requirements correctly had already been recognized by the command. The General Mission Analysis Subsection of the ORS had studied the problem at least since April 1943 when consultants Edwin Hewitt and Frank Stewart arrived and began working on it. Two memoranda, "B-17 Fuel Consumption" and "Memorandum Concerning a Formula for Determining the Operating Ranges of the B-17F in Combat Flying," dated 11 July were prepared by Hewitt just after he was assigned to gunnery problems. Because data were inadequate and accurate information on fuel consumption was difficult to secure, the estimates were found to be too broad and conservative. It became evident that to devise a yardstick to precisely estimate fuel consumption for missions, an elaborate measurement system would have to be developed. The section negotiated with Wright Field in the United States for an aeronautical engineer and a test pilot to work on this problem. [70]

In the meantime Mr. Blair Bennett arrived on 29 September 1943 and was assigned to the General Mission Analysis Subsection. He earned an A.B. degree from Georgetown University and an M.A. degree from Columbia University in 1940. He had been working as a mathematician at the U.S. Naval Proving Ground at Dahlgren, Virginia, when he joined the ORS of Eighth Air Force. [71]

The problem of running out of gas during missions was stubborn and impossible to eliminate. The air force and its analysts continually strove to estimate their gasoline consumption with more precision. However, many gas shortages could not be remedied by accurate fuel estimates before a mission anyway. From 1944 on, the Eighth Air Force flew more and more sorties deep into Germany, Czechoslovakia, Austria, and Poland; more planes were flying to places closer to the limit of their range. On such a mission the bombers might find that their primary target, say in Czechoslovakia, was hidden by clouds. In that case they would proceed with their heavy bomb loads to a secondary target or targets of opportunity. Thus, planes using extra fuel because of engine trouble, heavy loading, or assembly problems found themselves in trouble.

The greatest breakthrough in the fuel shortage problem on missions came soon after D day, when the Allies established fighter bases in France and Belgium. These quickly were regarded as havens for bomber crews in times of trouble. However, the advanced fighter bases had been erected quickly for fighters, not bombers. They were not strong enough or long enough for extended use by bombers. Heavy bombers were not really welcome under any circumstances.

Not long after these bases were established in 1944, on our return from a mission, our pilot realized we did not have enough gas to cross the English Channel. We found an American fighter base at a village near Charleroi, Belgium. Our pilot radioed that we were out of gas and were coming in to land. As we approached, however, we were given a red light by the tower. We pulled up to decide what to do. The gas gauges were reading empty. In desperation we went around the traffic pattern again. The pilot instructed me to shoot red flares as we approached (the signal for wounded on board). I did so; we landed. At the end of the runway was an ambulance, which fortunately we did not need. After a miserable night spent in our freezing plane, we flew back to base in England, but not before we expressed our gratitude by buzzing their control tower in our B-17.

Another personal experience also illustrates the extent of the gas shortage problem. After a mission deep into Germany in early December 1944, my whole squadron ran short of fuel on the return. We landed at an airfield in Belgium whose runway consisted of a metallic mat resembling chain mail, rolled out in the field outside of Liege. My plane was not only low on gas but also had a cracked cylinder in one engine. We eventually flew back to base in a transport plane and found that, since our plane had not returned with the others, we had been presumed lost.

Battle damage and its causes. Battle damage was measured and counted only on planes which returned from missions. Through 31 December 1943, for every 100 bombers returning from attacks, one had to be scrapped, thirty-six were temporarily put out of action (five with major damage and thirty-one with minor damage), and sixty-three were undamaged. This does not include lost aircraft.

Flak was by far the most frequent single cause of damage. More than one out of every four attacking aircraft returned to base damaged by flak. However, in almost nine out of ten cases where flak holes were found, the total damage to the aircraft was minor.

Enemy fighters were directly or indirectly responsible for most of the remaining damage to aircraft. The fighters caused damage directly with rockets, aerial bombs, cannon fire, and machine gun fire. Enemy fighters were also indirectly responsible for holes caused by stray shots from friendly aircraft, gunners who accidently shot their own planes, and empty shell cases trailing from the guns of one plane into other planes in the formation.

Averages for July through December 1943 showed that of attacking aircraft that returned to base, one out of every twenty-six (3.8 percent) had been hit by cannon fire; one out of every seventeen (5.9 percent) had been hit by enemy machine gun fire; one out of every seventy-one (1.3 percent) had been hit by stray shots from other friendly aircraft; one out of every forty-three (2.3 percent) had suffered self-inflicted damage, and one out of every twenty (5 percent) had been hit by empty shell cases.[72]

Although damage from ejected shell cases was relatively minor, these statistics indicate that it was frequent. I learned to respect the danger of ejected 50-caliber cases from friendly aircraft when shell cases trailed out of a plane ahead of ours, crashed through the Plexiglas nose of our plane, smashed a metal box filled with wiring for our nose guns, and thudded into my flak suit. As a result we finished the mission without using nose guns. The rest of the mission was especially cold and drafty for the navigator and me, as bombardier, and a shell case bruised my shin.

REFERENCES

1. Wesley Frank Craven and James Lea Cate of the USAF Historical Division, eds., *Europe: Torch to Pointblank, August 1942 to December 1943*, vol. 1 of *The Army Air Forces of World War II* (Chicago: University of Chicago Press, 1949), 844–45.

2. Ibid., 313, 321.

3. Ibid., 343.

4. ORS Report, Eighth Bomber Command, "Analysis of VIII Bomber Command Operations from the Point of View of Bombing Accuracy—1 January 1943–

15 October 1943," 31 October 1943, Archives, Simpson Historical Research Center, Maxwell Air Force Base, Alabama.

5. *Europe: Torch to Pointblank*, 843–45.

6. ORS Report, Eighth Bomber Command, "Reduction of Losses and Battle Damage—A Summary and Analysis of the Defensive Experience of VIII Bomber Command, 17 August 1942–31 December 1943," Archives, Simpson Historical Research Center, Maxwell Air Force Base, Alabama.

7. *Europe: Torch to Pointblank*, 347.

8. Ibid., 665.

9. Ibid., 666.

10. Memoir of Edwin Hewitt, "A Sketch of Gunnery Activities in the Operational Research Section Eighth Air Force, from June 1943 to August 1944," 17 July 1945.

11. "Eighth Air Force, History of Operations Analysis Section, October 1942–June 1945," Leslie H. Arps, 520.303-3, Archives, Simpson Historical Research Center, Maxwell Air Force Base, Alabama, 86.

12. "Gunnery Subsection, Operational Analysis Section, Eighth Air Force, June 1943–January 1945," W. L. Ayres, 520.303-2, Archives, Simpson Historical Research Center, Maxwell Air Force Base, Alabama, 1.

13. "A Sketch of Gunnery Activities."

14. Ibid.

15. Ibid.

16. Ibid.

17. Ibid.

18. Ibid.

19. Ibid.

20. Ibid.

21. Ibid.

22. "Eighth Air Force," 88.

23. "A Sketch of Gunnery Activities."

24. General James M. Gavin, "On to Berlin."

25. "Eighth Air Force," 85, 88.

26. "You Can't Miss It," ORS, Eighth Bomber Command, Archives, Simpson Historical Research Center, Maxwell Air Force Base, Alabama.

27. "Eighth Air Force," 53–55.

28. Ibid., 56.

29. Ibid., 56–58.

30. G. Baley Price, *Gremlin Hunting in the Eighth Air Force, European Theater of Operations, 1943–1945*, 1–2.

31. Ibid., 3.

32. Leroy A. Brothers, *Operations Analysis in World War II, United States Army Air Forces* (Philadelphia: Stephenson-Brothers, 1948), 3, 40.

33. *Gremlin Hunting*, 10–12.

34. Ibid., 13–14.

35. Ibid., 14–15.

36. Ibid., 16, 18–19.

37. *Operations Analysis in World War II*, 9–10.

38. "Report for Colonel W. B. Leach on the History and Development of the Bombs and Fuzes Subsection of the Operational Analysis Section, Headquarters Eighth Air Force," 10 April 1945, Bissell Alderman, 520.303-3, Archives, Simpson Historical Research Center, Maxwell Air Force Base, Alabama, 7–8.

39. Ibid., 10–11, 22.

40. Ibid., 13.

41. *Europe: Torch to Pointblank*, 690.

42. "Eighth Air Force," 95–98.

43. *Europe: Torch to Pointblank*, 691–92.

44. ORS Report, Eighth Bomber Command, "Memorandum on Blind Bombing Aspects of Missions of September 27 and October 2, 1943 (Emden)," 27 October 1943, Archives, Simpson Historical Research Center, Maxwell Air Force Base, Alabama.

45. *Europe: Torch to Pointblank*, 693–94, and "Memorandum on Blind Bombing."

46. "The Army Air Forces in World War II, Combat Chronology, 1941–1945," Headquarters USAF, 1973, Kit C. Carter and Robert Mueller, Archives, Simpson Historical Research Center, Alabama, 210.

47. *Europe: Torch to Pointblank*, 720–21.

48. "Reduction of Losses and Battle Damage," 42.

49. *Europe: Torch to Pointblank*, 694, 696.

50. ORS Report, Eighth Bomber Command, "The Operational Effectiveness of the Radio Countermeasure 'Carpet'," 7 November 1943, Archives, Simpson Historical Research Center, Maxwell Air Force Base, Alabama.

51. ORS Report, Eighth Bomber Command, "A Comparison of Losses and Flak Damage Between Carpet Protected Groups and Other Groups Going to the Same Target on Ten Carpet Operations," Archives, Simpson Historical Research Center, Maxwell Air Force Base, Alabama.

52. Thomas Parrish and S. L. A. Marshall, eds., *The Simon and Schuster Encyclopedia of World War II* (New York: 1978), 259–60.

53. ORS Memoranda, Eighth Bomber Command, "Preliminary Memoranda as to Possible Uses of Window in the Operations of VIII Bomber Command," 19 September 1943, and "Supplementary Memorandum Relative to the Use of Window for the Confusion of the Enemy Gunlaying Radar Sets in the Immediate Vicinity of the Target," 30 October 1943, Archives, Simpson Historical Research Center, Maxwell Air Force Base, Alabama.

54. *Europe: Torch to Pointblank*, 694.

55. "Combat Chronology," 235.

56. *Europe: Torch to Pointblank*, 691.

57. "Combat Chronology," 240.

58. "History of the Battle Damage Subsection, Operational Analysis Section, Headquarters Eighth Air Force, December 1943–May 1945," 520.303-1, Archives, Simpson Historical Research Center, Maxwell Air Force Base, Alabama, 1–3. This history actually refers to many things which happened throughout the year 1943 and even in 1942.

59. "Reduction of Losses and Battle Damage." During the period 17 August–31 December 1942 the Loss and Battle Damage Subsection wrote ten reports and seven memoranda. Reference six is a report which gives a synthesis of these.

60. Ibid., 3–4.

61. Ibid., 5–6.

62. Ibid., 27–28, and "History of Battle Damage Subsection," 9.

63. "Reduction of Losses and Battle Damage," 28–29.

64. Ibid., 29–30.

65. Ibid., 30–31.

66. Ibid., 31–32.

67. Ibid., 32.
68. *Europe: Torch to Pointblank*, appendix.
69. Ibid., 33.
70. "Eighth Air Force," 82–83.
71. *Operations Analysis in World War II*, 9.
72. "Reduction of Losses and Battle Damage," 35–40.

5

The Operational Research Section
of the Eighth Fighter Command
March–December 1943

BACKGROUND

Brigadier General Frank O'D. (Monk) Hunter was the first commander of the Eighth Fighter Command. On 14 May 1942, in the States, he assumed command of the Eighth Fighter Command, at that time called Interceptor Command. It was his responsibility to direct the movement of the first USAAF-manned aircraft to Britain. Between 18 June and 27 July, three groups, the U.S. Ninety-seventh Bomb Group (B-17s), the U.S. First Fighter Group (P-38s), and the Sixtieth Transport Group (C-47s) flew the "northern route" from the United States to Britain. The route started at Presque Isle, Maine, continued to Goose Bay, Labrador, to an outpost called Bluie West 1 Landing Ground in Greenland, to Reykjavic, Iceland, and finally to Prestwick, Scotland—a journey of about 3,000 miles. It was a dangerous journey flown by young men, most of whom had never been out of the United States before, much less into the strange "land of the midnight sun." The greatest dangers were engine malfunction over the icy North Atlantic and bad weather, which could make it impossible to find or land at the bases along the way. The first element landed in Britain on 1 July. The last, two B-17s and eight P-38s which included General Hunter and his staff, landed at Prestwick on 27 July. Of the 180 aircraft involved in the movement, five B-17s and six P-38s were lost. Amazingly, the crews were saved.[1] Thousands more men and planes, including the ORS of the Eighth Fighter Command, would travel some version of the northern route before the war was over.

The headquarters of the Eighth Fighter Command was established at Bushey Hall, a country hotel not far from either the headquarters of RAF Fighter Command or the headquarters of the Eighth Bomber Command at High Wycombe. General Hunter, a distinguished WWI fighter pilot, cooperated closely with the RAF even before USAAF aircraft arrived. In May 1942, for example, the pilots of the Thirty-first Fighter Group, leaving their

P-39s behind, were sent by ship to England, where in early June they began training in British Spitfire fighters. Thus, when the first elements of the U.S. First Fighter Group landed in England, they found an emerging American Spitfire group. Furthermore, many Americans had volunteered for the RAF long before the United States entered the war. Three RAF Eagle squadrons were composed entirely of Americans. These elite squadrons were finally incorporated into the USAAF in September 1942. [2]

In the last half of 1942 the Eighth Fighter Command not only provided escort for the Eighth Bomber Command on its bombing missions, but also provided training and experience for future fighter groups of the Twelfth Air Force preparing for the Northwest Africa campaign. By 20 October 1942, the USAAF had in Britain three fighter groups of P-38s, three fighter groups of Spitfires, one group of P-39s, one mixed group of Spitfires and P-39s, and several reconnaissance groups. After 26 October 1942, when the groups committed to the Twelfth Air Force were taken off operations in the United Kingdom, the only permanent fighter group left under the Eighth Fighter Command was the Fourth at Debden. This became the nucleus for rebuilding the the Eighth Fighter Command for the operations of the Eighth Air Force in 1943. [3]

In January 1943 the Eighth Fighter Command began to convert to the P-47. According to the plan, three fighter groups of P-47s would be operational by the end of March 1943. Furthermore, this was the beginning of a larger build up of the fighter force. At this point, early in March 1943, the way was cleared for the Eighth Fighter Command to have its own ORS.

In early 1943 the Eighth Fighter Command had two main tasks. The first was to escort the bombers of the Eighth Air Force on strikes against targets in France, the Low Countries, and Germany. The second was to absorb and train the early elements of the Ninth Air Force. The groups marked for the Ninth Air Force would not form until the end of 1943.

Perhaps the biggest problem of the Eighth Air Force in the latter part of 1943 was that, on one hand, fighter escort was a necessity for the bombers in a sustained program of attacking targets deep in Germany, while, on the other hand, in 1943 Allied fighters (Spitfires, P-38s, P-39s, and P-47s) had inadequate range for most missions into Germany. Thus, the command was faced with the problem of fighting Germany's best pilots at ever-increasing ranges.

RECRUITMENT

Colonel Harlan, chief of the ORS of the Eighth Bomber Command, spent most of February, March, and April 1943, in the United States recruiting analysts for his section. His deputy chief at the Eighth Bomber Command, Leslie Arps, received a cable from Harlan dated 6 March instructing Tuttle and him to ask General Hunter how many men he needed for his ORS.

After Arps and Tuttle saw General Hunter and his chief of staff, they cabled Harlan requesting one radar man, an assistant, three physicists, and two mathematicians for the ORS of the Eighth Fighter Command.

First, the section chief, Lauriston Sale Taylor, was recruited. Taylor, born on 1 June 1902, was just shy of his forty-first birthday when he became chief. He obtained a bachelor's degree from Cornell University in 1926. The next year he began work at the National Bureau of Standards as an assistant physicist. From 1935 to 1941 he was a senior physicist and chief of the X-ray section. From 1940 until April 1943 when he was recruited for the ORS, he was chief of a proving ground group in the Bureau working on various weapons projects for the NDRC.

In mid-April, Taylor, without advance notice, was called into a conference with W. Barton (Bart) Leach and John Harlan by Alexander Ellett, who was in charge of Bureau operations for the NDRC. Colonel Leach, chief of the headquarters section of operations research of the USAAF in Washington, D.C., described for Taylor operations research work in Britain conducted by civilian scientists. Then John Harlan, chief of the ORS of Eighth Bomber Command, told him of operations research work done by civilian scientists in the European and Mediterranean theaters. When Taylor had a chance, he asked why they were telling him all these things. The reply was, "We're here to see if you would be willing to organize a group of some six to ten scientists and technical people as an Operations Research Section to the Eighth FC which is just beginning to operate from its English bases." Before they left Taylor agreed to do it. Then he wondered how he would explain to his family what he had done. [4]

After the war Leach commented on the devoted service and sacrifices of the analysts.

> By and large they were men with families, developing careers, substantial war responsibilities in the zone of interior, and no obligation to go to war. They accepted the sacrifices and risks of service overseas in an untried enterprise because they saw in it the opportunity for a greater contribution nearer the fighting. [5]

Lauriston Taylor described how he told his wife that he had agreed to overseas duty as an operations analyst.

> That afternoon I decided that since many things were to be done, I had better go home first. This in itself was of course surprising, and a little alarming, and Zula wanted to how what was going on. I decided to use the same tactics that had been used on me, by telling her a little about the operations research in England and North Africa. Before I got around to the point of telling her that I had been tapped for the job, she turned to me and just said quietly. "Where are they going to send you and how soon do you have to

leave?" I guess she knew as well as I did that there was no use in asking how long I would be gone. So you can see, understanding wife that she was, she spared me the almost impossible ordeal of having to explain it all to her.

Leach helped Taylor recruit the men he needed by introducing him to key people. For example, Vannevar Bush of the Office of Scientific Research and Development explained some of the qualifications needed by the analysts. Dr. Wheeler Loomis, though he did not volunteer names of his staff members at the MIT Radiation Laboratory, arranged interviews with people Taylor learned about through other sources. During the war Loomis was professor and head of the physics department at New York University as well as associate director of the Radiation Laboratory at MIT.

The recruitment of Carroll L. Zimmerman demonstrates the work of what airmen often irreverently called "the fickle finger of fate." Taylor recalls the event.

> Among the names that I had on my list for the Radiation Laboratory was a Zimmerman, and arrangements were made for an interview. Zimmerman came in—a huge piece of man, very pleasant and easy to talk to. After a few minutes he interrupted to ask if I indeed had the right Zimmerman, because what I was telling him about seemed to bear very little relationship to what his technical background interests were. When I gave the initials he indicated I had the wrong one, but wondered if, since I had already been telling him about the program, I would have any objection to continuing. There was no other use for the time left in that period, so I went ahead, at the end of which he thanked me very much and disappeared. I later talked to the other Zimmerman without any success. On the next day I received a call from the first Zimmerman (Carroll L.) wanting to know if he could see me for a few minutes. Of course, I said yes and he came immediately to the point; he said that what I had told him sounded so interesting and potentially worthwhile to the war effort, that he thought that in case I had any interest in him he would like to explore the question further. I was delighted, and, to make a long story short, Zimmerman joined me and later became the head of one of the separate units that I had in operation first in England and then on the continent. [6]

With Zimmerman's help, Taylor recruited his friend, Roland W. Larson from the MIT Radiation Laboratory, who was engaged in microwave research. He had a B.S.E.E. degree from the University of Wisconsin.

Also recruited was Ralph P. Johnson, a research physicist with General Electric Co. at Schenectady, New York. Taylor describes him as "an outstanding physicist with both theoretical and experimental capabilities" who was suggested to him by Fred Seitz. Johnson had a bachelor's degree from the University of Richmond, 1929, a master's from the University of Virginia, 1930, and a doctorate from MIT, 1936. After the war he joined the Ramo Woolridge organization, and he later became vice president.

Because General Hunter requested two mathematicians, Taylor recruited Dr. Alva E. Brandt and Dr. Horace W. Norton, whom he describes as mathematical statisticans. Brandt, serving as chief of the Experiment Station, Division of Soil, Conservation Service of the Department of Agriculture in Washington, D.C., had a B.S., 1917, an M.S., 1926, and a Ph.D, 1932, all from Iowa State College. Furthermore, he had done postgraduate studies in biology and statistics at University College, London, in 1934. Dr. Norton had been working as a meteorologist with the U.S. Weather Service in Washington, D.C. His degrees were B.S., University of Wisconsin, 1935; M.S., Iowa State College, 1937; and Ph.D., University College, London, 1940.

Whereas Taylor had a natural inclination and ability to recruit physicists, Leach, the Harvard Law School professor, "showed a great leaning toward lawyers for this kind of work." Taylor resisted this, and "we ended up by a compromise whereby I agreed to have a lawyer at the outset, but no more until I had at least some experience in the field." The lawyer Taylor selected "after considerable thought and numerous interviews" was Theodore Tannenwald, Jr., an attorney with Weil, Gotshal, and Manges of New York City. Tannenwald had an A.B. from Brown University, 1936, and an LL.B. from Harvard, 1939. After the war he rose to chief judge of the Tax Court in Washington.

By the last week of May, a little over four weeks since his initial interview with Leach and Harlan, Taylor completed the roster of his section and reported it ready for departure.[7,8]

ARRIVAL AND ORIENTATION

On 1 June 1943 Taylor and his section were put on twenty-four-hour alert in Washington, D.C., for departure. On 9 June Taylor, Zimmerman, Tannenwald, and Larson flew to LaGuardia Airport. The next day they flew the northern route to Britain, from LaGuardia to Shediac, New Brunswick, to Shannon in southern Ireland (via Botwood, Newfoundland, twice for replacement of malfunctioning engines) and finally to a base in southern England. John Harlan met them in a London hotel and took them to the Eighth Fighter Command headquarters.

The headquarters of the Eighth Fighter Command had been established in what had once been an exclusive country hotel in Bushey, Hertsfordshire, near London. Although Harlan had been in touch with the Eighth Fighter Command and they were "somewhat expecting us—more or less" the greeting by the colonel, chief of A-1 (Personnel), was "I don't know why you men are here or what you are supposed to do but I guess as long as you are here we'll have to find you some place to sleep." [9] This section, like all operations research sections, had to demonstrate its value to the command.

The officers at headquarters, with few exceptions, were billeted with private families in the immediate neighborhood. Thus, the analysts too were placed in private homes. Taylor and Zimmerman, for example, were initially billeted at one of the larger homes in the area belonging to a wealthy resident.

On the second day the analysts met General Hunter. Taylor gives a fond, insightful description of the general.

> He was tall and thin and held himself very erect so as to display to maximum benefit his bristling black hair and his even more bristling handle-bar moustaches which to those who got to know him, proved to be one of the best weather vanes in the headquarters. When you were in conversation with him you learned to watch those moustaches; if they began to quiver a little you could detect that he was getting tense and that the weather was deteriorating. When they really began to go up and down—and I'm not kidding, they really went up and down—you knew that heavy weather was on you and that it was about time to take cover. As I got to know Monk Hunter better I learned that not only were these moustache signs very nearly infallible, but I learned also that he knew that the officers on his staff knew this, and on more than one occasion I have seen him scare the bejesus out of somebody just by getting those moustaches working when he really wasn't mad at all but just wanted to drive home a point. I'm not too sure that a great many of his staff officers knew this last little trait of his. [10]

At least one person in the command knew why the analysts were there, General Hunter; he requested them. He explained to appropriate people in his command what the analysts would do, and instructed them to cooperate fully. The analysts, passing security checks more severe than most of the people on Hunter's staff, were given access to all information.

For the first few days, while waiting for working quarters, the analysts spent considerable time in the officers' lounge. When it was discovered that these strangers in civilian garb were scientists, the officer in charge of the club asked for help with some half dozen or so slot machines. The machines were making more money for the club than was needed and were not returning enough to the players. Thus the "docs and scientists" readjusted the machines to give the players a better payoff and still give the club adequate income. According to Taylor, "This little operation turned out to be one of our real lucky breaks, because from that time on we were classed as geniuses who could do anything. Of course we already were aware of this, but it was the first time the Fighter Command staff had become aware of it. Anyhow we were in." [11]

After about a week the section was assigned working quarters—two small rooms in what had been the house of the hotel golf pro. Located in another room was the chief of the Gas Warfare Section, which consisted of a captain and one GI. With tongue in cheek Taylor said "Evidently they felt our usefulness was probably as great as that of Gas Warfare." In any case the captain was a fine young man—he was the officer in charge of the Officers' Club. Furthermore, he was very good for the spirits of the men in the operations research section "because no matter how lonesome and neglected we felt, he could always go us at least one better." Taylor admits that they must not have been considered total outcasts because the most popular section in the headquarters—the post office—was also housed in their little building. [12] In a more serious vein Taylor describes the problem of gaining acceptance.

> There were a few things that every operations research man learned about rapidly as soon as he tried to function. First, he was a civilian and, *ipso facto*, open to suspicion. This had to be overcome by somehow proving that he was not a government spy and usually that he was there at considerable personal sacrifice to himself. He also had to somehow demonstrate that he had no personal irons in the fire—his job was to help the Air Force, and that the worst that could happen to him would be that he would be fired and sent home and back to the work that he would really prefer to be doing. You have to prove that you are not bucking for any promotion and that while success will get you nowhere, failure will hurt. It was a hard job and most of our people in positions of leadership made it, some others never did. [13]

THE WORK OF THE SECTION

Ammunition belting. The section had arrived in mid-June. By 23 June Taylor had submitted his first memorandum to his chief of staff on a possible method of eliminating vibrations on the gun cameras of the P-47. By 9 July all of his men were at work on assigned projects. These were described to Leach in a letter from Taylor dated 9 July 1943. [14]

Most work assignments reflected the problems known to the command. One problem, however, was brought to the attention of the command by the ORS. All of the American planes—both fighters and bombers—were heavily armed with .50-caliber machine guns. It had become standard practice to use mixed ammunition consisting of armor-piercing (AP), incendiary (I), or a combination of armor-piercing and incendiary (API) projectiles. Taylor said "there was a great deal of voodoo about the selection of these."

The British had collected and analyzed a great deal of German aerial equipment. They calculated, for instance, the relative vulnerability of different portions of a plane to different kinds of ammunition. For example, in a given type of German bomber, 20 percent of the target might be vulnerable to incendiary ammunition (I), 30 percent to armor-piercing (AP), and 50 percent to armor-piercing, incendiary (API) ammunition. Accordingly, guns would be belted with ammunition in the ratio of 2-I to 3-AP to 5-API cartridges. Besides this, there were arguments as to whether you should put all five API together or distribute them in some other way.

> What should have been obvious, but clearly was not, was the fact that if any plane was more vulnerable to any one ammunition than the other it was a pure dilution of ammunition to put in any except the most effective. Ralph Johnson, who was the first one of us to notice this fact, was so dumbfounded that he was almost afraid to mention it. When it was brought up at the top echelons they were skeptical at first. Then when they saw the truth of it, even the 'high command' had a terrible time in convincing the squadrons at the fighting level that they should stop this silly dilution of ammunition. [15]

The section's first report was written by Ralph Johnson on "Mixed Belting of Ammunition for the P-47" and was dated 21 July 1943.

The analysts visited a number of fighter and bomber bases to convince the appropriate people that the analysis was valid. The effort paid off; two groups agreed to participate in an experiment. One group loaded ammunition the way the analysts recommended, all API, and another group loaded ammunition in the mixed-belt manner. Both groups went out on fighter escort for the same mission of B-17s.

> As luck, or statistics, would have it, the group with API ammunition clobbered the German fighters whereas the group with the mixed ammunition had poor hunting. None of them stopped to think about the luck or what it would be like tomorrow with the group positions reversed or a variety of other things. The result was that there was not enough API ammunition in all the UK to supply the overnight demands of the VIII FC [Fighter Command]. Nevertheless, knowledge and acceptance of these results came about slowly in some commands, and not at all in others.

The validity of the section's work on ammunition belting was established both theoretically and experimentally back in the States. Dr. William L. Duren, Jr., a mathematician and outstanding gunnery operations analyst with the Second Air Force in the United States, specialized in gunnery problems of the B-29. In his memoir, however, he told how he also tried to act as liaison between mathematicians in civilian research centers writing papers that "would never be read" and the military men for whom they were intended. Duren gave an example.

> Jacob Wolfowitz had written an elegant statistical analysis of the question, what was the best mixture of the several available types of ammunition to load on the belts of the .50-caliber machine gun against enemy fighters. His answer was clear cut, *based on his assumptions*. The conclusion was that the belts should be loaded 100 percent with the one API (armor-piercing incendiary) type. The assumptions, based on actual experiments at Wright Field, were that serial correlation in several successive hits was small or zero and thus that the probability of a kill in any shot was independent. Under these conditions the belts should be loaded entirely with bullets that had the highest probability of downing the fighter with one hit. This, the Wright Field tests showed, was the API. Not only did the ordnance sergeants not read Wolfowitz's report, but, in defiance of orders from the top, they considered it their right to load those guns as they deemed best. Each one had his own mixture formula including tracers and incendiaries as well as armor piercing bullets. On each base I undertook to "sell" Wolfowitz's result. The argument could be put on a common sense basis, free of the technical statistical qualification. But I do not know how successful I was. [16]

I will add a personal note on the ammunition belting procedures. Because I was the bombardier, I was also the gunnery officer of the crew. However, the crew had nothing to do with selecting ammunition for the belts of our machine guns. We shot, as the occasion arose, whatever ammunition was provided for us. Our most memorable gunnery episode occurred on 2 November 1944 while bombing the synthetic oil refineries at Merseburg-Leuna near Leipzig, Germany. Of 1,100 heavy bombers in five separate forces sent to Germany that day, 683 B-17s were sent to the notorious Merseburg oil refineries. A major air battle lasting forty minutes took place between the escorting fighters of the Eighth Fighter Command and the Luftwaffe in the Merseburg area. Hundreds of fighters on both sides were involved. The largest formation of German fighters encountered during the Merseburg battle was a force, mostly Me-109s, estimated at 150, 200, or 250 planes. The largest group of German jet fighters yet to be encountered, about fifteen Me-163s, rose to attack the bombers that day. At least nine broke through our fighters and made individual passes at the B-17s. Two attacked our group, the 493d Bomb Group, and one made two passes, from behind and overhead, at our squadron. I vividly recall the Me-163—a flying wing—going over us twice with trajectories of tracer bullets from our guns, especially the top turret guns, apparently going through the plane. Yet the fighter flew away without disintegrating. As late as 2 November 1944 and probably for the rest of the war, the ordnance sergeants of the Eighth Bomber Command were still mixing or diluting the ammunition in the ammunition belts. Although the glowing, visible tracers made us feel that we had come close to our target, if all our bullets had been APIs we might have destroyed our adversary. [17,18]

Gunnery and battle damage.   Taylor, as chief, was responsible for all the reports. He assigned work in accordance with the analysts' specialities and interests, and the perceived problems of the command. The analysts' reports reflect well its operations and problems. Johnson's work with ammunition loading is one example. In addition, Brandt analyzed machine gun malfunctions. Tannenwald studied ammunition expenditure, and Norton analyzed statistics of gunnery problems. The main gunnery reports produced by the ORS of the Eighth Fighter Command in 1943 were: "Mixed Belting of Ammunition for the P-47" dated 21 July 1943; "Combat Gunnery, August 15–September 15, 1943," dated 11 October 1943; "Combat Gunnery, September 15–October 20, 1943," dated 4 December 1943; "Note on Gun Stoppages in Combat," dated 31 December 1943; and "Shot Patterns, September 15–December 31, 1943." [19,20]

Each fighter plane was fitted with a gun camera operating at the rate of eight frames per second for as long as the pilot held the trigger and for a few seconds after the last shot was fired. This photography helped evaluate the "kills" reported by the pilots. Knowing whether planes were being destroyed at the rate claimed by the pilots at their briefings was critical. For example, when two or three planes converged on a single German plane, the plane would explode and each plane claimed the kill. Careful analysis often proved that the same plane was in the eyes of two or more gun cameras when it was destroyed. [21] The gun camera photos also showed that in the summer of 1943 German planes were firing jet-propelled rotating rockets with no fins at our B-17s. [22]

Taylor and Brandt were the analysts primarily involved in analyzing gun camera film. Two reports were written on this topic, "Assessability of Gun Camera Films," dated 4 September 1943 and "Analysis of Recent Gun Camera Films," dated 23 September 1943. [23]

A letter from Judge Theodore Tannenwald, Jr., (United States Tax Court) dated 22 July 1983, explains Bart Leach's rationale for having lawyers as part of the mix of personnel of operations analysis sections and how it worked out in his case.

> He [Leach] had the attitude—and quite correctly—that lawyers were useful in two respects: first, to handle much of the administrative work of the Section; second, to put the analyses of the scientists in language the operations people could understand. Throughout the life of the Section [at Eighth Fighter Command] I per-

formed the second role. After Taylor left, I performed the first role for Johnson. Thus when you refer to the film analyses by Taylor and Brandt, I was deeply involved in those, not only in terms of the actual analyses, but also in terms of the drafting of the reports.

Johnson initiated a series of studies on battle damage. The first report was titled "Battle Damage to P-47s, August 14–December 1, 1943" and was dated 23 December 1943. [24]

Radio and radar. Zimmerman and Larson had previous radar experience. They concentrated their activities on the uses of radar by both the Allies and the Germans. They also worked on some problems of the identification system carried by the U.S. bombers and fighters, known as the IFF (Identification, Friend or Foe). As far as the crews of the planes were concerned the IFF was a "black box" located in each plane which could be activated by a suitable signal from the ground in order to tell whether the plane was friend or foe. There was a suspicion that the Germans had obtained or reproduced some of the "black boxes" and were using them for deceptive flying over England. While flying missions as a bombardier from England in the last six months of 1944, I remember that as a back-up and supplement to the IFF, bomber crews were given special identification signals for the bombardier to flash with a light from the nose of the bomber as the plane approached the English coast after a mission. This was especially useful when the plane or planes returned on a course out of the ordinary.

Zimmerman and Larson were also involved in plane-to-base communication systems. VHF (very high frequency) was in use when they arrived; UHF (ultra high frequency) was introduced soon after.

Taylor, though involved to some degree in all the work, was more deeply involved in radar studies, especially at the beginning. In order to do their work, Larson and Zimmerman needed to know more about the early warning and fighter control radar gear in England. Working with British operations research counterparts, Taylor arranged for Zimmerman, Larson, and himself to visit two main sites. One was located on high cliffs overlooking the English Channel on the Isle of Wight, and the other was located on high cliffs at a spot called Beachy Head, close to the southern beaches of Eastbourne. They set out with a command car, driver, British road maps, and "umpteen copies of our orders (which said almost nothing)." The British, worried about the possibility of invasions or infiltration by saboteurs, carefully removed all road signs and other means of identifying locations. Thus, it was necessary to ask directions from time to time. Three civilians in an American car with a uniformed driver were clearly suspicious. In Southampton, while asking directions, they were surrounded by a crowd of people who would not let them leave until the police arrived to check them out.

The radar stations they visited possessed unsurpassed radar views across the channel. They could detect German planes far inland forming up over their bases for an attack. These stations were among the most important British assets during the Battle of Britain. With them the British obtained long enough warning of impending attacks to scramble their fighter planes into positions ready for the German bombers. Because of this the stations were prime German targets. While visiting the radar station near Beachy Head, Taylor and his men stayed at a small hotel used by the staff of the radar station. All the buildings around it had been bombed out. They spent the night on the top floor and were warned to get down below in case of an air raid. The top floor was not the best place to be when the Jerries' "skip-and-run" bombers skimmed in across the waterfront. Shortly after Taylor's visit the skip-and-run boys came in and bombed out the hotel. [25]

Two reports came out of these radar and radio studies by the end of the year. The first was "The General Use of Type-16 Fighter Direction Stations" dated 26 November 1943, and the second was "Air Tests of Modified SCR-522 for Assessing Reduction in Freya [German radar] Interference" dated 14 December 1943. [26]

Operations research by the assistant secretary of war.   Just about a month before the Eighth Fighter Command ORS arrived in England, a bit of operations analysis was done at the highest level by civilian analyst Robert A. Lovett, Assistant Secretary of War for Air. The general he advised was none other than General Henry H. Arnold, the commanding general of the USAAF.

Lovett was met in London on 13 May by General Eaker, commanding general of the Eighth Air Force, which included the Eighth Bomber Command and the Eighth Fighter Command. Lovett came to see what the Eighth Air Force was doing. In particular he visited all the fighter groups and talked to "a large proportion" of the approximately one hundred pilots in General Hunter's fighter command. From them, the bomber crews, and their commanders, he obtained a front-line assessment of one of the greatest problems that confronted the Eighth Air Force in the last six months of 1943. On one hand the Eighth Bomber Command needed, and knew it needed, fighter escort for its strikes against German targets. On the other hand the Eighth Fighter Command did not have a plane with adequate range to provide this escort.

As a result of his observations Lovett wrote two memoranda to General Arnold, the first dated 18 June and the second 19 June. In them he advised General Arnold that

1. fighter escort would have to be provided for the bombers on as many missions as possible;

2. the P-47 could serve as top escort cover only if satisfactory auxiliary gasoline tanks were developed;

3. the Eighth Air Force needed P-38s and P-51s with wing tanks in order to meet the increasing German fighter opposition;

4. the Eighth Bomber Command needed more replacement crews, more forward firing power for the B-17, and, for its crews, better training in gunnery and formation flying over 20,000 feet. [27]

Even with this advice and more from other quarters, it was not until the end of 1943 that the Eighth Fighter Command was able to fly escort all the way. Two groups of P-38s were sent to England in August and started operations on 15 October. On 1 December a group of P-51s with British Rolls Royce Merlin engines became operational. The P-38 had little experience flying from Britain in winter. The extreme cold it encountered at high altitudes caused many operational problems. More importantly, it had already been found in North Africa that, although the P-38 outperformed the German planes below 18,000 feet, the tables were turned at altitudes above 18,000 feet. Thus the P-51 Mustang, not the P-38, was the plane for the European theater. [28]

In a July 1983 letter Tannenwald discussed how his section participated in the attempt to use the P-38 in the European theater.

> We were involved in a general way with the efforts of Col. Hough to modify the role of the P-38 in order to accommodate a bombardier. One plane was so modified and Hough took it on a mission over Germany—a mission that he asked me to go on, but I declined because of the fact that had he been shot down, I would not have been accorded the status of a prisoner of war because I was a civilian and would probably have been shot.

A good discussion of Colonel Hough's work with the Droop Snoot bomber, a modified P-38, and its use appears in Roger Freeman's *The Mighty Eighth*, page 148.

Operational efficiency. Because fighters routinely flew to the limits of their range, operational efficiency was a major concern of the command. At one time or another every member of the section was involved with some facet of this problem. In a letter to Leach on 9 July 1943 Taylor described the initial work assignments of the section. Zimmerman and Larson were assigned to study gasoline consumption and develop methods to record data on the maximum range of the P-47. Brandt, Norton, and Tannenwald also worked on the problem of gasoline consumption. One report on "Operations Efficiency of Fighter Command Aircraft" dated 14 August 1943 was produced on the subject. [29,30]

On 13 August 1943 Tannenwald wrote a report reflecting another major concern of the command titled "The Relative Effectiveness of Using Fighters to Escort Bombers." The report begins with the statement, "A subject often discussed in connection with Air Force operations is the desirability of using fighters to escort bombers compared with other uses. It occurred to thisSection that an analysis of existing data might furnish some mathematical basis for this discussion." The section wanted to compare the probabilities of bomber loss when there was fighter escort and when there was not. It also intended to compare USAAF and enemy fighter casualties while our fighters were on escort duty and while they were on fighter sweeps.

The report indicates that not enough data existed to answer the bomber loss question. Not enough was known about the causes of bomber loss. The reports on bomber losses did not specify when on the mission the damage occurred which caused the loss. Such information was necessary for this study. On 17 August, four days after the report was filed, missions of B-17s to Schweinfurt and Regensburg rendered the first question academic to the bomber command. Sixty out of 376 planes were lost, and many more were heavily damaged—mainly by German fighters during the unescorted part of the mission. The study's other question remained relevant, however, and unfortunately received much less attention than it deserved.

Often when the Eighth Bomber Command sent planes out on a mission it would send a smaller group of planes to a secondary target as a diversion. This confused the enemy and divided his forces. Thus, the fighters performed several functions. In addition to escorting bombers during primary attacks and diversionary sweeps, the fighters often flew non-escort missions or independent sweeps of their own. Using data compiled during 1 April–30 June 1943, Tannenwald compared destroyed enemy aircraft with lost Allied fighters and killed or missing personnel for the three types of missions. The data indicate that the fighters had a substantially greater chance of engaging in combat as they escorted main bombing attacks. Also, the chance of destroying an enemy plane on such a mission was better. Furthermore, though the pilot casualty rate was higher during escort missions to main targets than during independent sweeps, the risk of casualty per combat was less. In other words, once our pilots engaged in combat they had a better chance of surviving if they were escorting planes than if they were on an independent sweep. Although the conclusions were based on meager data, the overall indication was clear. Our fighters were employed most profitably when they escorted main bomber attacks. Ralph Johnson signed this report for Taylor.[31]

THE EIGHTH AIR FORCE COMMAND STRUCTURE RESHUFFLES[32]

By April 1943 General Arnold was convinced that the Eighth Air Force could improve its bombing campaign of the continent from England. He suggested that General Eaker replace General Newton Longfellow, commander of Eighth Bomber Command and his chief of staff, Colonel Charles Bubb. Though he eventually complied, Eaker resisted at first. While reluctant to lose Longfellow, Eaker was more willing to replace his fighter commander, General Hunter.

Eaker and Hunter apparently disagreed about the best use of fighter planes. Hunter tended to believe that it was most effective for fighters to sweep an area and clear out the opposition, so the bombers could fly unmolested. Eaker, on the other hand, wanted the fighters to accompany the bombers, above, to each side, and below, in an effort to hold off the Germans to and from the target. The P-47s, of course, did not have the range to do this. However, Eaker felt that the P-47, using auxiliary gas tanks, could fly further if the fighters would fly to maximum ceiling and fly as far as possible on their drop tanks. They should even avoid combat if necessary until those tanks were emptied and released. The fighter pilots, on the other hand, were eager to release the drop tanks as soon as possible. They were just as eager to use up gasoline in the auxiliary tank behind their seats before engaging in combat. A hit there could turn them into a flaming torch. Thus, Hunter's pilots commonly dropped their belly tanks as soon as they reached ceiling, regardless of the amount of gasoline still in them.

Early in June, Eaker asked Arnold to send him a new fighter commander. One man suggested, Major General William Kepner, succeeded General Hunter as commander of the Eighth Fighter Command on 29 August 1943. Taylor, his men, and probably Hunter, did not know when they reported for duty in mid-June that they reported to a commander on his way out.

THE SECTION HELPS EIGHTH AIR SUPPORT COMMAND

In mid-summer 1943 Taylor discussed with General Hunter problems in his command that the section might look into. Hunter mentioned that the outfit with real problems was the Eighth Air Support Command under General Robert C. Candee. [33]

On 7 March 1943 the first two squadrons of the 322d Bomb Group arrived at Bury St. Edmunds. They were the first of several medium bomber groups—B-26s—which remained in the Eighth Air Force almost until the end of the year. Indeed, at first they were part of the Third Bombardment Wing, with headquarters at Elveden Hall and airfields in Suffolk and southern Norfolk. The B-26 Marauder was a two-engine bomber which could carry 4,000 pounds of bombs at speeds well over 200 miles per hour (top speed of 317 miles per hour) for hundreds of miles. It was manned by a crew of six or seven men.

The planners in Washington had designated it, in contrast to the heavies, as a low-level (treetop-level) bomber. Accordingly, on 14 May twelve B-26s, each carrying four 500-pound delayed action bombs took off on a low-level mission against an electrical generating plant near Ijmuiden on the Dutch coast. The mission was ineffective. The bombs hit the target area but missed the plant. The planes that returned were riddled with antiaircraft fire—one plane had 200 holes in it—and seven men were wounded. On the night of 16 May the 322d Group received orders to return the next day with twelve planes loaded as before. Six of them were to bomb the plant at Ijmuiden; the other six were to hit another generating station at nearby

Haarlem. The mission began as scheduled. One plane turned back thirty miles from the Dutch coast with engine trouble. The others, including one containing the group commanding officer, Lt. Col. Robert M. Stillman, did not return. The planes and men were listed at the Eighth Bomber Command as "missing in action, cause unknown."

After this disaster the 322d Bomb Group was removed from operations. By 6 June three groups of B-26s were in the Eighth Air Force. A fourth was on the way to the United Kingdom from the United States. General Eaker transferred the B-26s from the Eighth Bomber Command to the Eighth Air Support Command under General Candee. The Eighth Air Support Command was an organization whose purpose was to support ground forces. Up to this time, it had very little part in the Eighth's operational activity. All of that changed; the B-26s were moved to bases in Essex on the coast near Colchester.

All four B-26 groups had been trained for low-level bombing. However, the USAAF in North Africa stopped using B-26s for low-level bombing and began using them at altitudes well above the range of light antiaircraft fire. The Eighth Air Support Command decided to do the same. This meant implementing a new training program for the crews. Norden bombsights were procured and installed along with strike cameras to gather bombing accuracy data and downward-firing rear hatch guns for the gunners. [34]

General Hunter, after telling Taylor that Candee might discuss these problems with him, called Candee on the "scrambler" phone. Candee's reaction was instantaneous. "Get them over here as fast as you can." Taylor noted how differently the two commands regarded his section. According to Taylor, when the section arrived at the Eighth Fighter Command the chief of A-1 said, " I don't know why you men are here or what you are supposed to do, but I guess as long as you are here we'll have to find you some place to sleep." Though the chief may have intended no malice by this remark, to Taylor it symbolized a continuing problem between his section and some of the Eighth Fighter Command staff.

> At least while I was with it, the Fighter Command continued to resist our efforts to help them whereas the Bomber Command [at first called Eighth Air Service Command but soon to become the nucleus of the Ninth Bomber Command] at times appeared so anxious for our help that they would be almost willing to turn their whole operation over to us if we could just make it work. [35]

Taylor, Zimmerman, Larson, and Johnson were given a royal reception at Candee's office. Candee called in his principal division officers to talk to the analysts and to discuss their problems. "The whole atmosphere was fantastic. Every Division had problems, and knew they had them, and wanted any kind of help they could possibly get." The analysts spent weeks listening to their problems and giving help or advice when they could.

Soon the section was working more for the Eighth Air Support Command than it was for the Eighth Fighter Command. Taylor said, "Somehow Monk Hunter became aware of this; I should remark that he always seemed more aware of us than all the rest of his Command put together." Toward the end of the summer General Hunter called Taylor to discuss the section's work. Hunter's section heads and a few others, such as the signals officer, were present also. Hunter quizzed Taylor at length about what the section was doing and what he thought it could or should be doing. As Taylor responded relative to each section, Hunter turned to each section head and asked if they were cooperating. Each one in turn indicated they were cooperating. Finally he got to the Signal Corps Section. The colonel who headed this section had been a real problem to the ORS by withholding needed information. They worked around him. Taylor discussed ORS work with the Signal Corps Section in such a way that the colonel heading the section could not claim to be cooperating without contradicting Taylor. "Hunter caught this and really tore things apart. This resulted in some improvement in our access to information but a clear deterioration in personal relations." [36]

Hunter, discussing the section's activities with the Air Support Command, became upset because the section spent so much time with them and because the Air Support Command sought its assistance so often.

> Without any warning he picked up the scrambler phone and called General Candee to find what was going on and to find out how come Candee was poaching so much on his (Monk's) territory. We couldn't hear the other end of the conversation but by watching Hunter, you could see first the light twitch and finally the bristle of moustachios. Pretty soon he was talking to Bob Candee (using his first name) like a dutch uncle and telling him, by god, he had to have his own Operations Research Section and he had to have it fast and Monk would help him get it. You could almost hear the yes sirs and no sirs coming back on the phone although they were not in line of command. To listen to the conversation you wondered why the wires did not melt, but it soon ended and Monk turned around to the others in the room who had been listening more or less with their mouths open. His moustaches quieted down, his eyes began to sparkle and he began to chuckle, says he "Poor Bob, he's so serious and he's got so many troubles, and he doesn't know when I'm serious and when I'm not." He then turned to me "Taylor, Candee needs and wants an Operations Research Section, you get yourself ready to go back home and get him one, we'll make the necessary arrangements." Within less than a week I was home. [37]

THE SECTION IS SPLIT

Taylor arrived in Washington to recruit four or five new analysts for the Eighth Air Support Command. He expected to manage the operations research for the two commands jointly, borrowing analysts back and forth as necessary. However, he soon heard the rumor that the Eighth Air Support Command was to become the nucleus of a revamped Ninth Air Force. General Lewis H. Brereton, the commanding general of the Ninth Air Force in North Africa, would soon move his headquarters staff from Africa to England, where the Ninth Air Force would reform into a tactical air force. On 1 August 1943 Brereton's Ninth Bomber Command, under the command of General Uzal Ent, made the low-level attack on the oil refineries at Ploesti, Romania, from Bengazi, North Africa. When Taylor learned that Brereton was at the Pentagon, "not wanting to be caught in the middle of organizing something for one Air Force that might be lost in the organization of another," he sought a conference with Brereton. Taylor asked if Brereton wished him to go ahead with the plans developed with Candee and Hunter. Brereton's experience with operations research in North Africa was positive. He had access to British operations research at his headquarters in Cairo. Furthermore, one of the crack operations analysis groups of the war was sent to his own Ninth Bomber Command to help get ready for the Ploesti mission. Brereton's answer was an immediate yes; he wanted the planning to go forward, but with changes. He wanted the section completely separate from the Eighth Fighter Command. He also wanted the section to start with twice as many staff members as planned. Furthermore, he wanted operations research to operate as a division out of his headquarters, reporting to him but also establishing as many units in the other commands as was desirable. [38]

In a period of about three weeks, operating out of Washington, D.C., Taylor recruited nine new men whose duty as operations analysts for the Ninth Air Force began in November of 1943. He also made important contacts with people who joined later. (This, however, is part of the story of the Ninth Air Force ORS.) [39]

When Taylor returned to the Eighth Fighter Command he told the section members about the new developments. As a result, Zimmerman, Larson, and Brandt shifted with Taylor to the new Ninth Air Force section. Johnson, Norton, and Tannenwald stayed with the Eighth Fighter Command. Johnson was designated chief. General Hunter agreed to these proposed changes, and he had the orders prepared. Also, Hunter told Taylor that General Kepner was replacing him and that he was returning to the States. Kepner was not happy when he learned about the split up of the section. However, after some discussion with Ralph Johnson and Taylor, he agreed to the arrangement. The shift from the Eighth Fighter Command to the Ninth Air Force became effective in November 1943. [40]

REFERENCES

1. Roger A. Freeman, *The Mighty Eighth, A History of the U.S. 8th Army Air Force* (London: MacDonald, 1970), 7.

2. *The Mighty Eighth*, 7.

3. *The Mighty Eighth*, 9.

4. Lauriston S. Taylor, *From the Cupboards of Lauriston S. Taylor*, unpublished, 365–66.

5. Leroy A. Brothers, *Operations Analysis in World War II, United States Army Air Forces* (Philadelphia: Stephenson-Brothers, 1948), 2.

6. *From the Cupboards*, 367–70.

7. Ibid., 368.

8. *Operations Analysis in World War II*, 13.

9. *From the Cupboards*, 376.

10. Ibid., 379.

11. Ibid., 380.

12. Ibid., 381.

13. Ibid., 411.

14. Letter from Taylor to Leach, Subject: ORS projects, Dissemination of Information, 9 July 1943, ORS history records of the Eighth Fighter Command, Archives, Simpson Historical Research Center, Maxwell Air Force Base, Alabama.

15. *From the Cupboards*, 389.

16. William L. Duren, Jr., *Operations Analyst, U.S. Army Air Force in World War II* (1982), 14–15.

17. "The Army Air Forces in World War II, Combat Chronology 1941–1945," Kit C. Carter and Robert Mueller, Albert F. Simpson Historical Research Center, Air University and Office of Air Force History, Headquarters USAF, 1973, 486.

18. *The Mighty Eighth*, 191–92.

19. *Operations Analysis in World War II*, 13.

20. List of Operations Analysis Reports as of 1 February 1945, Operations Analysis Division, Management Control, Headquarters, Army Air Forces, Washington D.C., 131.500, Archives, Simpson Historical Research Center, Maxwell Air Force Base, Alabama.

21. *From the Cupboards*, 390.

22. Ibid., 391.

23. List of Operations Analysis Reports.

24. Ibid.

25. *From the Cupboards*, 393–96.

26. List of Operations Analysis Reports.

27. Thomas M. Coffey, *Decision over Schweinfurt, The U.S. 8th Air Force Battle for Daylight Bombing* (New York: David McKay Company, 1977), 195–98.

28. *The Mighty Eighth*, chapter 12.

29. *Operations Analysis in World War II*, 13.

30. List of Operations Analysis reports.

31. Report No. 3, Headquarters Eighth Fighter Command, ORS. "The Relative Effectiveness of Using Fighters to Escort Bombers," 13 August 1943, 524.310, Simpson Historical Research Center, Maxwell Air Force Base, Alabama.

32. *Decision over Schweinfurt*, 199–200.

33. *From the Cupboards*, 391.

34. *The Mighty Eighth*, chapter 7.

35. *From the Cupboards*, 392.
36. Ibid., 396.
37. Ibid., 396–97.
38. Ibid., 398–99.
39. Ibid., 401.
40. *Operations Analysis in World War II*, 13.

6

The Operations Research Section
of the Eighth Air Force
January 1944–6 June 1944

ON COURSE FOR THE INVASION OF NORTHWEST EUROPE

By January 1944 the long-planned cross-channel invasion of northwestern Europe by the Allies had become the next objective. The target date for the invasion had been set for May 1944, though the actual day was 6 June. General Dwight Eisenhower had been named the supreme Allied commander, and he reached London in mid-January 1944 to assume command of the Supreme Headquarters, Allied Expeditionary Forces (SHAEF). Air Chief Marshal Sir Arthur Tedder, who had served with Eisenhower in the Mediterranean, was named deputy supreme commander.

As of 1 January 1944 the United States Strategic Air Forces in Europe (USSTAF) had been established with administrative control over both the Eighth and Fifteenth Air Forces. Lt. Gen. Carl Spaatz assumed command of USSTAF, and Major General James H. Doolittle replaced Lt. Gen. Ira C. Eaker as commander of the Eighth Air Force. General Eaker, in turn, assumed command of the newly established Mediterranean Allied Air Forces. Air Chief Marshal Sir Trafford Leigh-Mallory, former head of RAF Fighter Command, was designated air commander in chief of the Allied Expeditionary Air Force (AEAF). Under AEAF was the RAF Second Tactical Air Force and the rapidly growing U.S. Ninth Air Force, commanded by Major General Lewis H. Brereton. RAF Bomber Command, commanded by Air Chief Marshal Sir Arthur Harris, was not part of either of these commands and remained pretty much an independent entity with Prime Minister Churchill as its patron.

On 27 December 1943 General Arnold, commanding general of all the United States air forces, sent the following New Year's message to the commanding generals of the Eighth and Fifteenth Air Forces:

> a. Aircraft companies in this country [United States] are turning out large quantities of airplanes, engines and accessories.

b. Our training establishments are operating 24 hours per day, seven days per week training crews.

c. We are now furnishing fully all the aircraft and crews to take care of your attrition.

d. It is a conceded fact that OVERLORD [the cross-channel invasion] and ANVIL [the invasion of southern France] will not be possible unless the German Air Force is destroyed.

e. Therefore, my personal message to you—this is a MUST—is to, Destroy the Enemy Air Force wherever you find them, in the air, on the ground and in the factories." [1]

By January 1944 the Eighth Air Force was a powerful, experienced air force. It had been operating out of England against German industry and the GAF for almost a year and a half. In January 1944 the Eighth Air Force consisted of twenty-six heavy bomber groups. [2] Fifteen more heavy bomber groups would become operational in the Eighth Air Force between January 1944 and D day. By January the U.S. fighter escorts were finally capable of flying all the way with the bombers to the deepest targets, such as Berlin. As General Arnold's directive anticipated, bombing German airplane factories was not enough, because the Germans dispersed and hid their production sites. However, bombing important production centers, including oil, had a side effect which was devastating for the Germans. When the GAF rose to protect their industry, their airfields, and their oil from the bombers, they were now engaged not only by bombers, but also by fighters. Thus, they were flushed out and destroyed in large numbers.

Although the Germans replaced planes, their diminishing oil supply was making it impossible for them to train replacement pilots adequately.

BOMBING ACCURACY
JANUARY, FEBRUARY, AND MARCH 1944

Radar bombing. Before the invasion, and for months after, the Allies could strike against Germany itself only with air power. In the air war the weather was a great ally of the Germans because it protected them from bomber attacks. In the winter of 1943–44 the Eighth Air Force plunged into a large program of H2X radar bombing in an attempt to free itself from the weather's absolute control. In the summer of 1943, H2X was produced in the States. In order to gain precious time, the Radiation Laboratory at MIT hand made twenty sets, enough to equip a dozen B-17s and provide necessary spares. These twelve planes, manned by crews partially trained in H2X use, arrived in England in October 1943 to join the 482d Bomb Group. With them came scientists from the Radiation Laboratory who set up a laboratory in the United Kingdom (UK) to coordinate the work of the Radiation Laboratory with the Eighth Air Force. The H2X crews spent October in simulated bombing missions over England. They still needed more training, but, because bombing weather was so bad, the air force ordered the H2X crews to complete their training over Germany itself, each crew with a combat wing of sixty bombers behind it.[3]

The first Eighth Air Force Pathfinder-led mission—244 planes attacked—was to the port city of Emden, Germany, on 27 September 1943. These Pathfinders used the British H2S radars. The second Eighth Air Force Pathfinder-led mission—337 planes attacked—was again to Emden on 2 October 1943. The Pathfinders used the British H2S again. On 3 November 1943 the Eighth Air Force mounted its third Pathfinder-led mission, this time to Wilhelmshaven. Of the 555 planes dispatched, 528 attacked. This time the mission was led by eleven Pathfinders, nine of them using the American H2X and two using the British H2S.

In November 1943 the Eighth Air Force flew missions on eleven days. Pathfinders were used on eight of these days. In December the Eighth Air Force flew missions on ten days. Pathfinders were necessary on six of these days.[4]

In January the Eighth Air Force flew large missions to the German targets of Kiel, Münster, Ludwigshafen, Oschersleben, Halberstadt, Brunswick, and Frankfurt on six days. Pathfinders were used on four of these days. In addition, four large missions were flown against V-weapon sites in France.

In December 1943 radar bombing had made it possible to drop more bombs than ever before in any one month (13,142 tons) despite the foul weather. For the first time the Eighth Air Force exceeded the tonnage dropped by the RAF.[5]

The Bombing Accuracy Subsection attempted to shed some light on what had been accomplished. Reliable information on bombing accuracy was very difficult to obtain. No strike photographs were available to evaluate bombs dropped through the clouds. Evaluations were based on photographic reconnaissance made before and after the missions. Reliably reporting new strikes on targets like Wilhelmshaven and Ludwigshaven, which had been bombed many times before, was very hard. Nevertheless, the first report of the Bombing Accuracy Subsection in 1944 was "Report on Results of Pathfinder Bombing on Certain Targets," dated 31 January 1944. In his memoir Baley Price discusses the report.

> This report was prepared by Col. Scott with assistance from Major Darwin in the analysis of the photographic source material. The first blind mission was conducted on 27 September 1943, and there had been many since. Col. Scott assembled all the data he could get from PRU (Photographic Reconnaissance Unit) photographs and published the results. He came to the conclusion that these missions had averaged only 5% of their bombs within one mile of the aiming point.

The technical people were disappointed, discouraged, and not a little defiant. Some denied that the results were as bad as the report indicated; others insisted that Radiation Laboratory had built good equipment, but that the Air Force was making a hopeless mess of using it. The Bombing Accuracy Subsection itself was fearful that the Air Force was embarking on a program of inaccurate bombing that would inevitably absorb much energy and material that otherwise would have gone into visual bombing. Such doubts and criticism were suppressed for fear that we might hinder the development of instruments and techniques that eventually would be of the highest importance. [6]

The official USAAF history of this period corroborates the evaluation.

The bomb patterns made by pathfinder-led forces in November and December were too scattered to effect more than accidental damage to any particular industrial plant or installation of importance. The aiming point became a highly theoretical term. On only two missions did bombs fall in the assigned target area. Photo interpretation indicated that only 6 of the total 151 combat boxes (about 4%) depending on radar (data from 15 October to 15 December) dropped their bombs within one mile of the aiming point; 17 dropped within two miles; 30 dropped within five miles. These figures are of course only approximate, because they do not include the large number of bombs which fell in water nor do they do justice to the incendiaries, the pattern of which is more difficult than that of high explosives to trace. At Bremen, the city most heavily attacked, no high explosives fell within two miles of the aiming point, and only five combat boxes succeeded in placing their cargo within five miles. Especially discouraging were the results at Ludwigshafen on 30 December when the I. G. Farbenindustrie plant suffered little damage. Though an inland target, it should have been easily identifiable on the radar screen because of its position on the Rhine, and the radar operators had by that time the benefit of two to three months' experience. [7]

The heavy bombers were sent out whenever it seemed possible to bomb either visually or by radar. Often missions were "scrubbed" before takeoff, and often planes were recalled after takeoff because of weather. The following statistics reflect improving weather and increased daylight. The Eighth Air Force was able to mount bomber attacks on eleven days in January 1944, seventeen days in February, and twenty-two days in March. In each month radar bombing was a big factor. [8] The H2X Pathfinders were, in bad weather, invariably used for the longer missions. Gee-H was used for some of the shorter missions within its range.

Although the radar bombing of the big bombers with H2X improved some-what in January, February, and March 1944, it clearly was not precision bombing. Instead, it was a new kind of area bombing. Whereas the accuracy of visual bombing could be described in units of 500 feet, the accuracy of H2X bombing at this stage was described in terms of miles. Appropriate targets for H2X Pathfinders were seaports and large industrial areas. This type of bombing indirectly helped achieve General Arnold's directive of destroying the GAF. It served to keep pressure on the enemy. Sometimes too, on a Pathfinder mission, the weather cleared in the target area and visual bombing would become possible. Furthermore, these missions often provoked fighter attacks, resulting in losses the GAF could not afford.

Clearly, this new technique of H2X bombing assumed a larger and larger place in Eighth Air Force operations. The ORS needed to become involved with it. Thus, on Thursday, 30 March 1944, Colonel Harlan, chief of the section, called Dr. Baley Price and Dr. Forrest Immer, members of the Bombing Accuracy Subsection, to his office and assigned them to study H2X blind bombing accuracy.[9]

Visual bombing accuracy in 1943 and early 1944.   The Bombing Accuracy Subsection had prepared a major report titled "Analysis of VIII Bomber Command Operations from the Point of View of Bombing Accuracy—1 January 1943–15 October 1943," which was discussed earlier. This analysis was repeated for the next five-month period in "Report on Bombing Accuracy—1 October 1943–1 March 1944," which is dated 12 April 1944.[10]

In 1943 the Eighth Air Force grew from an operational force of four to twenty-six heavy bomber groups. By the end of March 1944 thirty heavy bomber groups were in the Eighth.[11] During the first half of 1943 the operations analysts had pretty much established, by scientific analysis of actual operations, the fundamentals of visual formation bombing. This knowledge had been put into use in subsequent operations. The accuracy of Eighth Air Force operations improved remarkably from 1 October 1943 to 1 March 1944.

That only 55 percent to 60 percent of the visual attacks made by the big bombers were against targets with preassigned aiming points may be surprising. Because bad weather decreased visibility over the targets, it was often impossible to bomb either the assigned primary or secondary target. Instead, bombers would drop their bombs visually on a "target of opportunity." The Bombing Accuracy Subsection did not include the results of this kind of bombing in their analyses. Table 6.1 on page 112 is based on the two reports on bombing accuracy described above and gives the results of visual attacks on targets with preassigned aiming points only.

In the report this remarkable improvement was put into perspective and explained by the bombing analysts. The target systems of the Eighth Air

Table 6.1. Bombing Accuracy During Visual Attacks

	Average percentage of bombs dropped that fell within:	
	500 feet of aiming point	1,000 feet of aiming point
1 Jan. 1943–		
1 Oct. 1943	5.5	16.0
1 Oct. 1943–		
1 Mar. 1944	14.5	37.0
Improvement	9.0	21.0
(percent)	163.6	131.3

Force for both periods under consideration were seaports, airfields, and various production centers such as ball bearing factories, aircraft factories, and shipyards. Intensity and magnitude of the attacks increased in January and especially February 1944. On 20, 21, 22, and 24 February the weather cleared sufficiently over Germany and Austria for the Eighth Air Force, in conjunction with the Fifteenth from Italy, to make heavy strikes against major aircraft production centers.

However, in December 1943 a large new target system demanded the attention of the Eighth Air Force. On Christmas Eve 1943 the Eighth Air Force mounted its first attack with 670 bombers against a number of "ski sites" (German missile sites) being built in the Pas-de-Calais. In January the Eighth Air Force flew approximately 1,034 sorties against missile sites along the French coast. It flew upwards of 733 such sorties in February. Two aspects of these targets positively affected bombing accuracy. Because the V-weapons were close to the bombers' home base, the danger of GAF attack was small. Attacking combat boxes could be smaller, and were often of squadron size rather than group size. Bombing altitude also improved accuracy. At first, antiaircraft defenses around the missile sites permitted heavy bombers to attack at altitudes considerably lower than their usual 20,000 to 23,000 feet. However, as the antiaircraft defenses around missile sites strengthened, the bombers were gradually driven up to higher altitudes.

The bombing analysts deleted all squadron bombing from the second period and compared again. Table 6.2 shows the result. [13] Comparing this with Table 6.1 suggests that more sighting and smaller combat boxes increased bombing accuracy.

The improvement in bombing, even with squadron bombing omitted, is still remarkable. Analysts gave the following reasons for this improvement.

Table 6.2. Bombing Accuracy During Visual Attacks
(Squadron Bombing is Omitted)

	Average percentage of bombs dropped that fell within:	
	500 feet of aiming point	1,000 feet of aiming point
1 Jan. 1943–		
1 Oct. 1943	5.5	16.0
1 Oct. 1943–		
1 Mar. 1944	13.0	34.0
Improvement	7.5	18.0
(percent)	136.3	112.5

1. The reduction in pattern size of group bombfalls in the past six months of operations has resulted in a marked improvement in the bombing effectiveness of the heavy bombardment units of the Air Force. Additional efforts along this line can be expected to contribute even further improvement.

2. A reduction in the average bombing altitude during the same period has likewise contributed greatly to improved bombing results. (The average bombing altitude during the first period was 23,000 feet whereas the average altitude during the second period was 19,000 feet.)

3. Under the methods of attack employed during the last six months, the combined effect of (a) splitting the attacking force between as many separate targets as feasible and (b) where possible, of increasing the spacing between attacking units, has been to increase the per-unit effectiveness of our Air Force and thereby our overall efficiency. [14]

The statistics on bombing accuracy showed that the growth of the air force to thirty-one groups had introduced a problem that was negligible when it consisted of only four groups. The data showed that if from one to three groups attacked a given target, 39 percent of the bombs could be expected to fall within 1,000 feet of the aiming point. If from four to six groups attacked the same target, 34 percent of the bombs could be expected to fall within 1,000 feet of the aiming point. If from seven to nine groups attacked, the percentage dropped to 25 percent; and if from ten to nineteen groups attacked the same target, only 20 percent of the bombs could be expected to fall within 1,000 feet of the aiming point. Such a finding virtually dictated the policy of splitting an attacking force among many targets.

It had been known since May 1943 [15] that the bombing accuracy of groups bombing the same target decreased as the number of groups bombing increased if they followed one another closely. This was caused by groups interfering with each other on the bomb run, and by smoke and debris obstructing the target. Bombing accuracy improved considerably for the following groups if they separated from one another by at least a few minutes. This, however, made the bombers more vulnerable to flak.

The Eighth Air Force in this period was growing rapidly. On 13 December a record-breaking 649 bombers were dispatched to targets in Germany. On 29 January a record-breaking 763 bombers were dispatched to targets in Germany again. Then on 20 February 1943 the Eighth Air Force, for the first time, dispatched 1,000 bombers to German targets to begin the "Big Week" campaign. [16]

The "Report on Bombing Accuracy—1 October 1943–1 March 1944" was prepared by bombing analysts James A. Clarkson, Forrest R. Immer, G. Baley Price, Philip Scott, and W. J. Youden. Dr. Immer was a new man in the section who began his service as an operations analyst on 31 January 1944. Dr. Immer received his B.S., M.S., and Ph.D. degrees at the University of Minnesota in 1924, 1925, and 1927 respectively. He was associate director of the Agricultural Experiment Station of the University of Minnesota before he joined the section. [17]

A separate report was made by the section on bombing accuracy for March 1944. The Eighth Air Force flew missions on twenty-three days in March. On thirteen days missions relied solely on Pathfinder. On four additional days they relied partly on Pathfinder. That leaves six days on which the air force was able to operate completely visually. Counting all V-weapon missions as one, the air force attacked twenty-eight preassigned targets, fourteen of them in Germany, and fourteen in occupied territories. In addition, five targets of opportunity were attacked, two in Germany and three in occupied territory. Excluded from evaluation were ten Pathfinder missions.

In February, 18,903,000 pounds of bombs, excluding frags, were dropped visually by the Eighth Air Force, whereas in March only 17,460,000 pounds, excluding frags, were dropped. However, excluding bombs dropped on targets of opportunity in February, 12,426,000 pounds were dropped with 41 percent within 1,000 feet of the aiming point and 72 percent within 2,000 feet. Excluding targets of opportunity, in March 16,240,000 pounds were dropped. Thirty-one percent fell within 1,000 feet, and 61 percent fell within 2,000 feet of the aiming point.

Table 6.3 shows the visual bombing accuracy statistics for the three bomb divisions and the Eighth Air Force as a whole for the months of January, February, and March 1944.

The figures used in Table 6.3 and the report in which they appear were

Table 6.3.

| | Average percentage of bombs dropped that fell within | | | | | | | |
| | 1,000 feet of aiming point | | | | 2,000 feet of aiming point | | | |
	Jan	Feb	Mar	3 Mos	Jan	Feb	Mar	3 Mos
First Bomb Div.	33.3	45.7	29.2	36.2	58.5	81.1	62.5	68.3
Second Bomb Div.	23.3	27.4	26.4	26.4	49.7	51.2	48.5	50.5
Third Bomb Div.	52.5	47.5	30.8	43.9	78.5	78.8	65.4	73.2
Eighth Air Force	39.1	41.4	30.8	36.6	64.8	72.3	60.5	63.9

primarily for internal use. The air force used the report to inform its commanders of how they were doing. Also, the analysts and the air force used this information to improve bombing accuracy. ORS scorekeeping created intense interest and competition among the groups, the wings, and the three divisions. According to these figures, the Second Bomb Division trailed the other two markedly in accuracy during this period. This, of course, increased pressure on the Second Bomb Division to do better.

BOMBING ACCURACY FIELD TRIPS

The February trip—Youden preaches the doctrine of small patterns. Late in February the Bombing Accuracy Subsection organized a field trip to the wings of the Second Division. Price recalls,

> Dr. Immer had joined the Section about the first of February, and a trip to the field would be good training for both him and me. Dr. Youden was the leader of the party, and Captain Veazey, assistant Eighth Air Force Bombardier, accompanied us.

Forewarned that accommodations at Second Division headquarters were not very good, they put up at the Red Cross Club in Norwich, which was located in the center of Second Division territory. The civilian status of the analysts prompted the manager of the Red Cross Club to question their right to stay there. When she learned that she and Dr. Youden had both been born in Townsville, Australia, things were soon smoothed over.

Typically, when they visited a wing or a group, a meeting with the staff members concerned and the bombardiers was arranged, and Dr. Youden gave a lecture. Pilots were also urged to attend because part of the message was for them. Price says,

> The story we had to tell at the meetings on this particular trip was a simple one. Dr. Youden first described the improvement

in bombing accuracy and explained how this improvement had come about. Then he explained how still further improvement could be obtained: make smaller patterns by releasing all bombs as nearly simultaneously as possible and having all planes on the same course with the same speed at the moment of release.

One of their stops on this trip was at Wendling, the base of the 392d Bomb Group. Captain Joseph B. Whittaker, group bombardier, was in charge of the meeting there. He was so impressed by the bombing accuracy story that he called a second meeting for the next morning for the benefit of the pilots who had not attended the first meeting. In the afternoon Captain Veazey, formerly assistant group bombardier of the 392d Group, arranged for the bombing accuracy men to fly in some B-24s that were going out to drop some practice bombs. Baley Price recalls,

> I was in the third plane off. Just as we joined the other two to make a nice formation of three, the flight engineer reported that gasoline was running out of the wings into the bomb bays, and that he thought we should return. Investigation showed that the gasoline tanks had been filled too full. We took off a second time, climbed to 10,000 feet, and went down to a bombing range near Ipswich to drop some 'blue bombs' [practice bombs]. We flew just inside the coast, and saw considerable flak over one of the ports. The British took strong measures to discourage airplanes— any airplanes—from flying over certain cities. This flight was my first one in a heavy bomber, in fact, in any military airplane. The date was February 27, 1944.

On the way back to ORS headquarters Price and the rest of the analysts stopped at Third Division headquarters at Elvenden Hall near Thetford. Here they had a brief conference with General Curtis E. LeMay to make plans for a similar tour through the Third Bomb Division in March. [19]

The March field trip—Colonel Castle becomes an ORS supporter. On the March trip to the wings of the Third Division, the bombing analysis group once again consisted of Drs. Youden, Price, and Immer, but this time Major May, Eighth Air Force bombardier, replaced Captain Veazey. After they visited one of the wings Dr. Youden left Price and Immer to complete the tour. Price notes that they had "graduated." They now had full responsibility to present and defend the bombing analysis findings and policies to the men in the Third Bomb Division who were actually dropping the bombs. Price may not have known, though Youden surely did, that Youden would leave the section in a few weeks.

Baley Price made an important contact for his later work in blind bombing on this trip. The Fourth Combat Wing of the Third Bomb Division had its headquarters on the base of the Ninety-fourth Bomb Group near Bury St.

Edmund. Colonel Castle was commander of the Ninety-fourth Bomb Group when Price visited there in March, and Castle presided over their meeting. Baley Price said this about him:

> It was my first introduction to him, a leader and airman of high ability. I did not realize what was coming in the months ahead, and he made little impression on me that day. Neither his size, his looks, nor his voice was impressive. He was widely known and respected throughout the RAF and the Eighth Air Force for his many accomplishments, however. West Point graduate, he had left the Army and become Vice-President of the Sperry Corporation. On the outbreak of war, he entered the Army again. Before I arrived at Pinetree, he was in charge of A-4 [Materiel] there; later he was Commander of the 94th Group and then of the 4th Combat Wing. [20]

Baley Price explained how Colonel Castle became one of the strongest supporters of Bombing Accuracy.

> Shortly after Bombing Accuracy began to publish monthly reports on visual bombing, General Le May called a meeting of his Group Commanders and publicly gave Col. Castle an unmerciful 'bawling out' because his Group was at the bottom of the Division on the basis of the ORS record. Col. Castle quickly came to ORS to learn what he could do, and Bombing Accuracy hastened to explain to General Le May that the accuracy figures were not a complete evaluation of the performance of any Group. General Le May replied he was well aware of this, but that he intended to use our figures as he had done to keep his commanders on their toes. But to finish the story about Col. Castle, he quickly threw a lot of effort into training, and his Group soon had the best bombing record in the Air Force.
>
> The incident explains how Bombing Accuracy gained some of its strongest supporters, and in addition it emphasizes the uncomfortable position which it often occupied as a result of the use to which its reports were put. [21]

The controversy over targets of opportunity and frags. Bombing Accuracy was often called upon to explain and defend its policies for assessing accuracy and preparing reports. One of the most significant incidents happened in April. In the first three months of 1944 the Second Bomb Division was behind the other two divisions in bombing accuracy. Feeling pressure, some of its officers raised questions about the reasonableness of the section's evaluation policies. Finally, about the middle of April, Colonel Scott was asked to pay a visit to discuss matters. Price recalled,

Col. Scott had a fixed rule that he would never go out on such an occasion without the company and support of a civilian scientist. The support was chiefly psychological: Col. Scott always did all of the talking, but he felt more secure when he had someone with him that could answer technical questions if they rose, and he felt also that the Army personnel stood somewhat in awe of mathematicians and similar civilians. On this particular occasion Col. Scott asked me to accompany him. The trip was set for a day in the third week of April.

Colonel Scott and Dr. Price were invited to be guests of General Hodges, the commanding general of the Second Division, during their stay. When they arrived at Second Division headquarters at Ketteringham Hall the afternoon before the meeting, they were given a nice room. That evening they had dinner at the general's mess.

The meeting opened the next morning at nine o'clock in the office of Colonel Bryan, assistant chief of staff, with Colonel Bryan presiding. He and Colonel Scott were well acquainted; when he was corporation counsel for the city of New York, Colonel Scott was a lawyer there. They met on opposite sides of a lawsuit involving Bertrand Russell. Some twelve or fifteen people were crowded into the small office, including the division bombardier, the Photographic Section officer—he was making independent assessments and evaluations of the bombing results—, members of the Statistical Control Section, and various other staff officers.

Colonel Bryan steered the meeting through a long list of items on his prepared agenda. The discussion revolved around the way in which Bombing Accuracy treated attacks on targets of opportunity and attacks with fragmentation bombs. No percentages were recorded for attacks on targets of opportunity. The captain from the Photographic Section, in particular, felt that the practices of Bombing Accuracy were not in the best interests of winning the war. As he saw it, the crews went out, but for reasons completely beyond their control, they frequently were unable to reach the primary or secondary target. They nevertheless exercised their best judgment in selecting targets of opportunity and inflicted a great deal of damage of military importance. In spite of this, they were never given credit in the records of Bombing Accuracy. Price conveyed the following dialogue between Colonel Scott and the captain.

> "All of the things you say are correct," Col. Scott replied, "but you must remember the purpose for which our records are compiled. The record we keep is designed fundamentally to determine the capabilities of the Air Force in attacks on assigned targets. In an invasion of the French Coast the Air Force will be assigned to hit certain targets in the path of the invading troops, and it won't help to have an Air Force that is capable of hitting some other targets

fifty miles away. Bombing Accuracy simply cannot afford to water down its figures with attacks on targets of opportunity."

"Would the Colonel explain that remark further," requested the Captain from the Photographic Section.

"Well, the situation is simply this," continued Col. Scott. "We kept a lot of records on attacks on targets of opportunity, and they showed that the percentages obtained were about twice those on assigned targets. And it is easy to see why this should be so. In the first place, there is no preassigned aiming point, and the bombardier's report of the aiming point he used may very well be influenced by what he saw of the bombfall on the strike photographs after he returned to base. In the second place, there is no problem of target identification. When a target of opportunity is attacked, it is selected because it has been identified already and is on course. If the percentages on targets of opportunity are included in the record, the figures are raised to such an extent that an entirely false idea of the capabilities of the Air Force is obtained."

"But such a policy is bad for morale," said the Captain, his blood pressure still rising. "These men risk their necks, and there ought to be some way to give them credit for their efforts."

"I am sorry," replied Col. Scott, "but the reports of Bombing Accuracy were not designed for the purpose of boosting morale."

This reply only infuriated the Captain further.

"And your treatment of frags is just as bad," he shot back. "Take the case of Joe Palooka, star bombardier of the 392nd Group. A couple of weeks ago his outfit went after an airfield down in France and met plenty of fighters and flak, but he went right through everything and smeared the target. His plane was so badly shot up that it crash-landed in the southern part of England. He was so pleased with his performance, however, that he rushed to a telephone to tell his Group how he had cleaned all the planes off of that airfield. When he finally returned to his base, he looked in the ORS report, and what did it say? 'Frags! Just Frags!'"

Price recalled that, though the tension was quite high by this time, Colonel Scott kept himself under control, even under constant and sometimes unpleasant provocation from the captain. The capable Colonel Bryan kept the meeting moving. Colonel Scott explained the many difficulties involved in efforts to assess the accuracy of bombing with fragmentation bombs.

The meeting lasted all morning and produced two results:

1. The Second Division Headquarters understood the difficulties involved in assessing bombing accuracy and the reasons for the policies followed by ORS.

2. Colonel Scott had agreed that Bombing Accuracy would show the results

on targets of opportunity by making a plot which contained the bombfall and an outline of the target area—with no aiming point and no percentages.

Price says,

> The meeting adjourned for lunch, and afterward Col. Scott and I took a walk through the gardens behind the Hall. We needed to calm ourselves in preparation for the afternoon session that was still to come.

The afternoon meeting was held in the intelligence room on the first floor of the hall. The meeting's purpose was to discuss certain additional problems with the four combat wing bombardiers and to report to them the accomplishments of the morning meeting.

Colonel Bryan was most pleased to report that Colonel Scott had agreed, for the sake of the morale of the crews and in recognition of their outstanding accomplishments in attacking targets of opportunity, to include in the bombing accuracy reports the plots for targets of opportunity as described above. For the bombing analysts Scott and Price, the high point of this meeting then occurred. Joe Feno, one of the wing bombardiers said,

> I don't want to have anything to do with targets of opportunity. You can leave them out completely so far as I am concerned! If anybody wants to see where the bombs fell at a target of opportunity, he can look at a strike photograph.

The question of plots for targets of opportunity was put to a vote, and three out of four of the wing bombardiers voted against including them. Price then says,

> The great effort of Col. Bryan, the Captain, and other members of the 2nd Division Headquarters on behalf of the morale of the crews had been defeated by the men themselves. It was our experience that they were not easily fooled by cheap efforts at morale building, and that nothing boosted their spirits so successfully as a good showing on the basis of a severe evaluation.
>
> It had been a long and hard day. As we walked away from the Hall, we were greeted by clouds of tear gas: the post security officer was holding a bit of gas mask drill. Col. Scott and I, away from home without our masks, did a bit of crying. So did the English family that still lived in one end of Ketteringham Hall: they had not been informed of the realistic drill! [22]

It happened all too frequently on missions that not all of the bombs would drop at "bombs away." For reasons not fully understood, some of the bomb rack mechanisms would occasionally not release their bombs when the release switch was activated. Bomber crews would find themselves on their way home with live bombs in the bomb bay. Once, for example, I called "bombs away," and only two of the four 1,000-pound bombs we were carrying dropped. We were unable to get the other two to drop in the target area—a German industrial target—and we had to take the bombs back to our base in England.

Bomber crews did not like to return to base with bomb loads. The unplanned-for weight of the bombs on the return might cause the plane to run out of gas if the tank were already low. Furthermore, the crews had an unshakeable belief, well-founded if the plane were damaged, that it was dangerous to land with a plane loaded with live bombs. Thus, it was the practice of the bomber crews to somehow, anyhow, drop unused bombs wherever they could on the way home. Higher headquarters did not have to worry about complaints about bombs dropped on German soil. Many of these bombs, however, were dropping on German-occupied territory in France and the Low Countries.

One morning all the bombardiers and pilots of my group were called to headquarters. A brigadier general from higher headquarters, in an understanding, friendly, but firm way, informed us that randomly dropping hung bombs on German-occupied territory, especially the Netherlands, must stop. According to the new policy, when bombs would not release over the target, bombardiers had to reinsert the pins in the arming vanes of the bombs and bring them them back to base. This, incidentally, required the bombardier to put on his portable oxygen mask and sometimes his parachute and crawl from the nose of the plane into the bomb bay to reinsert the pins in the bombs.

When Germany invaded the Netherlands in 1940, Queen Wilhelmina ruled that country. She, with members of her family and ministers of government, fled to London, which she proclaimed to be the new seat of her government. Dutch forces continued to take part in the war. The general from higher headquarters told us that every time the Dutch underground reported to Queen Wilhelmina that American aerial bombs fell on nonmilitary Dutch soil, the queen got her umbrella, marched over to the appropriate American authorities in London, and protested. This courageous sixty-four-year-old lady, standing up for her country and her people, made a strong, positive impression on us young crew members.

Dr. Youden leaves the section. Dr. W. J. Youden was one of the original six analysts who constituted the section at its beginning in October 1942. Two of the original six, physicist H. P. Robertson and mathematician James W. Alexander, left in early January 1943 after slightly more than two months' service. That left John M. Harlan, chief, Leslie H. Arps, Norris W. Tuttle, and Youden of the original six. Dr. Youden helped lay the foundations of the Loss and Battle Damage Subsection by instituting data-gathering procedures on battle damage, and having them in place when Richard Gettell arrived. Even more importantly, he had been the scientific leader of the Bombing

Accuracy Subsection and played a leading role in identifying the major variables determining the accuracy of visual formation bombing. However, most of the innovative part of his work in bombing accuracy had been done by the end of March 1943. A year later Bombing Accuracy's work in visual bombing was routine. The big new direction for his subsection would be assessing the accuracy of blind bombing. However, just as this was beginning under Baley Price's leadership, Youden left. Dr. Youden's last day with the section was 8 April 1944.[23] He went from the European theater to the India-Burma theater, where he served for six months as an analyst in India. Then Youden returned to the States and served for ten months as a bombing accuracy analyst with the Twentieth Air Force at the Pentagon, where he prepared a manual combining the best of European and Far Eastern bombing theory and techniques. On V-J (Victory over Japan) day Youden was part of the OAS of the Twenty-first Bomber Command (Twentieth Air Force) based at Guam.[24] He was one of the great operations analysts of the USAAF, and he went on after the war to become one of the great statistical scientists.[25]

Gunnery Related Matters
January, February, and March 1944

The Eighth Air Force battles the GAF in the air.   On 5 January 1944 an Eighth Air Force report concluded that the U.S. daylight bombing program would be threatened unless the enemy's fighter force was reduced. The GAF had strengthened in the west because it stepped up production, strengthened firepower, and transferred fighters.[26] In accordance with General Arnold's New Year's message, the Eighth Air Force had begun to strike the GAF wherever it was found: on the ground, in the air, and in the factories. One of the most effective arenas was in the air itself. In increasing numbers and with increasing frequency the big bombers were striking targets the GAF had to defend—airfields, aircraft factories, oil, Berlin. In the ensuing air battles between the bombers and their escorts on one side and the GAF and flak on the other, both sides lost heavily.

In January the Eighth Air Force lost upwards of 146 aircraft; sixty bombers were lost on 11 January alone. This was 10.5 percent of the attacking force. In February 1944, 124 bombers were lost, and in March 240 aircraft were lost. According to "Combat Chronology," sixty-nine bombers were lost—10.5 percent of the attacking force—on the 6 March mission to Berlin and nearby cities. This was the largest number of bombers lost by the Eighth Air Force in a single day.[27] Was the Eighth Air Force defeating the GAF in the air? Would the Allies have control of the air over the invasion beaches by June?

Hewitt spreads himself thin—January and February 1944.   Edwin Hewitt had been doing all he could to prepare the bomber gunners for their air battles.

Although he continued lecturing to the gunners of the bomb groups during the winter of 1943–44, he was increasingly drawn into the work of the command staff.

> Matters in which I assisted the responsible officers were ordering new equipment from the United States, sitting on boards to determine what gunners should return to the United States as instructors, procuring equipment from the British, and in general acting as contact man for the gunnery officers at Headquarters Eighth Air Force. [28]

ORS records show that Hewitt wrote seven memoranda in January and February. For example, he wrote "Notes for Gunnery Instructors," "Fire Power of B-17 Group Formations," and "Memorandum for General O. A. Anderson *Re* Deficiencies In Gunnery Programs at Bombardment Groups." [29] The memoranda illustrate how a determined, aggressive analyst, backed by his chief, could take his recommendations anywhere in the air force where they might do some good, from gunnery sergeants in the schools up to generals themselves. A gunnery officer in the air force, by contrast, was limited by regulations, channels, and rank. Of course, the recommendations of the operations analysts to the officers of the air force were only advisory. However, it was the job of the analysts to advise, and their recommendations often became air force policy. Thus, by January 1944 the zone system of aiming, largely because of the efforts of Edwin Hewitt, became the aiming system used by the Eighth Air Force.

Hewitt is sent to the United States on temporary duty. Meanwhile, the gunnery people in the USAAF were working out an aiming system to be used in all their gunnery schools in the United States. Hewitt writes,

> In the latter part of February, 1944, I was sent to the United States on temporary duty to assist in writing a gunners' manual and to reach an agreement on a single system of deflection shooting to be taught in the United States and the ETO [European Theater of Operations].

Hewitt was upset to learn that his colleagues in the United States were discarding the zone system which he had worked so hard to establish in the Eighth Air Force. They were adopting position firing which he described as "a supposed refinement of the zone system. At the time, I felt that this decision was a mistake, but I now do not believe that gunnery is much different under the two systems." [30] Actually, the two systems were the same in principle; the differences were largely a matter of nomenclature.

In his memoir Hewitt writes,

> While in the United States I obtained the services for the Eighth

of Dr. W. L. Ayres, who was on leave from his chairmanship of the Mathematical Department of Purdue University. He had been given a course of instruction in aerial gunnery, and was persuaded to sign up for duty in the United Kingdom. [31]

U.S. mathematical work in gunnery

Two research groups on war problems. The theory of air-to-air gunnery was mathematically complex. By June 1943 at Columbia University in New York City two groups of mathematicians and statisticians worked on this and numerous other problems. There was the AMG–C (Applied Mathematics Groups–Columbia) directed by E. J. Moulton and the SRG–C (Statistics Research Group–Columbia) directed by Warren Weaver. In June 1943 the AMG included, besides directors, Saunders Mac Lane, Churchill Eisenhart, Dan Lewis, Walter Leighton, and Jim Stokes. The SRG included Harold Hotelling, Allen Wallis, and Abraham Wald. As time went on some moved to other places, but many other distinguished mathematicians and statisticians were added. [32] Some of the best mathematical minds in the United States worked in these two groups.

AMG–C became an authority on airborne fire control and, in particular, air-to-air gunnery. Together the AMG–C and SRG–C conducted a gunnery school to train mathematicians in mathematical aspects of gunnery problems which they would encounter as members of operations analysis sections in the field. W. L. Ayres, as one of the early "graduates" of this school, got specialized instruction in probability and statistics and learned about aiming rules for flexible gunners in bombers shooting at fighters. [33]

The training of gunnery analysts. The best information on Ayres' training comes from Dr. W. L. Duren, Jr. Like Ayres himself, Duren was a university professor of mathematics—Ayres at Purdue and Duren at Tulane University in New Orleans, Louisiana. Both Ayres and Duren had been recruited for gunnery work by E. J. Moulton of the Applied Mathematics Group at Columbia. Duren tells how he was recruited.

> In the spring of 1944 I was called to the telephone from my victory garden in New Orleans. On the phone was Professor E. J. Moulton summoning me to join an important scientific service in the war effort. I was to fly that weekend to New York for a confidential meeting in the offices of the Rockefeller Foundation. I had never been in an airplane and my scope of life had involved only family, the university, teaching and research in mathematics.
>
> In New York a group of 13 of us met with Moulton, Warren Weaver, T. C. Fry, and George W. Taylor, a senior operations analyst and Chief of the OAS of the 14th AF in China, who had initiated the plan to recruit a gunnery adjunct to each of the 13 air commands. [34]

Moulton recruited a group of mathematicians and one physicist, all of whom would receive special training before being assigned as gunnery analysts. They included W. L. Ayres (chairman of mathematics, Purdue University), A. C. Berry (professor of mathematics, Lawrence College), Ruel Churchill (professor of mathematics, University of Michigan), W. L. Duren, Jr. (professor of mathematics, Tulane University), Alex A. E. S. Green (physicist and instructor, California Institute of Technology), Ralph Hull (chairman, Department of Mathematics, University of Nebraska), Pierce Ketchum (professor of mathematics, University of Illinois at Urbana), Carl Rees (head, Department of Mathematics, University of Delaware), Richard Wolfe, and J. W. T. (Ted) Youngs (assistant professor, Purdue University).

Duren recalls the training they received.

> Our training combined some special crash course work provided by the NDRC Applied Mathematics Groups of Columbia University headed by E. J. Moulton. Our "Academic Dean" was Churchill Eisenhart, who also taught us statistics. Also involved in the teaching were Saunders Mac Lane, George Sheffé, the economist Milton Friedman, Alex Green (who was converting from his previous position as physicist in the Research Division of the AAF Flexible Gunnery School at Laredo, Texas) and others. The practical part of our training put us through gunnery schools at Buckingham Army Air Base in Fort Myers, Florida, and at the Laredo, Texas gunnery school. There we learned to fire the 50-calibre machine gun, to dissemble and reassemble it (blindfolded), to diagnose its malfunctions. We also played gunner in various training simulators that attempted to present the trainee with a target having the kind of relative velocity seen by a gunner in a rapidly moving bomber. [35]

Duren described the training program as "remarkably well constructed and helpful, given the conditions of wartime." The school attempted to anticipate the kinds of mathematics the analysts would use, including error analysis applied to gunnery and bombing, experimental design and testing of hypotheses, decision theory, and Wald's new sequential analysis. According to Duren,

> Mac Lane put us through a well-conceived course in the differential equations that model the performance of servos [automatic control systems], gun sights and other predictors using smoothed data from the operator's tracking of the target. We studied some excellent papers of British analysts. We had a crash course in ballistics at Aberdeen. And we spent a couple of days at Schenectady with the General Electric engineers who had designed the amazingly clap-trap electro-mechanical, analog computer-director system of the B-29. Another mathematical component of our training was

a study of the pursuit curve of a fighter attacking a bomber, both in its simple non-aerodynamic form and in the aerodynamic form worked out by the topologist Leon Cohen. [36]

Hewitt meets newsman Porter Henry, who becomes part of the section. Hewitt's account of meeting Porter Henry is brief.

> At Training Aids in New York I met Mr. Porter Henry, who is on the staff of the *New York Daily News* in peacetime and who was at that time editing various gunnery manuals! He expressed interest in an assignment with the Eighth Air Force which was eventually arranged for. [37]

The signing of a newspaperman as gunnery analyst demands explanation. Porter Henry was the only newsman to serve as an operations analyst in the twenty-six operations analysis sections of the USAAF. His job at the *New York Daily News* was that of a writer and reporter. As a rewrite man he collected facts of an event phoned into the office by the reporters in the field, and wrote them up into stories for the *Daily News*. [38] Henry served as an internal rewrite man for the Eighth Air Force for the news made by bomber crews.

Before Hewitt met him, Henry had served a kind of apprenticeship in aerial gunnery in New York City. The air force prepared three encyclopedic books called *The Pilot's Information File*, *The Navigator's Information File*, and *The Bombardier's Information File*. Each aspect of the pilot's job, together with the equipment entailed, was written up lucidly and simply, and was attractively illustrated. These books quickly proved their value. The gunnery people in the air force wanted a *Gunner's Information File* prepared and published. However, outside bids for this work were outrageously high so the gunnery people tried another tack. They searched the army for people who had been artists or writers as civilians. They turned up a surprising number of talented people, including artists and writers who had worked for magazines such as *Time* and *Life*, such as Willard Burton and Max Schwindt. When the project needed another writer, someone suggested Henry because he had a good technical mind. Thus the air force hired Porter Henry to write the machine gun section for *The Gunner's Information File*. Henry obtained a leave of absence from the *New York Daily News* to stay in New York to work on this project. [39] Apparently, Hewitt also helped with this project.

"While in the United States, I helped with the editing of the Gunner's Information File, a publication designed to give gunners all the information they would need." [40]

No doubt it was then (March 1944) that Hewitt met Henry. According to Henry,

> Position firing (in March, 1943) was being taught in all the gunnery

schools in the United States. On the other hand all the gunners in the Eighth Air Force were now using the Zone system. Ed Hewitt, being the gunnery man at Eighth Air Force ORS, had the job of seeing that all the gunners were instructed by somebody in this new position firing system. He and I got acquainted in New York and took to each other. He wanted to know if I would go to England and help convert the gunners to position firing and I said, "Sure!" So I took leave of my job with the *New York Daily News* and went to England as a civilian. [41]

A few details had to be worked out so Porter Henry could join the section. Henry had a deferment from his draft board because of his work on *The Gunner's Information File*. Understandably, his various bosses didn't want him to leave. However, with Hewitt's help, he worked out a solution. He let the draft board know he was ready to go into the army, and at the induction center a letter from General Doolittle, commander of the Eighth Air Force, would be waiting ordering that Henry be put on inactive status with the army and then sent to England as a civilian to report to the Eighth Air Force ORS.

At the induction center events almost took a nasty turn when a staff member asked, "Do you want to go in the army or the navy?" Porter Henry replied, "Wait a minute, there's a request here from General Doolittle to send me to England." His response was, "You're out of your mind. Where do you want to go, the army or the navy?" Finally after searching the records, Doolittle's request to send Henry to England was found. Porter Henry concludes, "So I got to England." [42]

Thus, as far as the Eighth Air Force was concerned, Porter Henry was a civilian analyst.

Hewitt calls on the assistant secretary of war for air, R. A. Lovett. Robert Lovett, the man under Secretary of War Stimson, was responsible for air matters. He had earned the respect of those he worked with and for. General H. H. Arnold, commanding general of the USAAF throughout the war, spoke well of Lovett.

> On November 7, 1940, however, another name was added to the top level of the War Department which was of towering importance to our Air Force. Robert A. Lovett came to Washington as Assistant Secretary of War for Air. I found in Bob Lovett a man who possessed the qualities in which I was weakest, a partner and teammate of tremendous sympathy, and of calm and hidden force. When I became impatient, intolerant, and would rant around, fully intending to tear the War and Navy Department to pieces, Bob Lovett would know exactly how to handle me. He would say with a quiet smile: 'Hap, you're wonderful! How I wish I had your pep

and vitality! Now ... let's get down and be practical!' And I would come back to earth with a bang. [43]

Lovett was called on to solve all kinds of problems. Arnold explains that in the big expansion phase of the air force,

> We encountered a distinct shortage of propellors, engines, aluminum, and other accessories in the aircraft proper .... . Mr. Lovett took that problem up and worked it through the various agencies until a just solution was found. The difficulties Bob Lovett encountered in trying to correct these defects in programming and distribution may be imagined when one realizes that at least nine men had to be seen before an air production could be made. One of the first things Bob Lovett did was to straighten that situation out: he reduced the number to two. [44]

Lovett's major achievement concerning the defense of our bombers took place in May and June of 1943. Indirectly, it may have had some bearing on Hewitt's assignment to gunnery analysis. In May 1943 Bob Lovett visited the Eighth Air Force. He interviewed a significant number of fighter pilots—he had been a navy pilot in WWI—and looked into bomber problems as well. When he returned to the States he wrote two memoranda to General Arnold, one on 18 June and the other on 19 June. The first recommendation, about improving fighter escorts for bombers, helped pave the way for adequate fighter escort by December 1943. The second called for, among other things, "better training in gunnery." [45] Such memoranda from such high authority caught the commanding general's attention and got results. Late in June 1943 John Harlan assigned Hewitt the task of studying the possibility of working out simple rules for aiming the bomber guns.

Not long before Hewitt returned to England in April of 1944 he became interested in "new types of compensating and computing gunsights for use on B-17 and B-24 airplanes" which were being developed in the States. Hewitt believed that some of the delays in procuring the gunsights were unnecessary. Bob Lovett had a reputation as a trouble shooter and expediter. He was also willing and able to talk with fighter pilots and bomber crews as well as generals. It was natural, then, for Hewitt to wonder if Bob Lovett could help.

> I secured an appointment with Mr. R. A. Lovett, Assistant Secretary of War for Air, and asked his help. He was highly cooperative, and as a result of his interest, I was able to present my problems to Wright Field and various responsible officers at Headquarters AAF.

Despite all of these efforts Hewitt remarks, "So far as I could tell, however, very little was ever done to speed up our new gunsights." [46]

The General Mission Analysis Subsection

By January 1944 the two projects handled by the General Mission Analysis Subsection were the "ORS day raid reports" of each mission and the gasoline consumption studies. Since early in the history of the section, the day raid reports had been written by Mr. Louis Lusky. He used as his basic data a report from each group commander on each mission flown by the group. In 1943 this project was manageable; only four groups were operational. However, by D day forty bomb groups were operational. One thousand planes or more were often dispatched on missions, and missions were being flown with increasing frequency. Captain Edward J. Kobeske, Sgt. Howard L. Spies, and Cpl. George F. Meyer, Jr. were assigned the task of assisting Mr. Lusky in policing the incoming reports and drawing off the information needed by the various subsections. [47]

When Hewitt left the General Mission Analysis Subsection to establish the Gunnery Subsection in mid-1943, his fellow mathematician Frank M. Stewart remained to struggle alone with the complex problems of the bombers' gasoline consumption. On 29 September 1943 Blair M. Bennett, a civilian mathematician from the U.S. Naval Proving Ground at Dahlgreen, Virginia, joined the section and worked with Stewart until April 1944, when Bennett left the section. The gasoline consumption problems were intractable, but very important to the command. Thus, on 3 January 1944 Major Emil Sorenson, a test pilot at Wright Field, was assigned on temporary duty to the section to help with gasoline consumption studies. Then, on 16 March 1944 1st Lt. Robert W. Bratt, an aeronautical engineer, was also assigned to the section on temporary duty. Finally, mathematician Dr. George W. Mackey, a consultant with OSRD (and after the war a distinguished professor at Harvard) arrived on 11 March 1944 to round out the group (Stewart, Sorenson, Bratt, Mackey) that would produce the definitive studies that year on gasoline consumption. [48]

The Loss and Battle Damage Subsection
January through D Day

By January 1944 the Loss and Battle Damage Subsection consisted of three analysts, Dr. Richard G. Gettell, George Shettle, and William J. Pilat, and four enlisted assistants, T/Sgt. William Weintraub, S/Sgt. William T. Parry, Sgt. Shirley E. Emhoff, and Cpl. Richard E. Garrison. The subsection had kept combat damage reports and cumulative combat summaries beginning with the first day of operations of Eighth Bomber Command. Arps notes, "These combat damage reports and summaries soon became the official damage figures for the Eighth Air Force. They were thus used by A-4, and later Materiel and Maintenance for damage record purposes." [49]

The subsection's report, "Reduction of Losses and Battle Damage—A

Summary Analysis of the Defensive Experience of VIII Bomber Command, 17 August 1942–31 December 1943," was completed on 12 February 1944. This masterful report brings to life the dry facts gathered from mission to mission in a meaningful way. For example, on the basis of the data, they were able to assess the defensive importance of fighter escort in 1943. They concluded that seven losses could be expected on unescorted missions and five on partially escorted missions for every one on a fully escorted mission. By closely analyzing trends in battle damage, weak spots in the bombers which could only be found in the course of combat were brought to light, and steps were taken to eliminate these weaknesses. Precise knowledge of the cost of past missions in terms of loss and battle damage enabled the subsection to speak with authority on various aspects of tactics such as the size and type of attacking formation, and the spacing of groups over a target.

According to Pilat,

> It became regular practice for engineering officers at various echelons to refer to us a large variety of questions relating to modifications. Medical officers concerned with the design of oxygen equipment or armour protection for crews did likewise. Technical representatives of aircraft manufacturers were not infrequent visitors at ORS. Brief memoranda, buckslip comments and conversations over the phone in person rather than formal reports became the measure of ORS's activity in the field, and all were frequent. [50]

Memoranda written by the Loss and Battle Damage Subsection during this period covered topics like: damage (to hydraulic or electrical systems, to oil tanks, oxygen bottles, etc.), ammunition expenditure, effects of loss of propellor control, body armor, cost of making more than one bomb run, probability of survival of combat crews reported missing in action, comments on proposed modifications of aircraft, and parachute failure on bail-out. The memoranda often responded to requests from the engineering section, the quartermaster general's office, or elsewhere in the command. Pilat notes,

> Perhaps one of the most useful memos we ever wrote was a very brief one pointing out a number of instances in which it had been reported to us that no extra parachute had been carried on the aircraft and that as a result, one or more crew members whose parachutes had been perforated by flak or set on fire, or who were cut off from their parachutes by fire in the aircraft, had been unable to bail out. This memo resulted in making the practice of carrying extra parachutes almost universal. [51]

Flak becomes the major menace. In 1943 the principal enemy threat to the operations of the Eighth Air Force was the German fighter force. Even then, however, the data of the Loss and Battle Damage Subsection showed that flak was the major cause of battle damage. The subsection began to suspect that loss due to flak was being underestimated. This was confirmed when crew members of lost aircraft escaped from occupied territory and returned to tell their story. Pilat explains,

> It was only after interrogations of crew members of lost aircraft had begun that the true importance of flak as causing straggling with resultant vulnerability to enemy fighter attack became apparent.... During 1944 fighters steadily declined in importance as a cause of loss, and from the middle of that year until the end of the war flak became the principal cause of loss. [52]

The section works to reduce flak risk. Beginning early in 1944 a comprehensive study of all available methods of reducing flak risk was undertaken by Gettell, Pilat, Shettle, and Kenneth Norton. To Norton, the analyst in charge of radio countermeasures against flak for the section, assessing the potential usefulness of those countermeasures under various conditions and establishing tactics to maximize their usefulness was vital. Because of this he was a logical person to be a part of the group to study methods of reducing flak risks.

Gettell had a Ph.D. in economics, Pilat had an M.B.A. from the College of the City of New York, and Shettle, an investment analyst, had a B.S. from the College of the City of New York. They did an excellent job gathering the data on aircraft damage and loss and interpreting this data. Indeed, the work of this subsection eventually benefited the whole USAAF, not just the Eighth Air Force. Their success was partly due to their willingness and ability to cooperate with people like Norton, who was specially trained in radio countermeasures, and Hewitt, the mathematician and flexible gunnery expert for the section. However, most importantly, the subsection cooperated with the flak intelligence officers of the command. Pilat describes this cooperation:

> [Effective work of the section to reduce flak loss and damage] necessarily involved a very close association with the flak intelligence officers at VIII Bomber Command and later Eighth Air Force. ORS was able to provide accurate statistics as to the trends in flak damage and loss, to perform various special studies which the flak officers needed, and above all to devote reflective thinking to the broader problems of reduction of flak loss and damage, with which the Air Force flak officers, immersed in routine day-to-day problems of keeping up-to-date flak intelligence and participating in mission planning, had little opportunity to deal. ORS, on the other hand, was able to acquire from the flak officers much detailed knowledge both as to the specific nature of enemy equipment and as to the basic nature, capabilities and limitation of anti-aircraft

fire, without which thinking, defense against flak could not progress far. [53]

Flak analysis in the Eighth Air Force—January to June 1944. According to Pilat, since February 1943 the Eighth Bomber Command flak officers had been planning routes into and out of the target area using a computer "to determine the effectiveness of each plotted ground battery against aircraft flying at a given altitude and air speed along various courses." In the fall of 1943, Colonel Thompson, Eighth Bomber Command flak officer, and Lt. Col. R. E. Devereux, on temporary duty from the United States to help Colonel Thompson, were improving the computer system.

> Their work involved reexamination of basic curves as to the probability of securing a hit on a single aircraft at various slant ranges, and also the modification of those curves so as to take into effect [account] the fact that we flew in tight formations and that enemy accuracy appeared to be such that shells aimed at one aircraft had almost an equal chance of hitting another in the formation. ORS was asked to perform certain calculations in an attempt to explore the differences between various curves for the variation with altitude of the probability of a flak hit. Likewise we were asked for information as to the size of formations as actually flown. [54]

The studies of Thompson and Devereux made it apparent that at altitudes flown by the Eighth Air Force, German antiaircraft fire had such poor accuracy that it depended on a large volume of fire to produce kills. Because the probability of a plane being hit was low, a battery's effectiveness largely depended on how long it could engage a formation. Colonel Thompson pointed out that sending the maximum number of airplanes over the same area of the defense in as short a time as possible was desirable.

Since Colonel Thompson's studies showed that the way the bombers flew over the target had a significant effect on flak risk, ORS decided to study the subject further. Calculations based on various hypothetical spacings between formations showed that flak risk could be decreased substantially if separate targets for the ground gunner—whether individual aircraft or formations— were flown sufficiently close together. That way, a gunner could not fire at each target, as Colonel Thompson assumed. He would be forced to let some targets go by without firing at them or to divide his fire so that few, if any, targets were fired at the whole time they were in the gun's effective range. Pilat states,

> Further calculations, based on the best data we were able to get from our flak officers as to the range and rate of fire of enemy guns and the probable firing policies of their gunners, led to the creation of a Flakometer—a device by which would be determined

the number of shells which could be fired at each of successive targets flown at various altitudes and with various spacings in trail. This was used both for visual demonstration to A-3 officers, flak officers and others of the principle that closing up spacings in trail would reduce flak risk, and for ready calculation of the relative flak risks of various types of formation spacing. [55]

Illustrated here are the compromises the command had to make. By separating attacking combat boxes on the same target by as much as five minutes, allowing smoke to clear, bombing accuracy was improved. However, when combat boxes attacking the same target flew in one right after another, little or no space was left between boxes, and flak risk was much less.

Flak as a dominant cause of loss by June 1944.   In his 1944 New Year's message General Arnold called for the destruction of the GAF. The success of the Eighth Air Force in its campaign against the GAF is reflected in the data gathered by the Loss and Battle Damage Subsection. In January 1944 the GAF was the greatest factor in the losses of the Eighth Air Force. By the end of May 1944 flak had become the chief cause of loss. Furthermore, flak was now causing ten times more damage than fighters.

The subsection's main study for the period January to June 1944, the report "Reduction of Flak Risk," was completed in May. After consultation with operations officers some revisions were made, and the report was circulated in the command in July 1944.

The subsection found that the major tactics to reduce flak risk were:

1.   Avoidance of flak defenses *en route* to and from the target area—by route selection and careful navigation.

2.   Entering and leaving the target area on courses of lowest flak risk.

3.   Flying at maximum altitude consistent with other considerations.

4.   Planning spacing and axes of attack of bombing units to make the fullest possible use of radio countermeasures.

5.   Minimizing the number of bombers flying together as a bombing unit.

6.   Increasing formation spreads and breadth.

7.   Closing up in trail to saturate enemy defenses using aimed fire.

8.   Evasive action. [56]

Item one, avoiding flak defenses on the route to and from the target, had become very important. Each navigator was given a map showing the flak defenses *en route*, at the target, and in the vicinity. Often combat boxes or individual planes separated from the main force before or after the target. These smaller units, separated from the main force, were the most likely to fly needlessly over defended areas or meet the GAF.

Item five, minimizing the number of bombers flying together as a bombing unit, is the only other tactic that also increased bombing accuracy. The other six tactics, though each reduced flak risk, generally reduced bombing accuracy as well. Thus, the command routinely chose tactics to balance the need for bombing accuracy with the desire to reduce risk.

Balancing these two needs was not easy. Higher altitudes reduced the flak risk. However, lower altitudes improved bombing accuracy. The path of least risk into the target often was not the best axis of attack for bombing accuracy. Close spacing of following groups attacking a target reduced flak risk, but also reduced bombing accuracy. Evasive action on the bomb run, highly detrimental to bombing accuracy, was only recommended just before and just after the bomb run. Nevertheless, loss and damage due to flak was so great that the command increasingly sought the advice of the section on these matters.

GEE-H BOMBING AND RADIO COUNTERMEASURES

Gee-H bombing.   The work of Dr. W. N. Tuttle and Maj. Warren E. Bales with the Gee-H blind bombing program finally began to pay off when the first mission was flown on 28 January. On this mission, forty-three B-24s bombed a V-weapon site at Bonniers. Recall that Gee-H bombing depended upon radio signals sent out from beacons located in England. The range of Gee-H was limited—between 200 to 300 miles—but it was more accurate than H2X. At first, Gee-H missions were flown only against NOBALL (V-weapon) sites. After D day, however, their use was extended to other targets within their range. In June 1944 alone, 3,000 Gee-H–led sorties were flown.[57]

In the first five months of operations with Gee-H, Tuttle and Bales found time to write some memoranda. On 4 January a memorandum on the Gee-H training program was released. On 21 February they put out a "Memorandum on the Use of the Gee-H Warning Period Method with Glide Bombs." In April and May they assessed accuracy in "Memorandum on Operational Accuracy of Gee-H Bombing at 2nd Division" and "Recent Data on Accuracy of Gee-H Bombing."[58]

Dr. Tuttle worked with the Intelligence Section in determining targets suitable for Gee-H bombing. He or Bales attended the operations conferences and advised on the setting up of each Gee-H mission. Elaborate grid maps were drawn showing the range of Gee-H and possible approaches to the targets within range.

Radio countermeasures.   Kenneth Norton, the section's RCM man, cooperated in the spring 1944 study of the reduction of flak risk. He also worked on a number of other projects. The bombers would rendezvous over southeast England before beginning the bomber stream toward their targets. This rendezvous might be at an altitude of 20,000 feet or higher, at a point visible to the German early warning radar. Norton worked with the Signal Section to screen the rendezvous from enemy radar. He wrote three memoranda on this, one in January, one in February, and one in March 1944.

Norton was continuously involved in using Window (Chaff) and Carpet to jam radar-aimed German antiaircraft guns. He wrote two memoranda on the use and effectiveness of these countermeasures during this period. In addition, he conducted a study described in "The Operational Effectiveness of Window on Four Visual and Four Blind Bombing Operations in February 1944," dated 6 May 1944. [59] At this stage of the war there was still much to learn about Window. For example, when and how should the silver foil be released from the bombers? Was there any difference in its use on visual versus blind missions? How should attacking and following groups be spaced to get the most benefit?

BUZZ BOMBS SUCH AS THE V-1—PHASE ONE

A large unexpected target system for the Eighth Air Force during the first five months of 1944 was the network of ski-sites and large sites. A few basic facts put the Eighth Air Force's involvement with the V-weapons into perspective.

By the third week of December 1943 Allied intelligence confirmed that a chain of ski-sites in France, ten to twenty miles wide, extended more than 300 miles along the English Channel from Cherbourg to Calais. The first ski-site was discovered on 24 October. A typical ski-site consisted of half a dozen steel and concrete structures. The largest resembled giant skis laid on edge. These were, it was realized, the launching sites for some kind of missile. By the third week of December, seventy-five ski-sites were identified. Those between Le Havre and Calais pointed toward London. Those on the Cherbourg peninsula pointed at Bristol. In addition, seven large (or heavy) sites had been identified, five in the Calais area and two near Cherbourg. The ski-sites were the intended launching sites of the V-1, a flying bomb, and the large sites were, it was later learned, intended as storage and assembly sites for the V-1 or V-2 and for other German weapons in development.

The air force gave the code name NOBALL to operations against the V-weapon sites and the code name CROSSBOW to the entire Anglo-American campaign against German long range weapons at any stage including experimenting, producing, transporting, launching, and flying.

Obviously, the threat of the V-weapons could not be ignored. The Allied commanders were understandably concerned. With the cross-channel invasion just five months away, here were the Germans getting ready to bombard the Allied base of operations with long-range missiles of some kind.

This new emergency was met primarily by the British Second Tactical Air

Force, the U.S. Ninth Air Force, and also the Eighth Air Force. The RAF Bomber Command played a very minor role in the campaign against the V-weapons. It specialized in night bombing of large (area) targets, not precision bombing of small targets. Because the Eighth Air Force was so large, and because it preferred daylight bombing of specific targets, it reluctantly wound up carrying a large part of the load in the Allied campaign against V-weapons.

Some ORS involvement with the V-weapons. The Bombing Accuracy Subsection was, of course, involved in assessing the accuracy of each NOBALL mission. Also, during the bad weather of the winter and early spring of 1944, the Radar Subsection was kept busy studying the Gee-H bombing of V-weapon sites. In addition to its usual work of damage reports on each mission, in March and early April the Loss and Battle Damage Subsection participated in some conferences on the feasibility of various types of aerial attacks on V-weapon targets. They, together with the Eighth Air Force flak officers, estimated the probable cost of making heavy bomber attacks on the V-weapon targets. Pilat explains that "as the result of these discussions it was decided [to continue] to attack these targets with the heavy bombers." [60] Because the decision was made to continue using the B-24 and B-17 in attacks on the V-weapon sites rather than switching completely to light bombers or fighter bombers, and because getting the job done was urgent, the Eighth Air Force accelerated its bombing of the V-weapon sites in April and May.

Soon after the ski-sites started to be attacked, the Bombs and Fuzes Subsection was asked to make a study to determine the most effective weapon against the sites. Alderman observed,

> There had been several missions on these targets mostly with 500 pound General Purpose bombs [GPs] and a few 250 pound G.P.'s. A difficult job of interpretation followed mainly because the targets had been hit several times, sometimes with different weapons and different air forces. The targets were fairly well camouflaged, some buildings hidden in trees; the altitude of attack was low at first and therefore the patterns were tight which made it difficult to isolate direct hits, and the reconnaissance photos were not always adequate. Nevertheless a study had to be made.

Alderman, Kring, and Hedefine prepared a report, "Bomb and Fuze Selection," for General O. A. Anderson, dated 23 February 1944, which stated the following conclusions for heavy bombers:

1. If the objective was to cause maximum destruction, the most effective weapon was the 500-pound G.P. (fuzed .025 tail).

2. If causing maximum damage and causing at least some damage was, together, the objective, the most effective weapon was the 500-pound G.P.

3. If the objective was to cause at least some damage, the 100-pound G.P. was recommended.

According to Alderman, because most attacks had an objective of maximum destruction, the 500-pound G.P. was used when available.

> For the then current bomb loads of the B-17s and B-24s we found that under no circumstances would the 250 pound G.P. be the most effective weapon. Nevertheless we were eventually forced to use this weapon as well as the 500-pound SAP [semi-armor-piercing], 100-pound G.P. and 1000-pound G.P. when the bomb shortage became acute in the spring of 1944. [61]

Some evaluation. The Allied bombing campaign against the ski-sites was so successful that the sites were never used. The Germans abandoned them when they realized they were too easily identified. They began building modified sites which primarily consisted of a launching ramp. According to Alderman,

> It was largely prefabricated and assembled quickly on the site after concrete footings were poured to receive the A-frames which supported the heavy firing tube. Our recommendation against this as a target was the 250-pound G.P. and by the time of these attacks the enemy had thrown a lot of antiaircraft into the area and had forced the heavies from the original low altitudes of around 12,000 to 15,000 feet up to 20,000 to 26,000 feet. [62]

The United States Strategic Bombing Survey estimates that bombing the ski-sites set the German V-weapon assault on England back at least three months. It was not until the night of June 12 that the Germans could successfully launch the V-1 rockets from the modified sites. On 13 June 1944 General Eisenhower's aide, Captain Harry C. Butcher, noted in his diary, "About twenty-five pilotless aircraft crossed the Channel last night and nineteen are known to have hit land, four in the London area." [63] The Allied air forces had been able to stave off the V-1 attacks until six days after D day.

In 1943 Adolf Hitler threatened to use secret weapons against the Allies in reprisal for their aerial bombing of Germany. He made good on this threat with two weapons, the V-1 and V-2 (Vergeltungswaffe 1 and 2 Reprisal Weapons 1 and 2.) The V-1 was a pilotless flying bomb, and it was called the buzz bomb by the Allies. It was a pulse-jet-powered flying bomb, twenty-five feet long with a sixteen-foot wingspan, and carried a one-ton warhead for up to 250 miles at a speed of 400 miles per hour. The V-1 flew low at a pre-set altitude varying from tree-top level up to several thousand feet. It could be heard for miles. Its jet engine made a noise that some likened to the noise of a Mack truck of those times. Most observers, however, described the sound of the V-1 as a distinct and ominous buzz. Furthermore, as long as you heard the buzz you were all right. However, if the buzz suddenly stopped it meant that the bomb had reached its programmed destination and was diving toward the ground, and if you were near it you should dive for cover.

Fact and speculation on the V-weapon sites.   The first NOBALL target of the Eighth Air Force was not a ski-site, but something very mysterious at Watten on the channel coast of France.

> In May 1943, Flight Officer Constance Babington-Smith, a WAAF member of the Allied central photographic interpretation unit in London, had interpreted a small, curving black shadow on a photograph of Peenemunde, in the Baltic, as an elevated ramp and the tiny T-shaped blot above the ramp as an airplane without a cockpit. The V-1 had been seen and recognized by Allied eyes for the first time. Almost simultaneously, at Watten on the Channel coast of France, Allied intelligence observed with profound curiosity the construction of a large and unorthodox military installation of inexplicable purpose. [64]

Watten was the first of the seven large (or heavy) sites built by the Germans along the French coast across from England.   It was also the first V-weapon site to be bombed by the Eighth Air Force. On 27 August 1943, 180 heavy bombers attacked Watten. The Eighth Air Force bombed it again on 7 September. For the first five months of 1944 it was bombed, on the average, twice each month. [65] Why were the large sites given such attention? Although Allied intelligence knew they were there, they were not sure what they were for. Butcher's diary explains how they were viewed by at least some of Eisenhower's staff, as late as 20 June 1944.

> Beetle [Lt. Gen. Walter Bedell Smith, Eisenhower's chief of staff] has been ominously predicting that the Germans will start using their next secret weapon, the rocket [the V-2] said to contain ten tons of explosive in a fifty ton projectile, which is skyrocketed from a hole in the ground like a giant sunken stove pipe and encased by heavy concrete. There are seven known sites for launching rockets, five in the Pas de Calais and two in the Cherbourg Peninsula. Fortunately, the latter either have been or soon will be captured by our rapidly advancing American troops, and crews of experts are awaiting opportunity to examine them. [66]

The V-2 was indeed a very dangerous weapon which traveled faster than sound and, unlike the V-1, was noiseless.   However, the rocket actually weighed thirteen tons, not fifty, and it carried a warhead weighing one ton, not ten. [67] The horrible rumors about the German secret weapons spurred on these attacks against known V-weapon sites.

To the Bombs and Fuzes men of the Eighth Air Force, the large sites were just another target system. It was later found that these were for launching, storage, and assembly of the V-2 rockets. According to Alderman the Germans were bombed continuously as they built the sites. The bomb weight depended upon the amount of construction and the estimated thickness of the concrete roof slab. At first 500-pound GPs were used, then 1,000-pound, and finally 2,000-pound GPs. As soon as the slabs, estimated to be five meters thick, were completed, the attacks shifted to interfering with the construction work, by tearing up assembled reinforcing rods, form work, railways, shelters, and other service installations. [68]

This bombing only delayed construction; it did not stop the sites from being completed. The large sites were mainly underground. The walls were made of steel and concrete twenty-five to thirty feet thick—much thicker than the five meters estimated by the ORS. It was estimated that the larger of the large sites could have quartered 200,000 people. General Brereton, commanding general of the Ninth Air Force, examined the site at Watten after it was captured. He described it as "more extensive than any concrete constructions we have in the United States, with the possible exception of Boulder Dam." [69]

Controversy over the best way to bomb the ski-sites. Both General Arnold, commanding general of the USAAF, and General Spaatz thought that the use of heavy bombers for Crossbow would unnecessarily divert them from preinvasion operations. On 25 January 1944 General Arnold authorized General Grandison Gardner at the air force research and development base at Eglin Field, Florida, to conduct a crash program of research to determine the best plane, bomb, and attack altitude to destroy the ski-sites. Simulated ski-sites were built on the Eglin reservation and attacked at different altitudes by different planes and with different bombs. On 1 March 1944 General Gardner submitted his findings. They were that the tests at Eglin Field had established that minimum altitude attacks by fighters, carrying 1,000- or 2,000-pound bombs, if properly delivered, were the most effective and economical aerial countermeasure against ski-sites; medium and high level bombing attacks were the least effective and most wasteful bombing countermeasures. [70]

General Arnold pressed for the adoption of the Eglin Field recommendation. However, it was not followed. Over General Brereton of the Ninth Air Force was the British A/C Marshal Leigh-Mallory. Over General Spaatz was the British A/C Marshal Tedder. The British commanders were skeptical of the Eglin tests. Leigh-Mallory in particular believed that low-level fighter attacks would be too costly. [71] He overtly opposed using fighter bombers against the ski-sites. There is no indication that Tedder or Eisenhower supported General Arnold in the controversy over this matter.

In a curious twist to the controversy, General Spaatz on 6 May informed Arnold of a trial minimum-altitude attack carried out by the 365th Fighter Group. After intensive training and briefing by Eglin Field officers, four fighter pilots attacked four ski-sites with P-47s carrying two 1,000-pound delay-fuzed SAP bombs. Though very heavy machine-gun fire was encountered at each site, three of the four attacking P-47s achieved Category A damage (sufficient to neutralize a ski-site for several months) with no loss of aircraft. [72] Curiously, despite this incredibly good performance, the commanders of the Eighth and Ninth Air Forces chose not to use their fighter bombers in this project.

In a letter to the author dated 3 January 1985, Leslie Arps, deputy chief of the Eighth Air Force ORS at the time of the bombing of the ski-sites, wrote:

> I attended several conferences at Bomber Command where it was discussed as to the advisability of using fighter bombers, mosquitos, medium size bombers, and heavy bombers to bomb no-ball targets. At that time, all the ski-sites were protected by very heavy flak installations. All of the commanders pointed out that in order to fly the heights to make accurate bombing of the ski-sites possible it would subject the aircraft to almost certain destruction. So far as heavy bombers were concerned, all agreed that they could not fly at that low an altitude. The light and medium bomber [commanders] were very emotional about it and said that they would obey orders but headquarters could expect all aircraft to be destroyed. It was for these reasons that headquarters did not utilize fighter bombers and low-flying B-17s.

The men of the Bombs and Fuzes Subsection knew about the controversy surrounding which air force and which planes would wage the major attack against the ski-sites. They played a minor role in it. Alderman wrote a little about it in his memoir.

> Throughout all these attacks there was great concern as to which Air Force was the most effective against these targets. The Eighth, Ninth, R.A.F. Bomber Command, and the British Tactical Air Forces had all been active against them. Elaborate but sketchy studies were made by the Crossbow Committee and certain conclusions were published. These were expressed in terms of numbers of aircraft which were required to knock out a target, and were only fair approximations once the Heavies (although they required more sorties per target knocked out) knocked out the target more completely. In any event all the Air Forces continued to hammer at them except for the low-level fighter attacks which were discontinued.
>
> Our Command was anxious to be relieved of the responsibility of attacking these targets and anxious to spend full time on our more meaty industrial targets. A-3 requested a digest of all the Crossbow Committee's data and other best guesses. This digest was prepared by Hedefine and was submitted. [73]

The air force history gives some statistics which support the position of General Arnold and the Eglin Field Study.

> Relying largely on heavy and medium bombers, the Allies inflicted Category A damage (neutralization for three months) on ski-sites 107 times (including repeats) between the inauguration of ski-site attacks in December 1943 and the abandonment, early in May 1944, of operations against this type of target. Of this number, the Eighth AF accounted for 35, the Ninth for 39, and the British component of AEAF for 33. B-17's, expending an average tonnage of 195.1 per Category A strike, accounted for 30 of the Eighth's successful strikes, as contrasted with 5 by B-24's, which expended an average of 401.4 tons per Category A strike. B-26's achieved 26 Category A strikes, at an average tonnage of 223.5 per strike. B-25's were credited with $10\frac{1}{2}$ Category A strikes for an average 244 tons per strike and A-20's accounted for 4 Category A strikes, with an average tonnage of 313 per strike. Among the fighter-type aircraft employed during this period, the Mosquito (a British fighter-bomber) led with an average tonnage of 39.8 for $19\frac{1}{2}$ Category A strikes. Spitfire bombers achieved 3 such strikes with an average of 50.3 tons per strike. [74]

The heavies of the RAF dropped 3,500 tons on ski sites and did not achieve any Category A damage. [75]

The above figures are incomplete without a fuller accounting of cost. We know that the Eighth Air Force lost forty-nine heavy bombers and 462 men in the ski-site campaign. Thus, each Category A strike cost the Eighth Air Force 1.4 heavy bombers and thirteen men. We know that the Ninth Air Force lost thirty medium bombers and 148 men. Thus, each Category A strike cost the Ninth AF 0.77 planes and 3.8 men. No human cost figures are available for the Mosquito, but General Doolittle said, in a letter to General Arnold dated 27 May 1944,

> Mosquitoes are the most effective type of aircraft. The British fighter had achieved the highest degree of damage with less tonnage, fewer attacking sorties, and fewer losses than any other type of aircraft. [76]

Despite the higher cost in terms of planes and men for the heavy bombers on the ski sites, the typical mission of the heavy bomber to targets in Germany was far more dangerous.

MISSION PLANNING WORK OF THE BOMBS AND FUZES SECTION

Weapon and force requirement studies in general.   The Bombs and Fuzes Subsection was often called upon to study the weapons and forces required to destroy special targets or groups of targets such as aircraft engine factories at Halberstadt, Leipsig, Aschersleben, and many others.

In analyzing each target area, the subsection usually determined which bomb would be most effective first and then calculated how many would be required. These requirements would then be given to the Bombing Accuracy Subsection which would translate the number of bombs required on the target into the number of bombs that had to be dropped. On some occasions Gettell of the Battle Damage and Loss Subsection would be called in by the Bombing Accuracy Subsection to estimate the bombing altitude that would be used, for this would affect the force estimates. The final estimate appeared in a memorandum to the commanding general. [77]

Force estimates for the bomber offensive program.   One of the most unusual requests came from General Fred Anderson. He had been commanding general of the Eighth Bomber Command from 1 July 1943 until 31 December 1943. On 1 January 1944 he became part of the staff at USSAFUK (The United States Strategic Air Force in the United Kingdom). Because this organization's acronym was rather inappropriate, its name was soon changed to United States Strategic Air Force in England with the innocuous initials USSAFE. Early in 1944 Alderman of Bombs and Fuzes and Clarkson and Scott of Bombing Accuracy were called to General Anderson's Headquarters in USSAFUK. They were presented with a large-scale bomber offensive program and asked to estimate the weapons and forces required for all the targets of the program.

Alderman, Clarkson, and Scott analyzed over a hundred targets: aircraft engine and assembly plants, ball bearing plants, synthetic oil targets, synthetic rubber plants, and tire manufacturing plants. They estimated the number of bombs required for each target, and calculated the size of force on each target. Alderman says,

> We were given General Spaatz' office and were told we couldn't leave until the job was finished.   The Intelligence Section at USSAFUK, Col. Hughes, supplied us with target folders and special data. Upon completion of a given category of targets the data was turned over to General Cabell and Col. Glenn Williamson who submitted the final report to General Anderson. This was quite obviously the fastest job of analysis we were ever assigned, beginning at 0900 hours one Sunday and running continuously until 0500 hours the following morning.

Many of these force requirement assignments had to be completed in a very short time, and they often came on Sundays. Each one came without any advance warning and there were only a few which allowed as much time as Alderman thought the job deserved, but under the circumstances of war no more time was available. Alderman adds,

> I firmly believe that two of the factors which permitted us to work
> with the speed we did was that, in addition to having our working
> data in good shape and certain targets analyzed in advance, we
> knew our limitations and capabilities and those of the men of the
> Bombing Accuracy Subsection as well. We knew how to get along
> with them, we knew the form in which they liked to get our basic
> data, and we were able to collaborate efficiently in the preliminary
> analyses, in the summing up of all information, and in the drafting
> of our final joint reports. [78]

Zuckerman's transportation plan comes to the section.   Solly Zuckerman was
a distinguished British scientist who was a consultant to Allied headquarters
on the effects of bombing. He was especially involved in the development of
the Transportation Plan for disrupting German railway traffic in the invasion
area of France in 1944.

The battle for adoption of the plan. Zuckerman's transportation plan was
a strategy to paralyze the railroad systems of northern France and the Low
Countries around the invasion area by neutralizing seventy-nine marshalling
yards. [79] Later, fourteen more marshalling yards in southeast France were
added. Five weeks after the adoption of the marshalling-yard plan, a plan to
bomb the bridges of the Seine and the Loire was also added.

Solly Zuckerman's plan evolved out of his experiences as a British civilian
scientific advisor to Tedder in the Sicilian air campaign and his survey afterward of its impact on the railroad system of Sicily. Although Zuckerman was
the architect of the plan, Tedder became its chief backer. At various times it
was called the transportation plan, the Tedder plan, or the Zuckerman plan.

The plan's primary purpose was to block off German reinforcements during
and after the invasion and to disrupt German movement within the invasion
area as well. Since rail centers were large targets, often as large as several
hundred acres, the transportation plan required not only tactical air forces,
but the heavy bombers of the RAF and the Eighth Air Force as well.

No one opposed the plan's purpose. The plan's execution, however, was
questioned. Opponents criticized plans to hit the railroad system at its fattest,
strongest points—the marshalling yards. Instead, they suggested that fighter-
bombers should cut railroads at various points between marshalling yards.
Then, only when the marshalling yards became jammed with traffic should
they be bombed. Furthermore, they argued, bombing the marshalling yards
would not stop the flow of trains because rail lines could be laid around the
damage almost immediately.

The dispute took place at high levels over considerable time. Against
the marshalling-yard bombing plan were General Spaatz, Air Chief Marshal
Harris, and Prime Minister Churchill. In favor of the plan were Air Chief

Marshals Leigh-Mallory and Tedder, and General Eisenhower. [80]

Eventually things came to a head at a crucial meeting of the Allied commanders on 27 March 1944, when Spaatz made the following recommendation for the strategic air forces under his command:

1. They should continue to destroy the GAF and the industry which supports it.

2. They should attack Axis oil production.

3. They should join with SHAEF [Supreme Headquarters Allied Expeditionary Force], AEAF [Allied Expeditionary Air Force] and the air staff in producing a plan for the direct tactical support of OVERLORD. This plan should provide for attacks in great strength upon communications (railroads) and military installations of all kinds in the initial phases of OVERLORD (the cross-channel invasion).

Eisenhower's aide, Captain Harry C. Butcher, gives Spaatz's reasons for pressing the oil campaign.

> In support of his recommendation that the Eighth Air Force begin bombing oil targets General Spaatz argued that the weight of attack required for a large marshalling yard was about the same as that needed for a synthetic oil plant and the target areas were essentially the same size. He said further that only fourteen synthetic-oil plants produce eighty percent of all German synthetic gasoline and oil, whereas fourteen marshalling yards comprise only a fraction of the German railway system, which could be readily dispensed without seriously disrupting German military operations. He also noted that our intelligence showed the Germans were already critically short on oil. [81]

General Spaatz's cogent arguments supporting the oil offensive and giving a lower priority for the use of the heavies against marshalling yards were brushed aside. A/C Marshal Leigh-Mallory, commanding general of AEAF which comprised all the tactical air forces in the theater, instead of backing an alternate plan, approved the Tedder-Zuckerman marshalling-yard plan. Tedder went further, arguing not only for the Zuckerman plan but for a delay in beginning the oil offensive. Butcher describes a 30 March 1944 meeting, chaired by Sir Charles Portal, marshal of the Royal Air Force, attended by Tedder, Leigh-Mallory, Harris, Spaatz, Anderson, and others.

> Tedder won out in his advocacy of the transportation plan, and Spaatz, who strongly urged attacking synthetic-oil plants, has temporarily lost. However, it was decided that after OVERLORD is ashore and firmly established, the strategic bombers can attack the oil industry. [82]

The section works out the force requirements for the marshalling yards.   By

April 1944, Baley Price had spent time at nearly every task performed by the Bombing Accuracy Subsection in order to have an overall knowledge of the work of the section. The one thing he lacked experience in was calculating force requirements for missions. He began to get experience in this work in early April 1944. His account gives us a good picture of how force requirement analyses were handled by the section.

One Sunday morning in early April Bombing Accuracy received a hurry-up call to send someone down to the Operational Intelligence Office in the Ops Block. Such a call meant that a problem involving the planning of future missions had come up. Dr. Clarkson was the member of Bombing Accuracy who specialized in such problems, but on this particular Sunday he was not on the post. Therefore, Colonel Scott and Baley Price responded to the call. Baley Price finishes the story.

> When we arrived, we found the problem was one of major proportions. We were given a minimum of information at the time, but looking back now one can see that the RAF and the Eighth Air Force were planning a campaign that would smash all the marshalling yards and communications centers connecting Germany and France with the part of the French coast that had been selected for the invasion. The targets had been listed and assigned in about equal numbers to the RAF and the Eighth Air Force. In general the RAF took the closer targets in France that they could reach easily with their Oboe blind bombing equipment, and the Eighth Air Force was left to handle the more distant ones with daylight visual attacks.
>
> On this particular Sunday morning Colonel Scott and I were merely given the list of marshalling yards and asked to calculate the size of force required to put each out of commission. The first difficulty lay in the fact that the problem was not clearly defined.
>
> And when were the answers desired? Imagine our surprise when we were told that they were required that night—my recollection is that the list submitted to us contained thirty odd marshalling yards! And to cap the climax, we learned that General Anderson had been carrying the problem in his pocket for two days but had forgotten to mention it to the members of his staff!
>
> We set to work at once, but there was difficulty even in obtaining photographs and the necessary target material for some of the railway centers. It soon became apparent that it would be impossible to give an answer in the time set. It would be necessary to go through all of the usual steps involved in a calculation of size of force requirement.
>
> First the Bombs and Fuzes Subsection, headed by Mr. Alderman, was called in to specify the type and density of bomb

required. In this case, the target was of a completely new type, and Mr. Alderman was not familiar with the details of the construction of French and German marshalling yards, and he did not know what parts of the complex it was desired to damage. It was necessary to have all of this information before the weapon [type of bomb] and the aiming points could be prescribed, and it was only after these decisions had been reached that the size of force could be calculated.

In the end Mr. Alderman went to London the next day, talked with some of the British authorities on Continental railroads and with the British experts who were planning the RAF's part of the program. By this time Dr. Clarkson had returned and taken charge of the calculations for Bombing Accuracy.

The campaign in preparation for the invasion of France was about to open. [83]

Price's involvement with the marshalling yards began Sunday morning. That evening while Alderman and Colonel Harlan, chief of the section, were at the home of Dr. Dickens, chief of the RAF Bomber Command Operational Research Section, they got a telephone call from Dr. Youden who asked that they return to the base immediately to cope with an important rush job. Alderman continues:

Dr. Dickens surmised that it was the same problem which had been given to his Section the preceding day, and he told us of the progress that his Section had made. He told us that a special Sheaf committee under Dr. Zuckerman was involved, and that he planned to meet a special group in London to get more details of the targets and objectives the following day. It was arranged that I should join him.

The problem proved to be part of a Master Plan for the knocking out of the railway communications system in France, Belgium, and Western Germany. [84]

Mr. Brant, an expert of the British Railway Research Service, and Air Vice Marshal Oxland from RAF Bomber Command were both present at the London meeting to go over in detail the British list of targets and as many of the Eighth Air Force targets as time permitted. Alderman returned the next day with Clarkson to finish up the American targets with Mr. Brant. Alderman says of Mr. Brant,

He was helpful in determining the parts of the various targets which had to be knocked out, and in recommending the density of bombs believed required on each aiming point. He was indeed an expert for he had visited and inspected the majority of the targets before the war and had made studies of all German, British and American attacks on marshalling yards. [85]

A large part of Zuckerman's book *From Apes to Warlords* is devoted to his experiences in developing and defending the transportation plan. In it he refers to Mr. Brant twice. In one place he says,

> I was introduced to a Captain Sherrington and his colleague Mr. Brant who were known as the 'railway experts'.... while he and Brant knew a great deal about the layout and normal workings of the continental railway system, they knew absolutely nothing about bombing or about the relative vulnerability of different parts of a railway system to bombs. [86]

In another place Zuckerman refers to "our main 'railway expert', Brant." The quotes around railway expert above are Zuckerman's. He, by this time, had become a powerful authority on railroad systems at the top planning levels of the Allied air forces. The railroad experts Brant and Zuckerman, however, did not always agree.

In one instance, described by Alderman, it appears that Zuckerman, by clever use of his knowledge and authority, caused the recommendations on bomb size made by the Bombs and Fuzes Subsection to be changed.

> Zuckerman, who was supposedly long in experience on attacks on marshalling yards in the Mediterranean theater, had first called for a density of four 500-pound bombs per acre over the entire yard. This, according to Mr. Brant, was much heavier than his research had indicated was required. He judged that one to three 500-pound bombs were required per acre depending on its importance and its priority in the entire Master Plan, and we agreed to reduce Zuckerman's estimate.
>
> According to the objectives which were discussed with Mr. Brant and the British, it appeared that the attacks should be directed to the immobilization of the entire Railroad Communication system by disrupting traffic and destroying engines.
>
> To meet this objective we recommended 100-pound G.P. bomb loads for the following reasons:
>
> First, in both our B-17 and B-24 aircraft, the bomb loads of 100-pound G.P.'s would produce more crater area than any other bomb load, and this meant more area of trackage and rolling stock destroyed;
>
> Second, even though 100-pound craters would be smaller and take less time to fill, than for example, 500-pound craters, there would be over three times as many craters for B-17s and over four times as many craters for B-24s with 100-pound bomb loads, which

together would require more time to fill;

Third, 3 to 4 times as many direct hits could be expected on locomotives both in the yards and in the roundhouses;

Fourth, since one 100-pound crater could cut a double track and one 500-pound crater three tracks, 2 and 3 times as many lines of tracks could be cut.[87]

As soon as the required bomb densities were adjusted to meet the requirements of the smaller bomb, the Bombs and Fuzes men turned them over to the Bombing Accuracy men who estimated the number of combat boxes required on each aiming point, which averaged about two per target. The aiming points were transferred to the photographs in target folders. The report explained the reasons for selecting the final load and the conditions under which the estimates of the force requirements were made. Alderman continues his story,

> Dr. Zuckerman soon called a meeting of the O.R.S. groups at Eighth and Ninth Air Forces, R.A.F. Bomber Command, and the Tactical Air Forces. It was never very clear why we were called together. It did come out that Zuckerman expected that all the Air Forces were planning to use 500-pound G.P.'s and he pointed out that the 500-pound G.P.'s had been the most effective weapon in all his experience in the Mediterranean. When asked if he had ever observed the effectiveness of the 100-pound G.P., he replied, "No"! We told him our reasons for recommending the 100-pound G.P. and pointed out that they were not expected to be effective in destroying the marshalling yard buildings.
>
> When the directive finally came through the regular channels to begin attacks on marshalling yards, we were informed that the targets were to be the maintenance and repair facilities meaning in particular the locomotive sheds and the engine and wagon repair shops. This amounted to a complete change in objective, and hence we used 500-pound G.P.'s when available since they were the most effective weapons against the structures of these buildings.[88]

The credentials of Alderman, Kring, and Hedefine for bomb damage analysis were excellent. Zuckerman, an anatomy professor at Oxford, first studied wound damage assessment by experimenting on laboratory animals and reviewing data from bomb casualties of early German bombings of England. After Sicily was captured in the summer of 1943, Zuckerman studied damage to the railway system and became an expert. Alderman, however, was an assistant professor of architecture at MIT, and Kring and Hedefine were construction engineers. Moreover, all three had worked for nearly a year as bomb damage analysts with the Eighth Air Force.

Which would have been the best weapon to use against the marshalling yards? Unfortunately it was not decided on the basis of practice, though there was ample opportunity.

Preparation for the bridge bombings. The members of the Bombs and Fuzes Subsection were given free access to all target information so that they would be as familiar as possible with the characteristics of a target when it was selected.[89] Alderman says,

> Long before any bridges were laid on as primary targets, we had discussed bombs and fuzes for such attacks. Soon bridges became a hot subject and the ORS groups of the various Air Forces were given bridges to analyze and to study for attack.[90]

Kring and Hedefine were bridge engineers by profession. With Alderman and Clarkson of Bombing Accuracy they prepared a general report covering the type of bomb required, the number of hits required on the many different types of bridges, and the force required. The targets were studied from two points of view: requirements for complete destruction (collapse of a main span) and requirements for temporary damage (deck, flooring, tracks, and secondary structural members).

Soon after their report was distributed men of other ORS groups visited, particularly, Mr. Derald West of the Ninth Bomber Command, an architect; Dr. Smith, a physicist, of the Ninth Fighter Command; Johnson, a physicist, and Tannenwald, a lawyer, both of Eighth Fighter Command; Dr. Beards of RAF Bomber Command, and other British analysts. Kring and Hedefine piloted this work and these conferences.[91]

Kring and Clarkson are BIGOTED. The importance of the work of the Bombs and Fuzes and Bombing Accuracy subsections in mission planning is shown by the fact that several weeks before D day, Kring of Bombs and Fuzes and Clarkson of Bombing Accuracy were selected to represent their subsections in planning D day missions.

All of the section members had secret clearances and worked with secret matters daily. However, Kring and Clarkson were given a special top secret clearance called BIGOTED. They attended frequent meetings in London and at headquarters where final decisions were being made on bombs and fuzes and size of forces. A special weapons committee was formed to consider bombs for D day targets. Chiefs from the army ground forces, navy, and air forces attended some of these meetings.

One important task was finding bombs which would be effective, yet not crater. These were needed to clear obstacles from plane or tank landing areas as well as barbed wire entanglements. These areas called for 100-pound GPs fuzed instantaneous nose.

Other areas to be bombed were gun emplacements, antiaircraft batteries, and shelters. These called for 500-pound GPs fuzed .025.

Alderman and Kring were consulted on altitude of attack, number of bombs needed to destroy various targets, and spacing of bombs. They also recommended procedures to follow if the bombing was visual or if it was blind, and bombing distances to keep our troops safe. Alderman records:

> Complete secrecy was maintained by our two representatives. From time to time they would discuss certain fundamental questions of bomb size, fuzing and accuracy with their colleagues, but never did the rest of us know the what, why, when or where of the D day operations.
>
> The trend of the bombing gave us some clues as to when it might happen, for occasionally peculiar targets were laid on in the Ops Conference, but the actual day of the invasion was not known by us until late in the evening the day before when Mr. Kring announced that he had been given permission to go on a mission to the Channel coast the next day. The prospect of going on the mission was more exciting for him than the mission itself. His group saw no enemy fighters, no flak, no enemy coastline and no targets. The whole area was totally cloud-covered, and bombs were dropped on H2X. They did see many bombers of the Eighth, and through holes in the clouds saw part of the endless chain of landing craft and supply ships. [92]

D day was a busy day for Alderman and Hedefine. There was scarcely a break in their mission planning work. Missions ran all day. Some aircraft flew two missions, some three. The men in operations and intelligence ran themselves ragged laying on targets and planning routes. The bomb supply was very low. In some cases it was necessary to recommend fifth and sixth choice bombs. Aircraft were only partly loaded. Some were being fuzed at the very last minute. Alderman concludes,

> It was a busy and profitable day for the Eighth Air Force and an exciting day for us, but, all in all, it was just another day's work for the Eighth for an operation had to be laid on for another important job 'tomorrow.' [93]

The Section's Work with H2X Gets Underway

Introduction. Although H2S and H2X radar had been used by the Eighth Air Force since September 1943, it was not until 30 March 1944 that the section became active in the field of H2X bombing accuracy analysis. On this date Colonel Harlan assigned Drs. Baley Price and Forrest R. Immer the task of studying H2X bombing operations, which by this time had assumed a large place in the operations of the command. In fact, the Radiation Laboratory had installed its own civilian scientific adviser at the Eighth Air Force headquarters. This adviser was independent of the ORS. Thus, once the ORS began analyzing blind bombing, the need arose for coordination and cooperation between the two sets of advisers at the same headquarters—those of the Radiation Laboratory and those of the ORS. [94]

By the time the section began analyzing H2X bombing accuracy, great curiosity as to what was being accomplished had grown along the ranks of the command, from the men who delivered bombs to the beclouded target areas to the generals. American airmen, trained in the visual bombing of "pin-point" targets, were skeptical of large-scale plans for bombing targets they could not see, watching bombs disappear into cloud banks, and not knowing what they had accomplished.

Price and Immer's first move was to visit the 482d Bomb Group on 3 and 4 April 1944 at Alconbury. This group had become operational on 30 August 1943. It was the training center for H2X blind bombing operations. At first all H2X aircraft were stationed there. By April 1944, however, most planes had been assigned to groups in the three bomb divisions, and Alconbury had become entirely a training and development base. On the first day at Alconbury they met Dr. David Griggs and other personnel. They discussed H2X mission reports, causes of poor results on past missions, and phases of the missions that Bombing Accuracy might profitably study. On the second day Price and Immer saw the trainers and equipment for the first time. In the afternoon they went on a flight to observe the H2X equipment in operations. Price recalls,

> It was my first flight in a B-17. The flight was scheduled to cover one of the simpler training courses, one that lay along the coasts of East Anglia and Southern England, but the equipment failed. As a result we returned to base after only part of the course had been covered. We flew at 12,500 feet, and there were clouds from about 800 feet to 12,000 feet. The descent was the most interesting experience in the clouds that I have ever had.

Price gives no further details of the experience except to add,

> After about a week it became clear that Dr. Immer preferred an assignment that did not involve so much field work. Accordingly, he was returned to office studies of accuracy of visual bombing, and I continued on the blind bombing assignment alone. [95]

Early in April Price visited each of the three groups, one in each division operating the H2X aircraft. At each, he talked with the radar officer, the H2X navigator, and the reporting officer. Later, he visited each of the three divisions and instituted a special report to be made by H2X operators to obtain more detailed information about the missions. Price got excellent cooperation on this project. In the case of the Third Division, for example,

> Colonel Harlan had called General Kissner, Chief of Staff, to say

that I was coming out to discuss a new report that was needed. When I arrived, General Kissner called a meeting of four of five of the staff members that would be interested in such a report. They examined in detail the one that I proposed, agreed that it was reasonable and desirable, instituted it as a 3rd Division report, and forwarded a copy of it to me at Eighth Air Force. [96]

Early in May, Lt. Fred Graham was assigned to Price to assist in photographic analysis of blind missions. A little later Sergeant Jean Farrington was assigned to do secretarial work.

Price made the best analyses he could of the H2X missions in April and May of 1944. He commented on four April missions, each for a different reason. They represent the difficulties and potential of H2X bombing at this time.

The air force bombs the wrong country.   Price tells us that on 1 April,

The 2nd Division was sent to Ludwigshafen. The weather was exceedingly bad [the Third Division had been sent out also, but it turned back], the H2X equipment was not functioning well, and apparently the dead reckoning navigators were not on the job. The Division scattered over a wide area of Germany, but the 44th and the 392 Groups broke out of the clouds and bombed visually— the 44th Group hitting the center of the town of Schaffhausen, Switzerland. [97]

Another version of this mission from another source gives a few additional facts. On 1 April 1944,

... 438 B-17s and B-24s are dispatched to bomb chemical industry at Ludwigshafen (largest in Europe). All 192 B-17's of the lead force abandon mission over French coast due to heavy clouds. The 246 B-24's in second force became widely dispersed; 162 bomb targets of opportunity (Pforzheim and Grafenhausen); 26 bomb Schaffhausen, Switzerland, and Strasbourg, France, mistaking them for German towns. [98]

This mission illustrates several things. First, the weather was often too bad even for blind bombing, and the attacking force had to return. Second, the danger of getting lost on blind bombing missions was great. Third, the breakup of blind bombing missions, which often occurred because of weather or equipment failure, led to sometimes desperate searches for targets of opportunity. In such instances the results were dubious or even negative, as in the Schaffhausen case.

Colonel Castle pioneers a new bombing technique.   Another blind bombing mission in April discussed by Price involved one of the emerging Eighth Air

Force heroes, Colonel Frederick Castle.

On 31 January 1942 General Arnold designated General Ira C. Eaker commanding general of the Eighth Bomber Command and ordered him to England to begin its organization. Eaker took with him a staff of six young officers. One of them was Captain Fred Castle. Arnold had few first-class career officers to spare, so he suggested that Eaker seek out some well-qualified civilians who were willing to join the air force. Arnold said,

> You can easily take a smart civilian and make him into a smart officer but you can't take a dumb officer and make him a smart officer. So you find yourself some smart civilians and I'll commission them for you. [99]

Frederick Castle was assistant president of the Sperry Corporation when General Eaker asked him to re-enlist. Several years earlier Castle had been an air force pilot and was a friend of General Eaker. [100] After a year and a half on Eaker's staff in the United Kingdom, Castle finally succeeded in getting Eaker to assign him to a flying job. On 22 June 1943 Castle assumed command of the Ninety-fourth Bomb Group stationed at Bury St. Edmunds. That was just over a week after the Ninety-fourth Bomb Group lost nine bombers to German fighters on the way back from a mission to Kiel. Morale, already low, was not improved when their commander was replaced by Castle, who was at first perceived as a desk officer. Castle turned this feeling around on 28 July 1943 by personally leading the Ninety-fourth Bomb Group plus thirteen planes from the 388th on a mission against a Focke-Wulf fighter plant at Oschersleben. The clouds were so heavy few of the other groups—300 bombers were dispatched—were able to find their targets. However, Castle's planes broke through a small opening and bombed very effectively. Reconnaissance photos indicated that perhaps fifty FW-190s had been destroyed. [101]

Nearly nine months later, on 11 April 1944, Colonel Castle was on a similar mission. The Third Division was sent to Posen in Poland to bomb aircraft factories. The weather was bad, and they were forced to turn back after they reached eastern Germany. As a result they attacked various secondary targets and targets of opportunity. The major portion of the division went to Rostock, but the Fourth Combat Wing attacked the airplane factory at Arnimsvalde, just east of Stettin. Colonel Castle was on the mission, and he gave Baley Price this account.

> We were flying along in 'soup' so thick that my best pilots had vertigo. The H2X operator-bombardier team that was leading the Wing was on the ball, however. In spite of the fact that there seemed not the least hope of seeing the ground, the bombardier had his bomb-sight set up with information supplied by the H2X operator. Finally, about twenty seconds before bombs away, the formation broke out into the clear, the bombardier made some last

minute corrections, and succeeded in putting part of his bombs on the target. [102]

The combined use of H2X and visual sighting was an important step forward in bombing technique, as Price points out.

> Colonel Castle was obviously impressed with the performance obtained from the combined use of H2X and the bombsight. I do not know when the combined procedure was first introduced into combat, but this case of its use by the 4th Combat Wing is the earliest one known to me. [103]

Analysis of blind bombing accuracy requires new techniques.   On 11 April another combat wing of the Third Division attacked the synthetic oil plant at Politz. The strike photographs showed plenty of ground detail around the edges, but the spot where the bombs fell was covered by a large cumulus cloud. The accuracy in this case was easily determined by using PRU (Photo Reconnaisance Unit) photographs together with strike photographs. Price comments, "This is the first case known to me in which accuracy was determined from a combined use of PRU and strike photographs." [104]

The losses were heavy on the missions flown by the Eighth Air Force on 11 April. Of the 830 B-17s and B-24s dispatched, sixty-four of the bombers were lost. In absolute numbers this was one of the heaviest single-day losses of World War II for the Eighth Air Force. [105]

The Berlin mission of 29 April 1944.   On 29 April all three divisions went to Berlin. The strike photographs for this mission showed enough breaks in the clouds for Baley Price and Lt. Graham to plot all the bombfalls. The results were drawn up in a brief report showing only the organization of the force and where the bombs fell and no comment. The report was given limited circulation. It was the first of Price's reports on blind bombing approved for release.

The bombing results of the 29 April mission were very unsatisfactory. High winds made navigation and flying difficult. According to "Combat Chronology," 570 B-17s and B-24s were aiming at railway facilities in the Friedrichstrasse section in the center of the city. The bombers were opposed by an estimated 350 fighters. [106] A big air battle took place with heavy losses of men and planes on both sides. The force was sent in with large combat wings abreast in such a way that an error by one lead wing quite effectively prevented two-thirds of the force from reaching the target. Some of the incendiary bombs fell in a lake west of Berlin. The Second Division, bringing up the rear with B-24s which were faster than the B-17s used by the other two divisions, finally plowed through the First Division at the target. Out of eleven large combat wings dispatched, only one placed bombs closer than five miles from the assigned aiming point. [107]

Although this mission was a failure in terms of bombing accuracy, it was highly successful as part of General Spaatz's plan to attack targets the GAF had to defend. Time after time before D day, the GAF was forced to defend targets like airfields, airplane factories, oil refineries, and Berlin. Although the ensuing air battles were hard on our bombers and escorting fighters, they were taking an unbearable toll of GAF men and planes.

Blind bombing in May.   Price and Graham prepared reports on the blind bombing operations of 13, 19, 22, and 24 May. The targets were Stettin, Stralsund, Brunswick, Kiel, and Berlin. These reports were given full circulation: copies were sent to all groups, wings, divisions, to Eighth Air Force headquarters, to USSTAF, and to some of the British organizations. All but one of the May blind bombing missions stirred up strong fighter opposition. Reports on blind bombing activities began to attract notice in the command. Price explains.

> About the middle of May, Col. Castle telephoned to Col. Harlan and asked that I be sent out to the 4th Combat Wing. He had heard that I was working on H2X performance, and he was anxious to enlist my help.
>
> On May 17 Lt. Graham and I went to Bury St. Edmund. Colonel Castle immediately asked me to speak at a small meeting of staff officers. I have taught a lot of classes and spoken on a lot of occasions, but this assignment was one of the most difficult I have ever encountered. I did not know enough about the field to pose as an expert, and I had almost no information about the knowledge, interests, and background of the group I was supposed to talk to. It was necessary to step forward and take the lead however.

On the next afternoon, 18 May, Colonel Castle called a meeting of his crews and his staff. Once again Price addressed the group. He recalls that "this assignment was at least as hard as addressing the small group of staff members."[108]

By this time General Kissner had joined the sessions. It was agreed that a group of them, including Price, Colonel Castle, and General Kissner, would go on an H2X camera-bombing mission the next morning. Price relates the experience.

> We reported at Squadron Operations about 7:30 the next morning, but one by one Col. Castle, General Kissner, and Major Hines (wing bombardier) all made excuses, and I was left to go on the flight alone. I flew with Captain West, pilot, and Captain Cole, bombardier. We climbed to 20,000 feet and flew over Peterborough, Nottingham, Northampton, Lutton, and Cambridge making camera bombing runs. It was my first flight on oxygen and at high altitude. Col. Castle was intensely interested in the results,

and asked to see the pictures as soon as possible after we landed. But we had accomplished very little because we had found clouds practically everywhere. There seemed to be no adequate means of assessing the results of blind bombing training.

On the next day Price went once again on a camera bombing flight. However, the clouds were as thick as before, and little was accomplished. The two flights emphasized the need for some adequate means of training blind bombing crews. Baley wryly remarks that the experience constituted another contradiction of modern war:

> The flying Army personnel such as Col. Castle, General Kissner, and Major Hines stayed at home while I, who had never been to high altitude, went flying to improve training procedures. [109]

The Heavies Prepare to Bomb the Beach Defenses on D Day

Price's connection with H2X preparation. Kring of the Bombs and Fuzes Subsection and Clarkson of Bombing Accuracy were BIGOTED and helped in the D day planning—particularly for bombing the invasion beaches. Price and the rest of the section, who were not cleared for the D day planning, nevertheless could see by the operations of the air force in May that a campaign in preparation for the invasion of France was in full swing. Price, with insight provided by his new responsibilities as a blind bombing analyst, notes,

> Suddenly, on May 25, there was some bombing of gun positions on the French coast that obviously had special meaning. One formation of approximately 18 aircraft had gone out from each of the three Divisions, and, in spite of the fact that the strike photographs showed a crystal clear day, the bombing had been done by H2X. The targets were coastal defenses located within a half mile or less of the beaches at Fecamp and St. Valery-en-Caux. The performance was repeated in equally clear weather on May 27.
>
> Very full and detailed reports on this bombing were received. The character of the reports indicated that the bombing had been of an experimental nature—obviously so, since otherwise H2X equipment would not have been used on such clear days. The reports stated that the targets themselves gave no distinguishable return on the scope, but that the bluffs along the coast at these points gave strong returns that tended to obscure much of the finer detail. [110]

These experimental H2X missions were planned because the Eighth Air

Force was assigned to bomb coastal batteries and shore defenses on OMAHA (an American landing area) and on the British landing beaches. Furthermore, the bombing was to take place just minutes before the invading troops hit the shore. If the weather was bad the Eighth Air Force would use H2X. Therefore, H2X training was intensified.

Price learned later that a large amount of training took place over England in the particular type of H2X operation that might be required on D day. This training was directed by Colonel Garland, a bombing expert sent over on "temporary duty" to the Eighth Bomber Command early in 1943.[111] As D day approached, each of the three divisions had two groups which had H2X planes. The H2X crews were instructed to make ten runs on targets on the coast of East Anglia, which were similar to those that would be encountered in France.

In this training, cameras simulated bombs and recorded accuracy. This method, known as "camera bombing," was used throughout the air force. A vertical photograph was made in the plane at the instant of bombs away. A second such photograph was taken at the instant the sighting angle in the bombsight was zero. Assuming that the bombsight was set for a bomb with zero trail, the bomb would have struck the ground at this instant. Thus, the center of the second photograph indicated the point where a bomb would have struck. Colonel Garland had the pictures of over 200 of these camera bombing runs. Price recalls,

> Col. Garland examined the photographs and observed that the performance was satisfactory. He did not make any full and detailed analysis, however. When I learned that Colonel Garland had these photographs, I asked to have them so that I might make a complete study of the results. They presented a larger body of data than had been available previously from either practice or combat.[112]

Price gets an assistant by V-mail. Dr. J. W. T. Youngs arrived in England on 30 May 1944. He was one of the mathematicians who had received special gunnery training with Ayres and Duren. Youngs was eager to serve as an analyst in England and to be there at the time of the invasion. However, there appeared to be no need for Youngs as gunnery analyst in the Eighth Air Force. At that time both Hewitt and Ayres served in that capacity. According to Price,

> Dr. Youngs is probably the only man that ever got an overseas assignment through a V-mail letter [WWII mail to or from the armed services, reduced to microfilm, then enlarged and printed for delivery]. One day in the spring I received a V-mail letter from him in which he asked casually whether I needed an assistant. He had just received two months of special training in gunnery, but we lost no time in bringing him over for bombing accuracy work.

When Dr. Youngs arrived, he was keyed up to high pitch in anticipation of the invasion as a result of the publicity given to the coming event in the American press. Imagine his surprise when he found that everything was calm in England—that, in fact, everything was closed up because the English had gone off on a bank holiday.

Upon Youngs' arrival, Price was moved from the Nissen hut that he had occupied since his arrival at Pinetree to another one in the same beech grove. Dr. Youngs was his roommate. Price recalls the morning of the invasion.

The night of June 5/6 was a stormy one: it was cold, the wind was blowing a gale, and there were heavy clouds. About three or four o'clock in the morning I was awakened by the roar of the motors of large formations of planes—a roar that rose above the howling of the wind. We often heard the RAF planes at night, but this was different. This was it: the invasion of France was on! [113]

The aerial bombardment of the defenses at Omaha beach on D day.   The old enemy of air operations—bad weather—was out in force on D day. The Eighth Air Force had to bomb with H2X through complete (10/10) overcast. To protect invading troops an order was given to the Eighth Air Force Pathfinder bombardiers which, though it did protect the troops from air force bombs, made the bombs overshoot their targets. Even though the last bombs of the Eighth Air Force would be dropped ten minutes before the touchdowns of the landing troops, with Eisenhower's approval "Pathfinder bombardiers were ordered to delay up to thirty seconds after the release point showed on their scopes before dropping." The danger of shortfall was stressed in all briefings.

A total of 1,083 of the 1,361 B-17s and B-24s dispatched on this mission attacked Omaha Beach and the British landing beaches, flying at right angles to the beaches in formations of six squadrons abreast with H2X Pathfinders in the lead. They dropped 2,944 tons of bombs with instantaneous fuzes to avoid cratering. The deliberately cautious method of bomb release did indeed prevent shortfalls. The implications of waiting from ten to thirty seconds after the indicated drop point had been reached before releasing the bombs, however, was drastic. The cruising speed of the heavies was around 180 miles per hour, about three miles per minute. The bombardier who waited from ten to thirty seconds after the drop point showed on his scope before releasing his bombs would have flown from one-half to one-and-a-half miles past his indicated drop point. Thus, the bombs hit from a few hundred yards up to three miles inland. There was one unexpected dividend; some mine fields were detonated. Unfortunately, however, the intended targets, the Omaha and British beaches, were left untouched by the gigantic aerial bombardment. [114]

Paul Carell, in his book, *Sie Komen (Invasion, They're Coming)*, gives an account of this event from a German perspective.

The German soldiers in a particular German strongpoint on Omaha Beach near Colleville heard the roar of the bombers above the clouds on D day morning. They ducked their heads when they heard the inferno of bomb bursts begin. When it was over they found that only two bombs had fallen within the strongpoint area. Everything else had fallen on the open ground behind them. One of the men said, "Maybe they weren't really after us." Carell says,

> They had just been saved not by military design but by the prover-bial fortunes of war. Chance had worked in their favor.
>
> A force of 329 B-24 bombers had been instructed to smash the strongpoints along the four miles of Omaha Beach and to silence the batteries and their emplacements with 13,000 super heavy bombs. Because of the low cloud cover they had to make a 'blind' bombing—by means of instruments. Duration of flight and bomb release time had been calculated to the second. At the very last moment, however, Eighth Air Force Headquarters lost their nerve, and fearing that the bombs might drop among their own lines, among the disembarked troops, they ordered the dropping time to be postponed by a few seconds. Only a few seconds—and 13,000 bombs missed their target. They were to prove expensive seconds. They were to cost General Eisenhower the lives of many American soldiers. [115]

The general in overall charge of the American landings was Omar Bradley. His account of the aerial bombardment, especially the plan to delay bomb release time, is harsh. He says,

> The naval and air forces commenced softening up the beaches at 0550. First came the terrific (and reassuring) salvoes from the warships. This bombardment went on for a solid thirty-five min-utes. During it, commencing at 0600, some 480 U.S. B-24 heavy bombers dropped 1,285 tons of bombs. Historian Morison judged that the naval bombardment, though brief, was highly effective, probably reducing enemy resistance by "half to three quarters." The aerial bombardment, as at Utah Beach, was completely in-effective. Owing in part to poor flying weather, the 2.5 million pounds of bombs fell inland of Omaha Beach, killing some French civilians and many cattle, but few Germans. [116]

Less than half of the bombers sent out to bomb the beach defenses bombed at Omaha Beach. The majority bombed invasion beaches assigned to the British troops. However, no specific information exists about the accuracy of the bombing of the British beaches. Bradley's account of the naval bombardment compared with the aerial bombardment at Omaha is one that makes an airman wince. No doubt, however, Bradley is trying to give an unvarnished account of what he saw. For example, he tells that sixteen LCTs were carrying sixty-four amphibious tanks, half to be delivered to the western sector of the beach and half to the eastern sector. The seamen in charge of landing the western sector's tanks wisely (and bravely) decided the weather was too rough to launch them at sea and succeeded in landing twenty-eight of them directly on the beach. On the other hand, twenty-nine of the amphibious tanks intended for the eastern sector were launched two-and-a-half miles off the beach. All but two of these foundered in the heavy seas. [117] In this gigantic cross-channel invasion, all three branches, army, navy, and air force, were doing the best they knew how to do and experiencing both success and failure. The navy warships were doing some things warships had been doing for centuries—bombarding (visually) coastal defenses. The air force, on the other hand, was doing something new, bombing coastal defenses through a heavy overcast with H2X radar, just ahead of our troops who were about to land.

The Gunnery Subsection—April 1944 to D Day

The gunners of the Eighth Air Force get an official spokesman. One of the accomplishments of the Gunnery Subsection was to help the Eighth Air Force correct some organizational oversights about gunnery. All of the gunners on a combat crew, with the exception of the bombardier-gunner on the B-17, were enlisted men. Whereas each group, wing, division, and the Eighth Air Force itself had its specially trained bombardier officer and its specially trained navigation officer, gunnery did not. For a long time there were no gunnery officers trained as such. At first gunnery officers had been trained as armament officers, pilots, navigators, or bombardiers. Gunnery to them was an additional duty. Often, knowledge of gunnery came after their appointment as gunnery officer. Hewitt had a great deal to do with improving this situation. Indeed, he had become the spokesman for the gunners at headquarters level and had essentially played the role of air force gunnery officer until the middle of April 1944.

Upon Hewitt's return to England in April 1944 he participated in a conference of all gunnery officers in the Eighth Air Force. As a result of this conference, a report was written recommending major changes in Eighth Air Force gunnery administration and practice. Hewitt says,

> Very few of these recommendations were ever fully implemented, although we did get an Air Force gunnery officer, Major John S. Stark. Under Major Stark's direction, gunnery in the Eighth attained a considerable measure of uniformity and central direction. [118]

Ayres' first major project. Dr. William L. Ayres arrived in the section about the middle of May. Porter Henry arrived soon after. Ayres described one of his first projects.

During 1944 all units of the command endeavored to improve the equality of the harmonization of the gun positions (see also page 267). In May the Eighth Air Force gunnery officer, Major Stark, proposed that a school be founded to offer an intensive course on all the sights of the B-17 and B-24 airplanes, including their operation and their harmonization. He proposed that the section organize the school, plan the course of study, and supervise the instruction. After an inspection trip by Dr. Ayres, the school was located at Kirkham. The first class of four officers and six enlisted men entered on 5 June. The course was open on a quota basis to armament and gunnery personnel, both officer and enlisted. The weekly classes were limited to thirty men, except for one month when fifty men per week were taught. The section planned the course of study, operated the school during the first classes, and made monthly trips to Kirkham thereafter to consult with the head instructor. [119]

The section learns of nonpursuit curve attacks. In the spring months of 1944 numerous gunners had reported attacks on their airplanes that could not possibly be pursuit curves and which made position firing invalid. Hewitt says,

> Col. Cass Hough of VIII Fighter Command suggested that this phenomenon might arise through the German pilots' skidding their airplanes, and Wing Commander Low of the RAF Central Gunnery School believed that this type of attack might be carried out by fighters carrying offset guns. We made large numbers of theoretical calculations concerning both types of attack and ran a number of air tests. The skidding experiments failed, but with an offset gun fighter, it was demonstrated that highly destructive attacks could be carried out which would completely upset the standard rules for position firing. [120]

Ayres added that German planes were captured containing guns offset vertically. Evidence indicated that such planes were used against the RAF night missions. The proof of these vertically offset guns added support to the belief that the GAF was experimenting with horizontally offset guns on a small scale.

The section analyzed these attacks carefully in order to provide rules for defensive fire if necessary. However, since reports of such attacks declined and stopped after July, no information about attacks or possible countermeasures was offered to the gunners. However, Ayres says,

> Since the attack has some advantages as a surprise feature and might be worthy of consideration in other theaters where our fight-

ers oppose enemy bombers, a report was prepared containing the mathematical analyses and all pertinent information and transmitted to headquarters AAF and the Operations Analysis Sections of other Air Forces. [121]

Hewitt earns the Air Medal.   Arguing that he needed to observe these peculiar, nonpursuit curve attacks, Hewitt obtained permission, after struggling with authorities all the way to General Eisenhower's office, to fly missions. He flew seven missions, five in May and two in June—one of them on D day. [122] Thus, two members of the ORS at the Eighth Air Force flew missions on D day, but Hewitt was the only operations analyst in the USAAF to earn the Air Medal. [123]

In a sense all first combat missions provided an abrupt introduction to war for the airman. The psychological impact of flying for the first time over territory and through air claimed by the enemy is a feeling I will never forget. However, some introductions were more abrupt than others. So it was with Hewitt.

On 19 May 1944 Hewitt flew on a mission to Berlin—a place where the Eighth Air Force would almost certainly engage the GAF. They were not disappointed.   On that day, 493 B-17s bombed the Friedrichstrasse section of Berlin, forty-nine B-17s bombed the port facilities at Kiel, and 273 B-24s bombed an industrial area at Brunswick. Enemy resistance was heavy; twenty-eight bombers and twenty escort fighters were lost. The U.S. bombers and fighters claimed to have destroyed 164 German aircraft.

The next day, 20 May, Hewitt accompanied a mission to the marshalling yard at Orly, France. This was part of the transportation plan in preparation for D day.

On 24 May Hewitt was back over Berlin. On that day 447 B-17s attacked Berlin, and seventy-two attacked targets of opportunity in the area. Enemy opposition was heavy. Thirty-three bombers were lost.

On 25 May Hewitt once again participated in the transportation-plan bombings for D day by flying a mission against the marshalling yards at Blainville, France.

On 27 May 923 B-17s and B-24s bombed marshalling yards, aircraft industries, and airfields at various places in Germany. Hewitt was on the mission to Mannheim, one of the toughest targets. Twenty-four bombers were lost that day.

On 6 June, D day, Hewitt flew to a target on the Cherbourg peninsula.

Finally, Hewitt flew his seventh mission to Leipzig, Germany, on 29 June. The industrial area around Leipzig was one of the most heavily defended areas in Germany, comparable to Berlin. Hewitt says of his seven missions:

> Officially, I rode as observer, but I found it useful (and by no means repugnant to the bombardier) to ride in the bombardier's seat, and

consequently, on four missions, acted as bombardier-gunner. I did not observe any of the peculiar attacks that had been reported, and saw fighters only twice. I had the amplest opportunities, however, to acquaint myself with the appearance, sound, and effects of the German flak. Participation in these combat missions was an extremely valuable experience. [124]

Where was the Luftwaffe on D day? By D day Allied air power had rendered German airfields within easy striking distance of the invasion beaches unusable. Thus, any German flyers who attempted to attack had to come from a distance. During May, Eighth Air Force and RAF strikes against Berlin, oil refineries at Politz, Ludwigshafen, and Leipzig, and other industrial targets, plus similar strikes against Germany and Austria from the south by the Fifteenth Air Force, tied down what remained of the GAF (Luftwaffe) to defend the Reich. No significant component of the GAF within reach of the invasion beaches could penetrate the umbrella that the Allied air forces had created around them. According to Paul Carell, only twelve German fighter-bombers were able to fly into the invasion area. Ten of these were immediately engaged in combat and had to drop their bombs prematurely. [125]

Of the approximately 300 sorties the GAF flew in France on D day (about one for every fifty flown by the Allies) only two seem to have gotten to the invasion beaches. They were flown by the German ace, Major Joseph Priller, a fighter wing commander, and his wingman, Flight Sergeant Henry Wodarczyk. D day morning the pair were alone at their unit's former base at Lille, France. The rest of Priller's unit had been dispersed to bases in the interior by orders from higher up, though Priller had protested. On the eve of the invasion he and Wodarczyk, so the story goes, got drunk. Early on D day Priller and his wingman, nursing hangovers, flew their FW-109s from Lille to the Normandy beaches. From an altitude of about 100 feet they used up all their ammunition on the swarming British beachheads. They then made good their escape back to Lille. [126]

As its great contribution to the Normandy invasion Allied air power essentially nullified German air power in the area. Allied forces could move without interference from the GAF. The German troops, on the other hand, had air cover—Allied air cover. They could not move, except at night or in bad weather, without intolerable losses to tanks and men.

REFERENCES

1. Wesley Frank Craven and James Lea Cate of the USAF Historical Division, eds., *Europe: From Argument to V-E Day, January 1944 to May 1945*, vol. 3 of *The Army Air Forces in World War II* (Chicago: University of Chicago Press, 1951), 8.

2. *Europe: From Argument to V-E Day*, 18.

3. Ibid., 17.

4. Wesley Frank Craven and James Lea Cate of The USAF Historical Division, eds., *Europe: Torch to Pointbank, August 1942 to December 1943*, vol. 1 of *The Army*

Air Forces of World War II (Chicago: University of Chicago Press, 1951), 8.

5. *Europe: From Argument to V-E Day*, 17.

6. G. Baley Price, *Gremlin Hunting in the Eighth Air Force, European Theater of Operations, 1943–1945*, 27–28.

7. *Europe: From Argument to V-E Day*, 20.

8. "The Army Air Forces in World War II, Combat Chronology 1941–1945," Kit C. Carter and Robert Mueller, compilers, 1973, Office of Air Force History, Simpson Historical Research Center, Maxwell Air Force Base, Alabama.

9. *Gremlin Hunting*, 38.

10. "Report on Bombing Accuracy—1 October 1943–1 March 1944," 12 April 9144, Microfilm Roll A 1077, Index 131. 504B ND through 131-504C ND, volume 3, Simpson Historical Research Center, Maxwell Air Force Base, Alabama.

11. H. P. Wilmot, *B-17, Flying Fortress* (New Jersey: Chartwell Books, 1980), 61.

12. "Bombing Accuracy."

13. Ibid.

14. Ibid.

15. "Eighth Air Force, History of Operations Analysis Section, October 1942–June 1945." Leslie H. Arps, 520.303-3, Archives, Simpson Historical Research Center, Maxwell Air Force Base, Alabama, 51.

16. "Combat Chronology," 276.

17. Leroy A. Brothers, *Operations Analysis in World War II, United States Army Air Forces* (Philadelphia: Stephenson-Brothers, 1948), 10.

18. "Bombing Accuracy." See "Report on Bombing Accuracy for the Month of March 1944,"

19. *Gremlin Hunting*, 25–27.

20. Ibid., 27–28.

21. Ibid., 28–29.

22. Ibid., 29–34.

23. "History of Operations Analysis," appendix I.

24. *Operations Analysis in World War II*, 2, 22, 32.

25. *Dictionary of Scientific Biography*, 552–57.

26. "Combat Chronology," 243–44.

27. Ibid., 287.

28. Edwin Hewitt, "A Sketch of Gunnery Activities in the Operational Research Section, Eighth Air Force, from June 1943 to August 1944," 17 July 1945, 13 pages.

29. "Eighth Air Force, History," appendix II.

30. "A Sketch of Gunnery Activities."

31. Ibid.

32. Some reminiscences by Walter Leighton in a letter, 7 October 1980, Mathematical Association of America Archives, Science Library, University of Texas, Austin.

33. Letter of Herbert Solomon, Department of Statistics, Stanford University, 18 September 1980, Mathematical Association of America Archives, University of Texas.

34. William L. Duren, "Operations Analyst, US Army Air Force in World War II," 1.

35. Ibid., 2.

36. Ibid., 3.

37. "A Sketch of Gunnery Activities."

38. From a tape sent by Porter Henry to Charles W. McArthur, February 1983.

39. Ibid.

40. "A Sketch of Gunnery Activities."

41. From a tape sent by Porter Henry to Charles W. McArthur, February 1983.

42. Ibid.

43. H. H. Arnold, *Global Missions* (New York: Harper and Brothers, 1949), 195.

44. Ibid., 266.

45. Thomas M. Coffey, *Decision over Schweinfurt, The U.S. 8th Air Force Battle for Daylight Bombing* (New York: David McKay Company, 1977), 195–98.

46. "A Sketch of Gunnery Activities."

47. "Eighth Air Force, History," 81.

48. Ibid., 82, 83, and appendix 1.

49. Ibid., 41.

50. "History of the Battle Damage Subsection, Operational Analysis Section, Eighth Air Force, December 1943–May 1945," 520.303-1, Archives, Simpson Historical Research Center, Maxwell Air Force Base, Alabama, 19.

51. Ibid., 18.

52. Ibid., 26.

53. Ibid.

54. Ibid., 27–28.

55. Ibid., 29.

56. Ibid., 30.

57. "Eighth Air Force, History," 98.

58. Ibid., appendix 2.

59. Ibid.

60. "History of the Battle Damage Subsection," 53–54.

61. "Report for Colonel W. B. Leach on the History and Development of the Bombs and Fuzes Subsection of the Operational Analysis Section, Headquarters Eighth Air Force," 10 April 1945, Bissell Alderman, 520.303-3, Archives, Simpson Historical Research Center, Maxwell Air Force Base, Alabama, 21.

62. Ibid., 21.

63. Harry C. Butcher, USNR captain, *My Three Years with Eisenhower* (New York: Simon and Schuster, 1946), 578.

64. *Europe: From Argument to V-E Day*, 84.

65. "Combat Chronology," 979. See Watten.

66. *My Three Years with Eisenhower*, 586.

67. Thomas Parrish and S. L. A. Marshall, eds., *The Simon and Schuster Encyclopedia of World War II* (New York, 1978), 662.

68. "Report for Colonel W. B. Leach," 21.

69. *Europe: From Argument to V-E Day*, 90.

70. Ibid., 98–99.

71. Ibid., 100–101.

72. Ibid., 103–104.

73. "Report for Colonel W. B. Leach," 21.

74. *Europe: From Argument to V-E Day*," 105.

75. Ibid.

76. Ibid.

77. "Report for Colonel W. B. Leach," 26.

78. Ibid., 26–27.

79. Solly Zuckerman, *From Apes to Warlords* (New York: Harper and Row 1978), 215–58, especially 256, 257.

80. Ibid.

81. *My Three Years with Eisenhower*, 507.

82. Ibid., 510.

83. *Gremlin Hunting*, 35–37.

84. "Report for Colonel W. B. Leach," 24.

85. Ibid.

86. *From Apes to Warlords*, 200, 254.

87. "Report for Colonel W. B. Leach," 24, 5.

88. Ibid., 25.

89. "Eighth Air Force, History," 78.

90. "Report for Colonel W. B. Leach." 27.

91. Ibid.

92. Ibid., 30.

93. Ibid.

94. "Eighth Air Force, History," 100.

95. *Gremlin Hunting*, 40.

96. Ibid.

97. Ibid.

98. "Combat Chronology," 306.

99. *Decision over Schweinfurt*, 84.

100. Roger Freeman, *The Mighty Eighth, A History of the U.S. 8th Army Air Force*, (London: Macdonald, 1970), 51.

101. *Decision over Schweinfurt*, 251.

102. *Gremlin Hunting*, 41.

103. Ibid.

104. Ibid.

105. "Combat Chronology," 314.

106. Ibid., 329.

107. *Gremlin Hunting*, 42.

108. Ibid., 43.

109. Ibid., 45.

110. Ibid.

111. "Eighth Air Force, History," 44.

112. *Gremlin Hunting*, 47.

113. Ibid., 48.

114. *Europe: From Argument to V-E Day*, 190–91.

115. Paul Carell, *Invasion—They're Coming* (New York: Bantam, 1984), 74–75.

116. General of the Army Omar N. Bradley and Clay Blair, *A General's Life, An Autobiography* (New York: Simon and Schuster, 1983), 249.

117. Ibid.

118. "A Sketch of Gunnery Activities," 11.

119. "Gunnery Subsection, Operational Analysis Section, Eighth Air Force, June 1943–January 1945," W. L. Ayres, 520.303-2, Simpson Historical Research Center, Maxwell Air Force Base, Alabama, 13.

120. "A Sketch of Gunnery Activities."

121. "Gunnery Subsection," 11.

122. Letter from Edwin Hewitt to Charles W. McArthur, 20 April 1982. Hewitt provides the dates and targets of his missions.

123. *Operations Analysis in World War II* lists all analysts and their medals.

124. Hewitt, letter, reference 122.

125. *Invasion—They're Coming*, 71.

126. Ronald H. Bailey, *World War II, The Air War in Europe* (Alexandria, VA: Time-Life Books, 1981), 165.

7

Operations Analysis in the Eighth Air Force, 6 June 1944–July 1944

THE MILITARY BACKGROUND

On 6 June 1944 the Allied forces—British, Canadian, and American—under General Eisenhower launched an assault from England across the English Channel to the Normandy beaches, which extend along the channel on the French coast between Le Havre and Cherbourg. By the middle of July, the Allies accomplished the first phase of the invasion, establishing a beachhead. They had control of a strip of the French coast containing the city of Caen on the east end and extending west through the town of St-Lô and across the Cotentin Peninsula to the sea. The British and Canadians under Field Marshal Montgomery held down the part of the beachhead around Caen. The American forces under General Omar Bradley held down the rest. For seven weeks the beachhead expanded. The German lines were gradually but relentlessly pushed back, though they held until the American "breakout" near St-Lô which began on 25 July 1944. [1]

In June and July the Germans failed to "throw the Allied invaders back into the sea." A major reason for their failure was Allied air superiority. They failed because superior Allied air power succeeded in its quest to

1. eliminate the GAF as a factor in the battle for Normandy,
2. disrupt reinforcements of troops and supplies to the German troops in the Normandy battle area, and
3. disrupt the movement of German forces within the battle area.

In June and July the fighters and bombers of the Eighth Air Force were heavily involved in the Battle of Normandy. Nevertheless, on 8 June 1944 General Spaatz listed oil as a priority target for the Eighth and Fifteenth Air Forces. [2] Though the Fifteenth Air Force carried out most of the oil offensive during June and July, the heavy bombers of the Eighth Air Force did conduct important missions against German oil supplies.

On the night of June 12/13, Hitler forced another target system back into high priority for the Eighth Air Force. By daybreak, twenty-five V-1 flying bombs flew across the English Channel; four hit the London area.[3] Hitler's V-1 bombardment of London and other cities had begun. The earlier bombings of the V-weapon sites by the Allies only delayed this onslaught.

On 26 May the Eighth Air Force reached its peak strength in number of fighter groups when the 479th Fighter Group (P-38s) became operational. The Eighth Air Force now had fifteen fighter groups, four P-38 groups, four P-47 groups, and seven P-51 groups, with an effective fighter strength of 885 planes. By the end of 1944, all but one of these fighter groups had been converted to P-51s. By D day the Eighth Air Force reached its top strength of forty heavy bomb groups when the 493d Bomb Group became operational.

The Eighth Air Force had grown into a mighty force with awesome capabilities.

The ORS Adds (and Loses) Personnel

A development related to the huge size of the air force took place at the ORS headquarters in Washington, D.C., in June and July. Plans were made to set up a liaison ORS at the headquarters of each of the three bombardment divisions of the Eighth Air Force. Each bomb division was a large air force in itself (approximately thirteen bomb groups per division), and each division had its own general. Thus, in June 1944 ORS headquarters in Washington began to recruit a lawyer and a scientist to form the nucleus of each of the three new sections. Though each new liaison section would have its own chief, it would also be under the supervision of the main section at Eighth Air Force headquarters. These recruits arrived in August.[4]

In addition to Henry B. Ashton, two analysts came in June. William A. Hosier, a mathematician from Michigan State College, was assigned to Micro-H, a form of radar bombing, and other consulting calculation problems. L. Emery Katzenbach, who had been assistant to the president, Hazelton Electronics Corporation, New York City, was assigned to the Bombing Accuracy Subsection. Two analysts came in July.

Dr. Ray E. Gilman, who earned his doctorate at Princeton in 1916 and worked as a mathematical consultant for International Business Machines in New York City, was assigned to the Bombing Accuracy Subsection. William A. Mersman of the Radiation Laboratory, British Branch, was "loaned" to the section until V-E day to supervise Micro-H work.

In July one of the section's outstanding analysts left, Dr. Richard G. Gettell of the Loss and Battle Damage Subsection. Like Youden before him, he did not leave operations analysis work. He left the ORS of the Eighth Air Force to become an analyst, first with the Twentieth Air Force and then with Twenty-first Bomber Command where new needs were developing.[5]

THE GUNNERY SUBSECTION, JUNE–JULY 1944

Background. By June 1944 the heavy bombers were routinely well escorted to and from their targets by Eighth Air Force fighters. It had become the prudent strategy of the GAF to save their attacks for straggling groups of planes that had become separated from their escorts. However, on prime targets in Germany, such as oil, the GAF still often attempted to break through the escorts. Insulated as they were from the GAF by the escorting Eighth Air Force fighters, most bomber crews at this time seldom saw a German fighter. Some of the aircrews, particularly the gunners, became lax and were unprepared for trouble when it came. This state of affairs greatly concerned the gunnery analysts. They knew the GAF was "out there" waiting for stragglers, cripples, and breakdowns in the escort system. They also knew that, although flak was now causing most of the losses, the GAF was still taking a steady toll.

Even in June when GAF operations in France had ebbed, Eighth Air Force fighters claimed approximately 240 enemy planes destroyed in the air or on the ground. Most of these were in France. In July, the Eighth Air Force fighters claimed approximately 260 enemy fighters destroyed in the air or on the ground in France and Germany. These claims were based entirely on film. [6] We do not have figures for the Ninth Air Force, but its fighters would have surely added to these casualties for the GAF.

During several missions to Germany in June, the GAF did break through the fighter escort and engage some of the bombers. In the last half of July, on seven different days, some of the bombers were engaged by the GAF during missions to oil targets in Germany. [7] However, unless his own group or some near-flying group was attacked, the individual airman typically would know nothing of the attack. The newspaperman Porter Henry did a lot to enhance communication about the current dangers from the GAF and what should be done about them.

Short Bursts. Porter Henry began a monthly magazine called *Short Bursts* which furnished information on such things as German fighter tactics, accounts of the encounters during the previous month between Eighth Air Force bombers and German fighters, and new gunnery equipment. Each issue gave a box score of enemy aircraft destroyed, classified by groups and gun positions. The magazine was written in a humorous, down-to-earth style that made it both easy and fun to read. Many points were made with cartoons and clever drawings. The first issue of *Short Bursts* came out in July 1944. Porter Henry did the writing, and Corporal John Faulkner did the artwork and cartooning. Each issue contained feature articles. The July issue contained an article on Silver Star citations to gunners in June and an article on the different gun sights and their uses.

The magazine was an overwhelming success from the beginning. It met a need—the need for the gunners to realize that they were still important. They learned that every month a surprising number of them were called upon to defend themselves and their crews. Eleven hundred copies of the initial July issue were printed. Requests for more copies from the Eighth Air Force groups and requests for copies for gunners of the Ninth and Fifteenth Air Forces as well as the Royal Air Force increased printing in later months to 2,600 copies. The groups insisted on more copies, as their copies wore out through continual reading. [8]

One reason for such an intense interest in gunnery matters was the first sightings in July of the German rocket plane, Me-163, and the jet, Me-262. [9]

Porter Henry is threatened with court-martial. The scorekeeping activity of the bombing accuracy subsection had on numerous occasions caused some of the bomb groups, and even one of the bomb divisions, to question and sometimes attack certain section policies for assessing bombing accuracy. In each of these cases, when the subsection had the opportunity to explain and defend its policies—such as its policy on evaluating targets of opportunity—it had succeeded in making converts of the skeptics.

Likewise, the Gunnery Subsection, and Porter Henry in particular, were criticized. Henry, in a 1983 taped memoir, tells how his reporting got him into trouble. [10]

The incident followed an air force mission deep into Germany, when one of the groups got separated from the bomber stream and its escort and was hit by the GAF. Henry says:

> So big old dumb Henry, being an ex-newspaper reporter, when I got the information I published it just the way it was. Wow! When the general who was commanding that group saw this thing you can imagine he was set on fire. He called General Doolittle and wanted to know who was this civilian publishing this stuff. He was going to court-martial me for aiding the enemy. However, at air force headquarters was John Harlan, one of the loveliest, loveliest gentlemen in the world with a mind like a buzz saw.

Harlan arranged for the general, Henry, and Harlan to have dinner at the senior officers' club in London to talk things over.

As Henry recalls it, Harlan defended him "in this neat little way by only asking questions" such as:

> General, you don't think the gunners should know where the group is at any time? Do you feel that the more ignorant the gunners are the better off they are? Do you feel, General, Sir, that the gunners should be informed of what's happening?

In a quiet way Harlan just kept asking these awkward questions, awkward for the general, that is. Consequently, the general, perhaps realizing that at a court-martial Henry would be defended by Harlan or perhaps another of the section's lawyers, dropped the matter.

LOSS AND BATTLE DAMAGE, JUNE–JULY 1944

Recall that Gettell, Pilat, and Shettle of the Loss and Battle Damage Subsection, together with Kenneth Norton of Radio Countermeasures, had completed in May a major study entitled "Reduction of Flak Risk." [11] The report mentions no measures that could be, or should be, taken to reduce the risk of flak injuries to the men inside the planes—such as wearing body armor, for example. This seeming omission will be covered later.

The subsection attempted to translate the recommended tactics into concrete form by suggesting two maneuvers by which some of the tactics could be realized. One was an "accordion" maneuver by which bombing units flying closely together would diverge in course about three minutes before the bomb release line. Then, after about a minute, they would converge toward the target so as to cross the target defenses and reach the bomb line almost simultaneously on converging axes. The other was a "javelin" maneuver. Bombing units would dive or climb at the initial point (IP) of the bomb run so they would be flying one on top of the other. Then, by flying the same indicated air speeds on the bomb run, their true air speeds would vary because their altitudes would be different and spread them out enough to avoid self-bombing.

The subsection waged a campaign within the command to sell its ideas on reducing flak risk and stimulate debate and experiment. On 28 April a flak conference was held at Eighth Air Force headquarters. In the middle of May another conference was held with the operations officers of the Third Bomb Division. During July a trip was made to each of the three bomb divisions, where the principles to reduce flak risk and the proposed maneuvers were throughly discussed with division and combat wing commanders. These efforts of the section were solidly backed by General Doolittle, who on 8 August sent the following letter to each division:

> 1. Representatives of the Operational Research Section, this Headquarters, have recently presented to and discussed with the Commanding General and other representatives of your Headquarters a study on "Reduction of Flak Risk" representing the results of a large amount of research on this subject which has been done by the Operational Research Section over the past several months.
>
> 2. It is desired to have your comments on this study, particularly with respect to (a) the soundness of the methods therein proposed for reducing flak risks, (b) the operational feasibility of either or both of the formation tactics therein proposed, and (c) many other types of formation which in your opinion would achieve the desired result.
>
> 3. The matter of reducing flak hazards through tactical measures and otherwise is being made the subject of a continuing study at

this headquarters and a full statement as to your views as to the feasibility of the proposals already made will be of much assistance in this regard. [12]

The Third Division responded that it was already experimenting with the javelin maneuver. The Second Division rejected the javelin maneuver. Otherwise, all three divisions thought the principles enunciated in the report were sound.

Furthermore, they thought experimentation with and adaptation of the maneuvers would reduce flak damage.

THE GENERAL MISSION ANALYSIS SUBSECTION JUNE–JULY 1944

Gasoline consumption.   At this time the analysts in the General Mission Analysis Subsection were the lawyer Louis Lusky, and the mathematicians Dr. George W. Mackey and Frank M. Stewart. In addition, on temporary duty with the section were the test pilot Major Emil Sorenson (since January 1944) and the aeronautical engineer Lt. Robert W. Bratt (since March 1944).

The data collected in the section's early work on fuel consumption had supported range estimates which were necessarily very broad and conservative. It had become evident that if any yardstick was to be devised for a relatively precise measurement of estimated fuel consumption for the purpose of determining range, an elaborate program would have to be undertaken.

A B-17, nicknamed "Petrol Packing Mama," was placed at the disposal of the subsection for the purpose of conducting experimental flights. In addition, two B-17 operating groups had cameras installed in the cockpits of their aircraft for the purpose of taking pictures of the relevant portion of the instrument panels during operational flights. These pictures were taken periodically throughout the entire flight. Elaborate control methods were employed to ensure precise measurements of the weight of the airplane before and after an operation and the amount of gasoline consumed.

Over a period of months an enormous amount of data in the form of photographs and weight and gasoline measurements was accumulated. The data were thoroughly analyzed and the results incorporated in numerous memoranda. For example, on 7 July, Lusky and Stewart issued a memorandum on "Operational Weight and Balance Investigation—B-17." The results of the many months of work was a concise pamphlet, "More Miles Per Gallon," which was written in June by Major Sorenson. [13] The pamphlet was distributed throughout the command in July. It was a handbook for B-17 pilots to secure the maximum range with a minimum consumption of gasoline when flying in formation. In a preface to the handbook, General Doolittle says:

This booklet represents months of study and investigation on the part of keen, engineering minds, employing the best modern methods of measurement and analysis. The conclusions contained herein are considered sound. The operating principles announced are commended to you for your use and benefit.

The shuttle missions. An historic mission of the Eighth Air Force which very likely affected a number of ORS subsections is reflected, because of its special gasoline requirements, in the memoranda of the General Mission Analysis Subsection. The following account of the mission is pieced together from "Combat Chronology."

On 21 June 1944 the Eighth Air Force began shuttle bombing missions (code name FRANTIC) between the United Kingdom and bases in Russia. Two groups of P-47s escorted 145 B-17s from the German coast to Stendal, Germany, where a P-51 group took over the escort to the target—the synthetic oil plant at Ruhland, Germany, near Berlin.

After the attack at Ruhland the supporting P-51 group was relieved by sixty five other P-51s, which accompanied the bombers to Russia. Near Brest Litovsk twenty to thirty German fighters attacked the bombers. In the resulting battle, one American and six German fighters were destroyed. A single B-17 was lost. Altogether, 144 B-17s landed in Russia, seventy-three at Poltava, and the rest at Mirgorod. The sixty-four remaining P-51s landed at Piryatin.

That night (June 21/22) the seventy-three B-17s that had landed at Poltava were attacked for two hours by an estimated seventy-five German bombers led by airplanes dropping flares. Forty-seven B-17s were destroyed on the ground, and most of the rest were severely damaged. Heavy damage was also inflicted on stores of fuel and ammunition.

The B-17s at Mirgorod and the P-51s at Piryatin were moved east further into Russia. The move was fortunate because the German bombers struck both Piryatin and Mirgorod on June 22/23.

On 25 June at daybreak the Eighth Air Force bombers and fighters flew from dispersal bases to Poltava and Mirgorod where they prepared to bomb the oil refinery at Drohobycz, Poland, and then proceed to Italy. However, bad weather forced the mission to be cancelled, and the planes returned to the dispersal areas.

On 26 June, seventy-two B-17s left Poltava and Mirgorod and rendezvoused with the fifty-five P-51s from Piryatin. The bombers attacked the oil refinery and marshalling yard at Drohobycz. (One bomber had to return to Russia because of engine trouble.) The planes then proceeded on to a Fifteenth Air Force base at Foggia, Italy. [15]

On 27 June the weather was too bad for the planes to return to the U.K. On this date the General Mission Analysis Subsection wrote "A Note on Fuel Consumption on Shuttle Missions." [16]

Unfortunately, this and many other notes and memoranda seem to have been lost. Very likely the subsection was consulted in the planning for the shuttle mission and again before the last leg of the shuttle mission.

On 5 July the remaining seventy B-17s of the shuttle mission (US, USSR, Italy, and UK) attacked a marshalling yard at Béziers, France, and finally returned to England. [17] The GAF had made the mission an extremely costly experience for the Eighth Air Force.

On 10 May 1945, in an interview of Hermann Göring by General Spaatz and others, Spaatz told Göring that the Poltava attack was the best attack the Luftwaffe ever made against the USAAF. The prisoner replied, "Those were wonderful times." [18]

Bombing Accuracy, June–July, 1944

Visual bombing. June and July were very active for the Eighth Air Force and hence for the Bombing Accuracy Subsection. The Battle for Normandy was raging. The V-1s were striking English cities from launching sites in France and the Low Countries, and oil targets in Germany and elsewhere had become top priority. The Eighth Air Force, now at maximum strength, flew record numbers of sorties in June and July. Large missions were flown, usually two per day, on twenty-eight days in June and twenty-six days in July. There was plenty of work for the new analysts, Gilman and Katzenbach. The subsection, pushed to its limit, plotted and analyzed bombfalls and kept the monthly accuracy reports going to the groups, wings, and divisions. Despite this, three memoranda were issued within the command in this period. The first, dated 13 June, responded to a letter of 3 June from General Spaatz. It was entitled "ORS Reports on Bombardment Groups' Bombing Accuracy." The second was dated 27 June and was titled "Relationship between Size of Force Employed to Attack Single Targets and Bombing Accuracy," and the third, dated 3 July, was on "Effect of Ground Speed and Size of Formation on Range Errors in B-17 and B-24 Formations." [19]

Radar Bombing

Gee-H. In August 1943 Dr. Tuttle recommended that the command use the British Oboe equipment for short range radar bombing and H2X for long range bombing. The British, however, for security reasons chose not to release the Oboe equipment for daylight bombing. As an alternative, Dr. Tuttle recommended British Gee-H equipment for short range bombing (less than 300 miles). The British cooperated fully with this plan. Dr. Tuttle and Major Warren E. Bales headed up the ORS activities with Gee-H.

From the beginning, the Radar Subsection was involved with every aspect of the Gee-H program. In particular, it helped train crews, prepare lattice charts, and compute data for the combat crews. It coordinated activities with RAF beacon operators and analyzed the operations themselves.

From the first Gee-H mission on 28 January 1944, until D day, Gee-H attacks were confined to V-weapon installations.[20] When visual sighting was not possible, Gee-H was, because of its reasonable accuracy, the logical method for this target system.

After D day, the scale of Gee-H operations expanded tremendously. In the month of June 1944 alone, approximately three thousand heavy bombers were led by Gee-H aircraft. The hard work of Tuttle and Bales had come to fruition. Memoranda written by the subsection reflected its work during this period. They included "Notes on Meeting of 17 June 1944 to Discuss Responsibilities of Signal Section and ORS in Connection with Gee-H Missions," issued on 21 June, and "Request for Additional Phasing Facilities at Gee-H Ground Stations to Eliminate Dead Spots," issued 17 July 1944.

In the latter part of July the Gee-H program was threatened by two factors. The more significant of these was that improved summer weather made visual bombing possible much more often for the targets in the range of Gee-H. Another factor, though less important, was that advancing Allied armies began to overrun some of the V-weapon sites along the French coast, which were the principal Gee-H targets up to that time. Gee-H Pathfinder crews became discouraged by the lack of activity, and many of the trained personnel were sent elsewhere.

The resourceful Tuttle and Bales, struggling to keep the program alive, began to explore the possibility of using Gee-H on tactical support missions.[21]

Micro-H. What was Micro-H bombing? In an article on navigation aids in WWII written by an air force historian,[22] Micro-H is described as a combination of Gee-H and H2X which was introduced operationally by the Eighth Air Force in November 1944. The article states that in the Micro-H technique, the bombers followed Gee-H beams emanating from stations in France until roughly thirty-five miles from the target, at which point the navigator switched to H2X.

Angus Taylor, an ORS analyst assigned to the Third Division, gives this slightly more detailed description of Micro-H bombing.

> Micro-H bombing depends upon the use of radar equipment. Aircraft are guided along a precisely determined course, and bombs are dropped after a synchronization process involving cooperation between the Mickey (H2X) navigator and the bombardier. The system differs from that employed in H2X bombing; in H2X bombing the planes are guided to their targets by the use of airborne radar alone, whereas, in Micro-H bombing the planes are positioned exactly with reference to the ground stations (beacons).[23]

The Micro-H technique was developed by the British Branch of the Radiation Laboratory (BBRL). Dr. Tuttle, together with other members of the command, participated in the early conferences with representatives of BBRL when it was decided to employ this form of blind bombing along with Gee-H and H2X. At that time, it was decided that BBRL personnel would supervise the installation of the equipment, help train crews, do essential calculation, and advise and command on operational problems.

As a result, a computation section was started at Eighth Air Force headquarters with BBRL men. When getting office space, telephones, enlisted help, and equipment became a problem, ORS offered to take on the Micro-H computation work, provided that BBRL would continue to furnish scientific personnel and that such personnel would, while on duty with Eighth Air Force, be considered ORS consultants. This was the way in which Dr. William A. Mersman and Mr. William A. Hosier became part of the Radar Subsection of ORS in June and July 1944. This arrangement worked well except in one respect. The men from BBRL at the ORS at Eighth Air Force headquarters claimed they were not qualified to study operational results, so they never analyzed them. [24]

By the time Micro-H became operational in November 1944 an analyst at Third Division headquarters, Angus Taylor, undertook the task of analyzing Micro-H bombing.

H2X—The Oxford Experiment gets underway. On 13 August 1945, seven days after the atomic bomb was dropped on Hiroshima, Japan, the following story appeared in a British paper, *The Daily Mirror*:

> Their A-bomb test-target was—Oxford
>
> American pilots used Oxford as a practice target for their atomic bomb raids.
>
> Oxford was chosen because an RAF Calibration unit, needed to assess bombing accuracy, was based nearby.
>
> With hints of German capitulation growing, the U.S. airmen got the job because it was expected that the Americans would drop the first atom-bomb on Japan.
>
> The Americans practiced with Mickey the magic black box with the television-like screen which shows a picture of the ground beneath.
>
> The "targets" were selected, an Eighth Air Force officer told me.
>
> One was a street intersection in the center of the city. The other a large manufacturing plant. Two aircraft of the 94th Bomber Group flew forty missions against each target. [25]

The above newspaper account, preserved in a memoir by G. Baley Price, is false in so far as it relates to the atomic bomb, but is otherwise true. Oxford was used as a "target" in an experiment to test the capabilities of H2X bombing. The results were published in a report called "The Oxford Experiment in H2X Bombing" which was widely circulated through the USAAF.

After studying the accuracy of H2X bombing for approximately three months (April, May, and June 1944) Baley Price went to his chief, John Harlan, and suggested that the ORS should experiment with H2X bombing in order to determine the capabilities of the equipment and the factors that affected accuracy. This may seem strange in the summer of 1944, after the H2X equipment had been used on a large scale in combat operations for nine months. Price gives his reasons for proposing the study.

> At this late date [July 1944] it was still true that almost no information was available. The equipment had been introduced after the war began; hence, there was no background of peacetime practice results such as we had for visual bombsights. It had been possible to gain all the necessary information about visual bombing from an analysis of combat missions. The strike photographs provided an ample record for accuracy studies. Blind missions, however, provided almost no data for analysis, at least very little had been accumulated up to the summer of 1944. A report was available from Radiation Laboratory which indicated the equipment should have an accuracy of 0.3 of a mile, but it added that someone ought to check the figure experimentally. The results of H2X in combat had not been entirely satisfactory—the errors often had been large. The answer to the entire situation seemed to be controlled experiments to determine the capabilities of the equipment; then we would have some idea about the errors that resulted from combat causes, and would know better how to go about improving the performances. [26]

Colonel Harlan at once suggested that Price, Dr. Youngs, and Mr. Ashton begin to explore the desirability and feasibility of running such tests. Ashton and Youngs had been with the section approximately one month, so Price, with over six months experience in bombing accuracy analysis, was the natural leader of the group.

Colonel Garland, the bombing expert at Eighth Air Force headquarters who had supervised the training for the H2X beach bombing on D day, was a logical person to go to for help. Although he seemed to approve of Price's idea, he did not offer to assume the responsibility of recommending the experiment to the Eighth Air Force. Price proposed that the experiment be started with two planes in the Third Division. Colonel Garland suggested that the work be done at the Ninety-sixth Bomb Group. However, Price insisted that the work be done by planes from the Ninety-fourth Bomb Group— Colonel Castle's Group. Price knew from experience that he could count on Colonel Castle's support. Garland also suggested that the test should be run at

Alconbury, the base where radar development was conducted and crews were trained. However, Price opposed the suggestion.

> For two reasons I opposed the suggestion: (a) I wanted complete freedom in conducting the test; (b) I wanted to run an operational test with combat crews and equipment, not a laboratory test with special planes and crews. [27]

After nine months of large-scale operational use of H2X, the section and the command needed to know the unvarnished truth about the operational effectiveness of the H2X equipment. Throughout this period the Radiation Laboratory had been unwilling to release H2X radar personnel to the ORS and instead had installed its own radar adviser at the Eighth Air Force. [28] In view of this history it seems natural and appropriate that Price should want an independent study.

Price acknowledges that

> The proposal [the Oxford experiment] was suggested at least partly by the practice runs on beaches that had been made in preparation for the invasion. The analysis of these runs had shown some surprising things (chiefly the equipment was more accurate on beach targets than most of us would have guessed from past combat experience), but it did not answer all our questions. All of these runs had been made on one type of target (and there was much evidence to indicate that the accuracy varied with the type of target) and at one altitude (namely 20,000 feet). What was needed now was further experimentation to complete the work begun in the practice runs in May. [29]

Price prepared the recommendation for the experiment and submitted it to Colonel Todd in A-3. Todd acted quickly; he scheduled a meeting for Sunday, 16 July, at Third Division headquarters to work out the details. Present were Lieutenant Colonel Thorup, the chief of staff of the Fourth Combat Wing and Colonel Castle's representative, and Lieutenant Colonel Riva, the commanding officer of the 333d Squadron in the Ninety-fourth Group, which would furnish the H2X crews and planes. Price outlined his first plan which was to elect three or four cities in England which were comparable to targets in Germany, simulate bombing runs, and assess them with camera bombing methods. Colonel Riva agreed to designate the crews and planes immediately. On Tuesday afternoon, 18 July, Price, Youngs, and Ashton reported to Bury St. Edmund to begin work. The next morning they learned which two crews and which two planes (B-17s) were assigned them.

One crew had a lead pilot of exceptional ability, Captain Samerdyke, who, after fewer than twenty missions was taken off combat flying because of combat fatigue. The pilot of the other crew was a Captain Smith. After installing appropriate cameras, waiting until Captain Smith flew his twenty-eighth and last mission, indoctrinating the crews, and waiting for appropriate weather, the first flight was finally made on Saturday, 22 July. Price flew with Captain Samerdyke at an altitude of 25,000 feet over Kings Lynn, Grimsby, Leeds, Sheffield, Derby, and back to Bury St. Edmund. Price assesses the first week of work:

> We had hoped to lay out a regular course over these cities. On this occasion a layer of solid clouds at low altitude prevented us from making any camera bombing runs, but we did get some scope photographs of the cities we expected to use as targets. I was thoroughly discouraged by our results for the first week. It seemed that the clouds would defeat the experiment just as they had nullified Colonel Castle's efforts to start camera bombing for H2X training in May. [30]

At this point Price found another way of simulating H2X bombing which did not use camera bombing. Specifically, it did not rely on obtaining pictures of the ground during the simulated bomb run. Price says,

> I spent a lot of time thinking about the situation. Photographs of the ground were not really needed, but they were only a means of locating the position of the plane. Couldn't we locate the position of the plane by some means that was independent of cloud? [31]

Price turned to his colleagues at the ORS of RAF Bomber Command. Like Hewitt before him, he and Ashton went to Bomber Command for help. In this instance they explained their problem to a Dr. Roberts. Roberts suggested GL (gun-laying), a method of using radar to detect approaching planes and aim gun-laying equipment at them. Radar, while it navigated bombers to targets, as with H2X, was also used to track approaching bombers and help aim guns at them. GL turned out to be the solution.

Roberts told Price and Ashton that the RAF had an installation, near Oxford, that had been used for the calibration of British blind bombing equipment. He gave Price names of people to call.

On Tuesday, 25 July, Price and Ashton called at the Air Analysis Section at Stanmore, the headquarters of the Allied Expeditionary Air Force (AEAF), in a suburb of London. There they met a Mr. Cornford who gave them permission to use the GL installation. The installation, located in a cow pasture near Oxford, consisted of two large pieces of radar equipment and several trailer vans. Captain George, the British officer in charge of the installation, and Price worked out the details of VHF radio communication which would be required in the simulated bombings.

On 1 August Price began working out the new procedures with the two crews. He selected two targets in Oxford, "one the main street intersection in the center of town and the other Morris Motor Works on the south east edge of Oxford." In the first week, 1–7 August, Price made numerous flights with each crew to set things up. Price says,

> Everything went well except VHF and my ears. In order to avoid interference with everybody concerned, Captain Levinson had suggested that we use a special "world wide" frequency. But the interference on this channel seemed world wide. The squeals and other noises in the ear phones did not add to the comfort of my ears, already hurting from repeated flights during the week. In the end we shifted back to the 4th Combat Wing's channel A to complete the experiment.
>
> At this point both crews had been checked out on the procedures, and I decided that I could be of more help on the ground than in the air. I became the operations officer of a little air force with two planes and two crews. And I learned to pity the generals that had thousands. [32]

As Price's story of the Oxford Experiment unfolds, it becomes evident that Price was aided every step of the way by the fact that the British had been there before him. They used gun-laying radar to check their Oboe blind bombing, and they loaned their range, equipment, and technicians to Price for his experiments. When it came time to calculate the track of the experimental bomb runs on the ground, the British furnished Price with their charts and techniques, which made the calculating and plotting manageable. By the end of the experiment, British experience enabled Price to predict that operational use of H2X blind bombing would be about twice as inaccurate as the experimental results.

Price's contribution lay in applying the British techniques and in showing what could be expected from H2X blind bombing in operations. His work will be described in more detail on pages 214 ff.

BOMBS AND FUZES

The transportation plan. In June while the Allies were establishing their beachhead on the Normandy coast, support of the ground battle was the overriding priority. It was typical for the Eighth Air Force to fly two large missions or more per day. On D day the Eighth flew four missions. Seventeen hundred and twenty-nine heavy bombers dropped 3,596 tons of bombs. On D day Eighth Fighter Command also put forth a tremendous effort. It had the threefold mission of escorting the bombers, attacking any movement toward the assault area, and protecting Allied shipping. The fighters flew 1,880 sorties including fighter bomber attacks against seventeen bridges, ten marshalling yards, and a variety of other targets including a convoy, railroad cars, sidings, rail and highway junctions, a tunnel, and a dam. [33]

Part of the air force's responsibility during the Normandy battle was to keep the GAF at a distance. In June the Eighth Air Force bombed airfields around the invasion area on twenty days and in July on ten days. On a mission when the Eighth went after airfields, it did not bomb just one, but would attack a cluster of them; on 13 June it bombed airfields at Dreux, St. Andre-de-L'Eure, Evreux, Beauvais/Nivillers, and Beaumont-sur-Oise. [34]

During the Battle of Normandy the Eighth Air Force also worked to keep German supplies and reinforcements from reaching the battle. They made it difficult and costly for the Germans to move about within the battle zone by bombing the marshalling yards and bridges in the transportation plan. The Bombs and Fuzes Subsection and Bombing Accuracy worked on force requirements for marshalling yards and bridges long before D day.

In June the Eighth Air Force bombed railroads and marshalling yards on fifteen days and bridges on seventeen. The air force approached these targets the way they did airfields. For example, on a day marked for bridge bombing, not one, but a cluster would be attacked. In addition to keeping up with these daily activities, the Bombs and Fuzes and Bombing Accuracy Subsections also helped plan future missions. Alderman recalls,

> Not long after D Day we were asked to prepare estimates for attacks on all the Rhine river bridges. The objective was the destruction of a main span; temporary damage was not to be considered. Material was available from A-2 on only some of the bridges, and these were studied in detail taking into account the vulnerable areas of the important structural members, the total length of the bridge, the lengths of the spans, the size and diameter of the bomb and its fuzing, and the number of direct hits required.
>
> For these studies there was no specific test data or operational experience available. Judgements had to be made as to how close to a heavy structural bridge member a bomb had to be in order to be able to take out that member. These factors had to be weighed against the probabilities of getting hits with the different sizes of bombs. [35]

The operations research sections of both the Fifteenth Air Force and the Mediterranean Allied Air Force had experience with interdiction campaigns and bridge bombing in Italy many months before the ORS at the Eighth Air Force did. Incidentally, all three sections discovered and enunciated the following principle:

> The direction of the bombing run is especially important in attacks on bridges. More of the vulnerable area of the structural members are exposed—taking into account the striking angle of the bombs— when attacks are made approximately perpendicular to the long axis of the bridge. [36]

The unprecedented activity of the Eighth Air Force in June led to serious bomb shortages. Quite often the Bombs and Fuzes Subsection had to accept second choice weapons. This is reflected in a memorandum written on 2 July for Ordnance, "Memorandum for Colonel Sims: Targets Classified According to Types against which Attacks Have Been Made by Other than the Preferred Weapon Because of Shortage of HE Bombs." [37]

V-weapons.   The Allied campaign against V-weapons begun in December 1943 was so successful against the "ski sites" that the Germans switched to extremely well-camouflaged, prefabricated, quickly assembled and self-defended "modified sites." By June 1944 the Germans had still not launched their V-weapons against the Allies. The Allied campaign against V-weapons had come to a standstill. This situation changed abruptly, however, when, during the night of 12/13 June, V-1 flying bombs began to fall on London. On Thursday, 15 June, "the British Chiefs of Staff formally asked General Eisenhower to resume bombing the [V-weapon] supply sites with everything that can be spared from the needs of the battle of France." [38]

The V-1, a pulse-jet-powered flying bomb, twenty-five feet long with a sixteen-foot wing span, carried a one-ton warhead 152 miles (later increased to 250 miles) at about 400 miles per hour. Although it was usually launched from the ground from concrete ramps, it was also fired from modified Heinkel He-111 bombers manned by a special Luftwaffe unit. The British had the Gloster, the only plane capable of catching the V-1 by matching its speed. [39] A technique that the British developed for defending against the V-1 weapons after they were launched was for their fighters to fly alongside and use their wing tips to tip the V-1 over, whereupon it would spin in and fall to the ground.

The Bombs and Fuzes Subsection recommended that the 250-pound GP bomb be used on the modified sites. Alderman also notes that "by the time of these attacks the enemy had thrown a lot of antiaircraft in the area and had forced the heavies from the original low altitudes around 12,000 to 15,000 feet up to 20,000 to 26,000 feet." [40]

On Tuesday, 20 June, a week after the first onslaught of the flying bombs, Captain Butcher, Eisenhower's aide, wrote in his diary:

> During the last three days we have had fairly continuous arrivals of Hitler's secret weapon, variously called "Diver," "Pilotless Air-craft," "Buzz Bomb," "Doodle Bug," or "Robot." Perhaps "June-bug" or "Jitterbug" would be appropriate. Certainly most of the people I know are semidazed from loss of sleep and have the jit-ters, which they show when a door bangs or the sounds of motors, from motorcycles to aircraft, are heard.

Butcher also notes that Eisenhower, who was the supreme commander, had, at the urging of Churchill, ordered the air forces to give first priority to the V-weapon sites over everything except the urgent requirements of battle, until it was clear that the V-weapon menace was under control. [41] Consequently, starting on 14 June and on nearly every day in June thereafter, the Eighth Air Force mounted attacks on V-weapon installations in France. However, in July, the Eighth Air Force mounted attacks on V-weapons on only seven days and these were in the first two weeks of July. [42] Alderman says, "Our Command was anxious to be relieved of the responsibility of attacking these targets and anxious to spend full time on our more meaty industrial targets." [43]

It is clear from Alderman's comments and even more clear from the daily record in "Combat Chronology" that in good weather, aside from ground support missions for the Battle of Normandy, German industrial targets had the top priority for General Spaatz.

How damaging were the buzz bombs in June and July? Eisenhower got a weekly report on the situation. In the first six weeks of the buzz bomb attacks, 12 June through the end of July—forty-two days,

3,407 bombs crossed the southeast coast of England,

1,594 bombs got to London,

4,175 people in the United Kingdom were killed by the bombs,

12,284 people in the United Kingdom were seriously injured by the bombs.

Thus, in the first six weeks approximately ninety-nine people were killed and 292 people were seriously injured each day. A large percentage of the damage occurred in London. In addition, in this same forty-two days, damage was done to seventy factories, seven railroads, three hospitals, ten schools, eighteen military installations, six docks, and forty-seven utilities. [44]

Is it any wonder that the British, especially those who lived in London or on the bomber paths, were concerned about the bombing?

A few excerpts from the radio broadcasts of Lowell Thomas give a sample of what people in the United States were told.

> June 16, 1944—"Tonight those new strange things of menace are flashing over the English countryside—the Nazi robot planes."
>
> June 20, 1944—"American Flying Fortresses and Liberators bombed the bases for the robot planes this evening."
>
> June 21, 1944—"The Allies have captured several robot launching platforms in their drive against Cherbourg."
>
> July 5, 1944—"In Southern England the buzz-bomb terror campaign was in full blast today—with robots coming across the channel in steady streams."
>
> July 11, 1944—"There was a great exodus from London today, 41,000 people leaving, mothers and children. They are fugitives from what Londoners are calling the "ersatz blitz". That is, the buzz-bomb assault. [45]

The oil campaign officially begins.   In March General Spaatz attempted to make oil targets his top priority. Instead, transportation targets, marshalling yards in particular, were given top priority until after D day. Thus on 8 June, two days after D day, General Spaatz placed oil targets in top priority for the Eighth and Fifteenth Air Forces. However, for the Eighth Air Force in June the requirements of the Battle of Normandy and the V-weapons actually had top priority. Nevertheless that month the Eighth Air Force managed to bomb targets in Germany on six days. In July the Eighth Air Force bombed industrial targets in Germany on twelve days. Several of these targets in July were synthetic oil refineries. The large one at Merseburg outside Leipzig was bombed twice.[46]

In anticipation of the attacks on synthetic oil refineries the men of the Bombs and Fuzes Subsection had made a study of them. Alderman writes,

> Our research included discussions with the British and American oil experts, a visit to two Synthetic Oil plants in North England, and analyses of all available information on the proposed German targets. It was unanimously agreed by the oil experts that the gas generator units were the most vital installations and that a synthetic oil plant could be knocked out of production by destroying only this one vital phase of the production system.
>
> The gas generator units were largely custom-made on the site, and we were informed that these installations would be the most difficult to replace. These units were housed in heavy steel-frame structures which would be difficult to destroy effectively with bombs of any size. For this reason it became obvious that the weapon should be selected which would most effectively knock out the gas generators themselves. Balancing the amounts of damage that could be expected of the different GP bombs with the number of bombs that could be carried, it was concluded that the most effective weapon which could destroy or seriously damage a generator unit was the 100-lb GP.
>
> During the first period of the attacks on Synthetic Oil targets the 100-lb GP was used on the majority of targets when it was available.[47]

Ground survey work.   As the Allied armies captured portions of Italy and France it became possible, for the first time, for ORS bombs and fuzes men to assess the damage Allied aerial bombing had caused at various liberated European targets. Thus, in October and November 1943, George Housner, the ORS Fifteenth Air Force counterpart of Alderman, Hedefine, and Kring, made studies of the bomb damage of an oil refinery and other targets in the Naples, Italy, area.[48]

In June and July 1944, after the Allies had established a substantial beachhead in Normandy, the ORS was able to make some ground surveys of targets in liberated areas. The first of these trips, several days long, was made in June. About a dozen people from Eighth Air Force headquarters, including Kring, investigated the damage to D day targets and coastal fortifications. Alderman says,

> Kring's reaction to this trip was that the group was much too large, that several jeeps could not stay together under the circumstances, and that all in all, because of the size of the party no intensive survey work was accomplished. Nevertheless he was able to gather certain information which we could apply to current operations. [49]

The second trip was entirely an ORS operation which took place 22–26 July. The orders were dated 18 July 1944. Colonel John M. Harlan, S/Sgt. George W. Adams, Mr. Charles U. Kring, and Mr. Bissell Alderman were ordered to northwestern Europe for approximately five days "for the purpose of conducting a survey of bomb damage to bridges, towns and airfields." These orders were issued by Lieutenant General Spaatz. [50]

The survey group spent nights at the Advance Headquarters Ninth Bomber Command, which was then at Grandcamp, France, This was also where the Ninth Air Force ORS had its headquarters. Sergeant Adams' role was that of jeep driver and photographer. Alderman says Adams "was a former Indianapolis race track driver and would have been an excellent man if his photography had been as fast as his driving." [51]

The main purpose of the trip was to study road interdiction attacks. This usually meant surveying destruction in small towns. However, on 25 July, while Colonel Harlan went to observe the aerial bombing at St-Lô, Derald West and Leonard Reinke of the Ninth Air Force ORS, and Alderman went to Caen to inspect the Caen-Carpiquet airfield, [52] which had been bombed four times (10 July 1943, 26 August 1943, 6 February 1944, and 23 May 1944) by the Eighth Air Force. [53]

Harlan and Alderman recommend against the bombing of French towns in road interdiction attacks. Beginning with D day, [54] the Eighth Air Force was called upon from time to time to attack some small town areas for the purpose of road interdiction. The intention was to crater streets and block roads by filling streets with debris from destroyed buildings. Aiming points were selected in the most vulnerable areas of the towns with this in mind. Both Eighth Air Force headquarters and USSTAF objected to these targets. Colonel Harlan, chief of ORS for the Eighth Air Force, and Alderman were requested to survey some of the towns that had been bombed. In the period 22–26 July they visited some of the towns and conducted a survey.

Alderman tells what they found and what they concluded.

> The only towns we could visit were those which had been bombed

by the Ninth AF: St. Sauveur-le-Vicomte, Isigny, Etienville, La Haye de Puits and Caen. These and others we visited were similar to the towns which were yet to be captured and which were targets for the Eighth. In our report [55] we pointed out that the effectiveness of these attacks had been very limited. In some towns no routes had been blocked, and in one instance where all routes had been blocked in a small town, bypass routes around the town were available nearby. It appeared to be an ineffective method of blocking roads. It was costly both from the point of view of the effort involved and the amount of property destroyed. The operations varied in effectiveness with the size of the town, with the type of streets, with the nature of the surrounding terrain, and with the weight and accuracy of the attack. We found that even in the most heavily bombed areas the rubble and debris was not uniformly spread, and it appeared that certain vehicles could get through with ease. We were told that temporary routes could be cleared in a few hours for one-way traffic.

If interdiction attacks had to continue, we recommended that targets be selected on roads through marshy areas, at cuts and fills, or in heavily wooded areas, that bridges should be bombed wherever possible, and that the number of attacks on towns should be reduced to an absolute minimum. [56]

Major Troop Support Activities of the Eighth Air Force in June and July The Breakout

Carpet bombing. Beginning with D day the Eighth Air Force and the section became involved in a new kind of mission—carpet bombing—in advance of our own attacking troops. Carpet bombing was a form of air support used to batter German forces in preparation for assaults by Allied ground troops on the German lines. It consisted of massive aerial bombardment of the part of the German lines that the Allies desired to penetrate. Clarkson of Bombing Accuracy, and Kring of Bombs and Fuzes, and no doubt Harlan had been given special clearance (BIGOT) in order to help the Omaha Beach bombing on D day. Kring even flew on a D day mission. A month later when Price was exploring the feasibility of running the Oxford Experiment, he had gone to Widewing (site of SHAEF, Eisenhower's headquarters in suburban London) to talk to the radar expert, Dr. Griggs. Griggs had urged him to make a study of the H2X performance on D day. This, of course, also meant a study of the Eighth's first carpet bombing experience. Price notes in his memoir, however, that it was now impossible to do so. "The results had been lost for all time as a result of clouds, rocket fire, naval bombardment, the action of ground troops, and so on." [57]

Alderman mentions in his memoir some of the "carpet bombing" or "breakthrough" type missions his subsection was involved with, including Caen, St-Lô, Eindhoven, and Metz.[58] At first the section did not write reports on these missions, though they did study them. Keeping a close record of the extent of the errors of each attacking unit had been part of bombing accuracy studies from the beginning on all missions in order to determine pattern characteristics and to estimate the probable dispersion of the bomb falls of an attacking force. Arps notes that this became important when the air force began major ground support missions such as the breakout at St-Lô. In his history of the section, Arps says,

> The Bombing Accuracy Subsection was charged with the responsibility of preparing after each ground air support operation a plot on a large scale map showing the bomb fall of each attacking unit. To mention only one instance where this became critical was the time that General McNair was killed.[59]

Lt. General Leslie J. McNair, chief of Army Ground Forces, was killed by bombs from Allied planes while observing the carpet bombing at St. Lô. (See pages 187, 189, and 191.)

Caen—Operation GOODWOOD

Purpose and size of force. The first time after D day that the Eighth Air Force used its heavy bombers to support attacking Allied troops was at Caen, the eastern end of the Normandy battle line. It had been General Montgomery's hope to capture Caen in the first few days of the invasion. However, five weeks later Montgomery's troops possessed only the northern part of the city.

The purpose of the 18 July Operation GOODWOOD was to break out from Caen and push toward Falaise. Operation GOODWOOD began with a gigantic air bombardment.

> RAF Bomber Command began with a heavy bombing attack by nearly 1,000 heavies at first light on the 18th; the Eighth Air Force followed with 571 of its heavies attacking three areas; and IX Bomber Command sent all eleven of its medium groups against five gun positions.[60]

Operation GOODWOOD as I experienced it. I flew as a bombardier in a B-24 with the 493d Bomb Group in Operation GOODWOOD. Though some things about this mission are still clear after over forty years, others are not. For example, although I recall pulling out the arming pins from the bombs after takeoff and then dropping the bombs on the signal from the group leader, I do not remember the size of the bombs. I think they were either 100-pound or 250-pound bombs. Though our bombs and fuzes men would probably have recommended 100-pound bombs for this kind of target, the British analyst Zuckerman was one of the planners for this mission, [61] so the bombs may have been bigger.

The bombers were to fly in at altitudes around 12,000 feet. Our pilot, S. R. Reid, told us that we would by flying low-low in the group; we were low squadron in our group and low element in our squadron. Our altitude, therefore, would be considerably lower than 12,000 feet. That, our pilot told us, made us more vulnerable to flak. He was right.

I remember approaching the bomb line. The light was eerie grey (morning) but we could see clearly, and we could be clearly seen. Just as we came within range of German antiaircraft, a piece of shrapnel crashed through the Plexiglas window to the right of the bombardier's compartment. It ricocheted and rattled around in my compartment before coming to a stop. Despite this distraction I got our bombs out on signal, and we returned to base with no further incident.

The bombing was accurate. On 21 July 1944 General Doolittle, commanding general of the Eighth Air Force, sent the following letter of commendation to General Partridge, commanding general of our Third Division:

> 1. I wish to commend the 92d and 93d Combat Wings of the 3d Division for the well-planned, highly successful attack made in support of ground troops on 18 July 1944.
> 2. Photographic coverage shows that the target area was completely covered with dense bomb patterns which materially reduced enemy opposition to the advancing Allied troops. [62]

A copy of this letter was placed in the records of each of the men of our group who went on the mission.

The accuracy of the bombing is also affirmed by Zuckerman, who made a survey of it immediately thereafter. [63]

Although the attack succeeded in capturing the rest of the city of Caen, the British offensive was stopped dead just south of Caen.

> Both ground and air commanders were concerned that no more substantial result should have been produced by the heaviest single bomber effort of the Normandy campaign, for a total of 7,700 tons had been dropped by the more than 1,600 heavies and 350 mediums combined. [64]

I recall one of our intelligence officers explaining to the assembled crews of our group why the attack had not succeeded. He said that the soldiers on each side of the bomb line had been stunned by the bombardment. Consequently, the Allied soldiers had not been able to turn the bombing to their advantage. Though that may be so, USAAF history indicates that Allied troops were separated from the bomb line by 3,000 yards. Furthermore, it asserts, most of the prisoners taken in the forward positions remained stone-deaf for a period of twenty-four hours in consequence of the air bombardment. [65]

German assessment of the attack.   The German view of the air attack is especially interesting. On 21 July, the very day General Doolittle had commended his Third Division, the German Field Marshal Gunther von Kluge wrote his evaluation of the battle at Caen for Hitler. On 3 July von Kluge had succeeded von Rundstedt as commander. To the führer he reported:

> My conference with the Commanders of the units of Caen, held just after the last heavy battle, forced me to the conclusion... that there is no way in which we could do battle with the all powerful enemy air forces... without being forced to surrender territory. Whole armored units... were attacked by terrific numbers of aircraft dropping carpets of bombs, so that they emerged from the churned up earth with the greatest difficulty, sometimes only with the aid of tractors... The psychological effect on the fighting forces, especially the infantry,... bombs raining down on them with all the force of elemental nature, is a factor which must be given serious consideration. [66]

The breakout at St-Lô

Bradley's plan—COBRA

> Surely History will give a name to the battle that sent us boiling out of Normandy, some name comparable with Saint-Mihiel or Meuse-Argonne of the last war. But to us there on the spot at the time it was known simply as the 'break-through'. [67]

The failure of the British offensive of 18 July at Caen to produce a breakthrough of the German lines made it all the more important to the Americans to succeed when they made their big push later, on 25 July.

Ernie Pyle.   Ernie Pyle was with a group of newspaper correspondents in the American lines one evening when Lieutenant General Omar Bradley, commanding all the American troops in France, came to their camp to brief them on the coming operation (code name COBRA). It would start, he said, on the first day there were three hours of good flying weather in the forenoon.

General Bradley told the correspondents that the attack would cover a segment of the German line west of St-Lô, about five miles wide. In that narrow segment the Americans would have three infantry divisions, side by side. Right behind them would be another infantry and two armored divisions. Once a hole was broken, the armored divisions would slam through several miles beyond, then turn right toward the sea behind the Germans in that sector in the hope of cutting them off and trapping them.

The attack was to open with a gigantic two-hour air bombardment by 1,800 planes—the biggest ever attempted by air in direct support of ground troops.

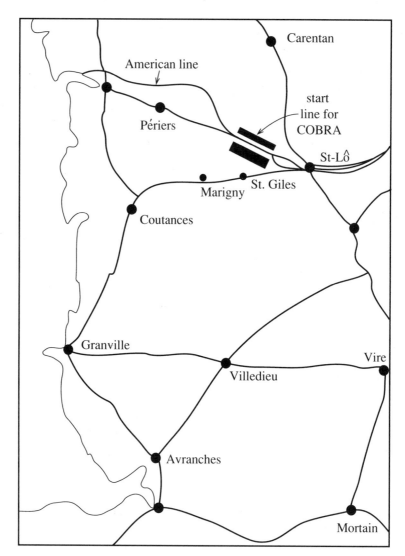

COBRA
The St-Lô Breakthrough

It would start with dive bombers, followed by great four-motored heavies, then mediums and then dive bombers again. Next, the ground troops would kick off, with air fighters continuing to work ahead of them. It was a thrilling plan to listen to, said Pyle. "Gen. Bradley didn't tell us that it was the big thing, but other officers gave us the word. They said, 'This is no limited objective drive. This is it. This is the big breakthrough.'" [68]

The air force's role in COBRA. The air force plan for COBRA was followed to the letter on 25 July. Fighter-bomber groups of the Ninth Air Force were to begin the operation with a glide bombing and strafing attack on a rectangular target 250 yards deep and 7,000 yards long, with its long northern boundary just south of the St-Lô–Périers road. There were eight of these assaulting fighter groups. After assembling over their bases, they were to check in with the controller at the Carentan airstrip at three-minute intervals, beginning at 0931 hours, and proceed to their targets, which were divided into eastern and western areas. The first group was to sweep the long axis of the eastern area, the second that of the Western area, and so on in alternation. As the fighter-bombers completed their blows, the heavies were to appear at 1000 hours and in successive waves deliver a saturation attack on an area one mile deep and five miles long. This area was parallel to and just south of the fighter-bomber area. The attack would be delivered at right angles to the long axis of the target. (The air force found this necessary to reduce the grave problem of flying more than 1,500 heavy bombers over the target within the space of sixty minutes.) At 1100 hours the infantry (Seventh Corps) was scheduled to jump off. At that instant an additional seven groups of fighter bombers would renew the attack on the eastern and western sectors of their assigned area. The medium bombers of the Ninth Air Force would then begin to bomb strongpoints and areas behind the German line which were inaccessible to artillery fire.

The heavies were to bomb visually and by groups. They were also to fly at minimum altitude consistent with precautions against enemy flak. Target boundaries were to be marked with red smoke shells fired at two-minute intervals. The army originally suggested withdrawing ground troops to a distance of 800 yards from the bomb line. The air force urged 3,000 yards. A compromise was struck at 1,500 yards, with the army forward lines marked with cerise and yellow panels. [69]

From the first fighter-bomber attack at 0938 until the last medium bomber attack at 1223, air force planes were able to adhere exactly to their rigid and intricate time schedule. A total of 1,507 B-17s and B-24s attacked, dropping over 3,300 tons; over 380 mediums dropped 137 tons of high explosives and more than 4,000 260-pound frags. Five hundred fifty-nine fighter-bombers delivered 212 tons of bombs and an unspecified amount of incendiary napalm. Thus, approximately 4,100 tons of bombs were dropped in the St-Lô aerial bombardment. By comparison, 7,700 tons were dropped by the more than 1,600 heavies—571 of these were American, the rest British—and 350 mediums in the Goodwood preattack bombardment at Caen. [70] The British Lancaster could carry at least twice the bomb load of the B-17 or B-24. They evidently did so on the GOODWOOD mission.

Bombing accuracy at St-Lô. On the positive side, the bombing was technically accurate. The mediums concentrated the bombs carried by twenty-one of their thirty formations in the proper areas. The First, Second, and Third Bombardment Divisions of the Eighth Air Force likewise covered their targets well, in spite of a change in the weather.

The preplanned bombing altitudes had been fixed between 15,000 and 16,000 feet, but the cloud base over the target area on 25 July forced readjustment of these plans after most of the aircraft were airborne. Some bombed from as low as 12,000 feet and few, if any, from the predetermined height; the bombardiers had been forced to hurriedly recompute their bombing data and reset their sights. The drop to the lower bombing levels loosened formations. This made the air over the target area more dangerous, and it tended to elongate patterns as units dropped on their leaders. Smoke markers proved of little value. They were not visible until their smoke had drifted high, and then the prevailing south wind quickly displaced it. Once the attack had begun, great clouds of dust and smoke had billowed up from the target area. Red smoke was difficult to distinguish from shell and bomb bursts or from the muzzle flashes of American artillery.

Under such circumstances it is remarkable that ORS experts, after elaborate scrutiny of strike photographs, found that bombing errors were actually less than anticipated. [71]

On the negative side, both air and ground commanders knew and anticipated the probabilities of gross errors in bombardment. They occurred on 25 July, and they were costly. For example, the lead bombardier of one group had trouble with his bombsight and released visually with bad results. Another failed to properly identify landmarks. Thus, frags and high explosives from a total of thirty-five heavies fell north (short) of the target areas and within American lines. Mediums of the Ninth Bomber Command likewise short-bombed; forty-two aircraft dropped their bombs within friendly lines because of faulty identification of target. The cost of these errors was reported as 102 army personnel killed, including Lieutenant General Lesley J. McNair, and 380 wounded. [72]

The COBRA mission as I experienced it. As bombardier on one of the B-24s of the 493d Bomb Group, I hit the switch which released over two tons of the more than 4,000 tons of bombs aimed at German lines that day. We had been extensively briefed to exercise the utmost care in following our instructions as to when and where to drop our bombs. We knew that dropping them too soon would mean dropping them on our own troops. We also knew the significance of our part of the action. On the ground were

1. Members of a B-24 crew. Left to right: (top) Stewart Reid (pilot), George Otto (copilot), Richard "Dick" Hicks (navigator), Charles W. McArthur (bombardier), (bottom) Melvin O. Stracner (engineer), Allen P. Coffee (radioman), Maurice Corrion (nose gunner), John P. Cook (waist gunner), Curtis Miller (ball gunner), and Edward P. Zilla (tail gunner).

2. The B-17 (Flying Fortress). The B-17 was a nonpressurized monoplane with a wingspan of 104 feet and length from nose to tail of approximately seventy-five feet. It was powered with four radial engines rated at 1,200 horsepower each. It had a maximum speed of 287 miles per hour at 25,000 feet and a tactical operating speed of 180–215 miles per hour at 25,000 feet. It had a tactical climbing rate of one hour and thirty minutes to 25,000 feet and a tactical flying radius of 650–800 miles, depending on the bomb load. It typically carried ten or more machine guns of .50-caliber—two in the nose; two each in the top turret; bottom turret; tail turret; and two in the waist, one on each side. The normal tactical bomb load was 4,000 pounds, but the B-17 could carry up to 9,000 pounds. The crew consisted of ten men: pilot, copilot, bombardier-gunner, navigator, engineer, radioman, ball turret gunner, two waist gunners, and tail gunner.

3. The B-24 (Liberator). The B-24 was a nonpressurized monoplane with wingspan of 110 feet and length of sixty-seven feet. It has four radial engines rated at 1,200 horsepower each. It had a maximum speed of 290 miles per hour at 25,000 feet and a tactical operating speed of 205 miles per hour at 25,000 feet. It had a tactical climbing rate of one hour to 20,000 feet and a tactical flying radius of approximately 700 miles. It was armed with ten machine guns of .50-caliber—two guns each in the nose, top, bottom, tail, and two in the waist. It normally carried a ten-man crew.

4. B-26 (Marauder). There were two types of this nonpressurized monoplane. Each had two radial engines rated at 2,000 horsepower each. The normal bomb load of each was 4,000 pounds. The small-wing B-26 had a wingspan of sixty-five feet and was fifty-eight feet long. It had a maximum speed of 317 miles per hour at 14,500 feet and a normal cruising speed of 200 miles per hour. Its normal combat range at 10,000 feet was 800 miles. It carried a crew of six and had nine or eleven .50-caliber machine guns. The large-wing B-26 had a wingspan of seventy-one feet and length of fifty-eight feet. It had a maximum speed of 282 miles per hour at 15,000 feet and a combat cruising speed of 195 miles per hour at 10,000 feet. Its combat range was 550 miles. It carried a crew of seven and had twelve .50-caliber machine guns.

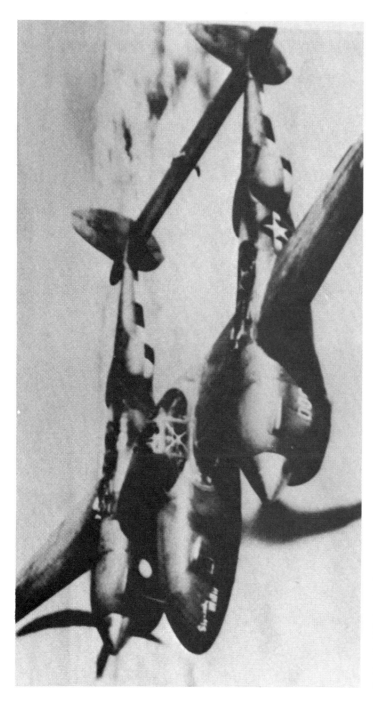

5. P-38 (Lightning). The P-38 was a twin-engine fighter powered with two Allison engines rated at 1,325 or 1,425 horsepower. Its wingspan was fifty-two feet, and its length was thirty-eight feet. Its maximum speed was 395 miles per hour at 25,000 feet, later increased to 414 miles per hour. It had a tactical cruising speed of 250–320 miles per hour and could climb to 20,000 feet in eight minutes. Its tactical radius was 200 miles per hour. It was armed with one 20-mm cannon and four .50-caliber machine guns. Two 2,000-pound bombs could be carried on wing racks.

6. P-47 (Thunderbolt). The P-47 had one radial engine rated at 2,000 or 2,100 horsepower. Its wingspan was forty-one feet and its length twenty-six feet. Its maximum speed was 433 miles per hour at 30,000 feet and later 473 miles per hour at 32,000 feet. It could climb to 30,000 feet in twenty minutes, and the latest model could climb to 32,000 feet in fourteen minutes. Its tactical radius was 250 miles. It was armed with eight .50-caliber machine guns.

7. P-51 (Mustang). The P-51 was powered by one engine. The P-51D had a Packard engine rated at 1,490 horsepower. Its wingspan was thirty-seven feet and its length approximately thirty-two feet. Its maximum speed at 25,000 feet was 437 miles per hour. It could climb to 30,000 feet in thirteen minutes. Its tactical fuel radius with internal fuel tank was 325 miles. This could be increased to 750 miles by adding two drop tanks. The P-51 was armed with six .50-caliber machine guns. Instead of drop tanks it could carry two 500-pound bombs.

8. Left to right: James A. Clarkson, Lt. Col. Philip C. Scott, and William John "Jack" Youden. This photograph and several others show Nissen huts used as living quarters and office space for the Operations Analysis Section, Headquarters Eighth Air Force, 1944. The huts were in a grove atop Dawes Hill on the grounds of Abbey School, High Wycombe, England.

9. Left to right: Clarkson, Scott, and Youden.

10. Members of the Bombing Accuracy Subsection. Left to right: Clarkson, Scott, G. Baley Price, Forrest R. Immer, Youden, and Charles R. Darwin.

11. Members of the Bombing Accuracy Subsection. Left to right: (top) Darwin, Youden, Sgt. Eileen Z. Hazelton, Clarkson, Scott, (bottom) Immer, S/Sgt. Carl J. Boria, T/Sgt. Ray J. Thompson, and Price.

12. Left to right: Boria, Hazelton, and Thompson.

13. John Marshall Harlan.

14. OAS members from the law firm of Root, Ballantine, Harlan, Bushby & Palmer in New York City. Left to right: (top) Scott, Harlan, Lt. Col. Leslie H. Arps, (bottom) Joseph J. Labriola, and Louis Lusky.

15. The B-17 airplane, nicknamed Petrol Packing Mama, used in the OAS gasoline consumption study. Left to right: Frank M. Stewart, Lusky, and two unidentified crew members.

16. Crew members of the Petrol Packing Mama. Major Emil Sorenson is in the middle.

17. Left to right: Sorenson, Lusky, and Stewart.

target study

18. The artist of these sketches is Richard C. Hicks, an Eighth Air Force navigator, friend, and fellow crew member of Charles W. McArthur.

briefing

bomb run

interrogation

two great armies opposing each other—our own American forces on one side and the Germans on the other. All the men I had any contact with believed that the battle would be decisive in the struggle for Europe. We knew that it was our task to blast a corridor through the German lines. Then, while the Germans were reeling from this assault from the air, our men on the ground were to take possession and pass through the corridor. We wanted to do our part well.

The bombers of the Eighth Air Force approached the German lines in orderly waves. Each bomb group was to drop its bombs simultaneously on a signal from its leader. This great air armada of over 1,500 heavy bombers approached the German lines in a giant column which took exactly one hour (1000–1100) to cross the target. My group was not among the first waves of bombers. As our group approached, we could see those ahead release their bombs. By the time our turn arrived a great cloud of smoke, fire, and dust had arisen which obscured details of the target area. Perhaps German antiaircraft guns had been silenced by the time we arrived, for we experienced no flak. We dropped our bombs and wheeled to the right according to the prearranged plan. As we flew away from the target area we could see the waves of bombers behind us still approaching to unleash their loads of bombs. It was a sight one does not forget.

The bombardment as experienced by newsman Ernie Pyle. Ernie Pyle elected to be with the infantry to observe the bombing and the assault. He chose a farmhouse about 800 yards behind the "kick-off" line of the assault from which to observe the aerial bombardment. He says:

> Before the next two hours had passed I would have given every penny, every desire, every hope I ever had, to have been just another 800 yards farther back. [73]

After describing the phase of the attack by fighter-bombers, Pyle then writes:

> And then a new sound gradually droned into our ears, a sound deep and all encompassing with no notes in it—just a gigantic far away surge of doomlike sound. It was the heavies. They came from directly behind us. At first they were the merest dots in the sky. We could see clots of them against the far heavens, too tiny to count individually. They came on in a terrible slowness. They came in flights of twelve, three flights to a group and in groups stretched out across the sky. They came in "families" of about seventy planes each. Maybe those gigantic waves were two miles apart, maybe they were ten miles, I don't know. But I do know they came in a constant procession and I thought it would never end. What the Germans must have thought is beyond comprehension. [74]

Pyle continues:

> I stood with a little group of men, ranging from colonels to privates, back of the stone farmhouse. Slit trenches were all around the edges of the farmyard and a dugout with a tin roof was nearby. But we were so fascinated by the spectacle overhead that it never occurred to us that we might need the foxholes. [75]

Pyle describes the dust and the sounds:

> For an hour and a half that had in it the agonies of centuries, the bombs came down. A wall of smoke and dust erected by them grew high in the sky. It filtered along the ground back through our orchards. It sifted around us and into our noses. The bright day grew slowly dark from it. By now everything was an indescribable caldron of sounds. Individual voices did not exist. The thundering of the motors in the sky, and the roar of bombs ahead filled all the space for noise on earth. Our own heavy artillery was crashing all around us, yet we could hardly hear it. [76]

Five heavy bombers were shot down by German antiaircraft fire. Pyle described in detail how one of them went down. And then he writes:

> But before it was down there were more cries of 'there's another one smoking—and there's a third one now.' Chutes came out of some of the planes. Out of some came no chutes at all. One of white silk caught on the tail of a plane. Men with binoculars could see him fighting to get loose until flames swept over him, and then a tiny black dot fell through space, all alone. [77]

As Pyle and his companions watched the bombing they became aware that the windrows of exploding bombs were easing back toward them instead of forward as the plan called for. Then they realized that the bombers were aiming at the smoke line on the ground and a gentle breeze was drifting the smoke line back over them. Pyle continues:

> All in an instant the universe became filled with a gigantic rattling as of huge ripe seeds in a mammoth dry gourd. I doubt that any of us had ever heard that sound before, but instinct told us what it was. It was bombs by the hundred, hurtling down through the air above us. Many times I've heard bombs whistle or swish or rustle, but never before had I heard bombs rattle. I still don't know the explanation of it. But it is an awful sound. We dived... I remember hitting the ground flat, all spread out like the cartoons of people flattened by steam rollers, and then squirming like an eel to get under one of the heavy wagons in the shed. An officer whom I didn't know was signaling beside me. We stopped at the same

time, simultaneously feeling it was hopeless to move farther. The bombs were already crashing around us. We lay with our heads slightly up—like two snakes—staring at each other. I know it was in both our minds and in our eyes, asking each other what to do. Neither of us knew. We said nothing. We just lay sprawled gaping at each other in a futile appeal until it was over. [78]

Pyle and his group of men were lucky. They came through this bombing unhurt. The air force had discovered what was wrong and corrected it. When they came out of their shelters the bombers were still coming as far as they could see. Pyle concludes his account this way:

The leading company of our battalion was to spearhead the attack forty minutes after our heavy bombing ceased. The company had been hit directly by our bombs. Their casualties in shock were heavy. Men went to pieces and had to be sent back. The company was shattered and shaken. And yet Company B attacked—and on time to the minute! They attacked, and within an hour they sent word back that they had advanced 800 yards through German territory and were still going. Around our farmyard men with stars on their shoulders almost wept when the word came over the portable radio. The American soldier can be majestic when he needs to be.

I'm sure that back in England that night other men—bomber crews—almost wept, and maybe they did really, in the awful knowledge that they had killed our own American troops. But the chaos and bitterness there in the orchards and between the hedgerows that afternoon soon passed. After the bitterness came the sober remembrance that the Air Force was the strong right arm in front of us. Not only at the beginning, but ceaselessly and ever-lastingly, every moment of the faintest daylight, the Air Force was up there banging away ahead of us. [79]

The bombardment as seen by a German general. Lieutenant General Fritz Bayerlein was commander of the Panzer Lehr division which met the full force of the American offensive at St-Lô. Bayerlein, an experienced tank commander who had served with Guderian in France and Russia and with Rommel in Africa, was taken prisoner in April 1945. In an interrogation on 29 May 1945 he gave the following assessment of the aerial bombing:

His communications had been destroyed in the first air attacks, and as the heavies began to come over soon after 1000 hours, he set out on the pillion of a motorcycle to visit his advanced Command Post at Le Mesnil Amey. There he observed the later stages of the bombing from a stone tower with walls two meters thick. What he could see of the battlefield he termed a Mondlandschaft (a lunar landscape). What he found there and at Hébécrévon and other points which he personally visited was half of his three batteries of 88-mm AA guns knocked out and his forward tanks pitched into craters or disabled by direct hits and by blasts which had thrown them on their backs. Communications both with his own regiments and with the corps was by runner only and 70 per cent of his personnel was 'either dead, wounded, crazed or dazed'. Not until night fall, when his forward lines had been overrun, was he able to gather a small combat group from his scattered and shattered division. [80]

In retrospect, von Rundstedt regarded the St-Lô bombing as "the most effective, as well as the most impressive, tactical use of air power in his experience." [81]

The assessment by General Omar N. Bradley. There were many observers of the St-Lô operation. "Ike hurried over to watch the jump off," and General Lesley McNair was in the front lines with a unit of Leland Hobbs' Thirtieth Division. [82] In his memoir Alderman reports that Colonel Harlan "went to the St-Lô area to observe the tactical bombing operations by the 8th and 9th Air Forces." [83]

Bradley gives us some details in his autobiography:

> The planes came on schedule... To our horror, reports of 'shorts' immediately flooded my CP [Command Post]. Quite soon so many reports had accumulated that we believed our own casualties were devastating, perhaps so great COBRA would have to be canceled. This proved to be an exaggerated fear, but the final toll was shocking and ghastly: 111 dead, 490 wounded. Among the dead was Lesley McNair. [84]

One of Bradley's aides, Chet Hansen, recorded:

> General Hobbs said afterwards it was horrible. The ground belched, shook, and spewed dirt to the sky. Scores of our troops were hit their bodies flung from slit trenches. Doughboys dazed and frightened. Huebner, who is an old front-line campaigner, said it was the most terrifying thing he had ever seen... A bomb landed squarely on McNair in a slit trench and threw his body sixty feet and mangled it beyond recognition except for the three stars on his collar. [85]

Bradley continues:

> Meanwhile Joe Collins had thrown his VII Corps assault troops into the hole....The GI's—somewhat dazed and demoralized by

the 'shorts'—charged through expecting to meet little or no opposition. All were shocked to meet heavy resistance. The assault bogged down. I was dismayed. Ike flew off to his headquarters in England dejected and furious at the Air Force for killing and maiming so many of our own men and determined never again to use heavy bombers in support of ground forces.... The heavy opposition we initially encountered was, in fact, merely the valiant and instinctive reaction of a few tough Germans. The bombing had done far more damage than we could possibly imagine.

Bradley then quotes Martin Blumenson, the official army historian, on the effect of the bombing on the Germans:

Bombs buried men and equipment, overturned tanks, cut telephone wires, broke radio antennas, sent messengers fleeing for foxholes or the nearest crater. Communications with forward echelons were completely disrupted. The bombardment turned the main line of resistance... into a frightening landscape of the moon.... No less than a thousand men must have perished in the COBRA bombardment. About one-third of the total number of combat effectiveness... were probably killed or wounded, the survivors dazed. Perhaps only a dozen tanks or tank destroyers remained in operation. Three battalion command posts of Panzer Lehr were demolished. The attached parachute regiment, virtually vanished. Only local and feeble resistance was possible against attacking American infantrymen.

Bradley then says:

Joe Collins soon sensed the confusion and lack of coordination within the German lines. Accordingly, he called on his reserves and threw Huebner's Big Red One into the fight. He then committed his armour.... Slowly it came to me that COBRA had not failed. It had succeeded; we had broken through. Joe Collins, absolutely justifying our faith in him, enlarged the rupture in the German lines and kept right on moving south, mile after mile. On his right flank, Middleton's VIII Corps, after a wobbly start, likewise broke through and Middleton cut loose his armour... The armour smashed through thirty-five miles to our long sought Avranches, at the base of the peninsula. The Germans, now completely routed, retreated in haste or surrendered.

Bradley's last comment on COBRA is:

COBRA would go down in history as the 'St-Lô breakout'. It was, in fact, a total and smashing breakin, breakthrough and breakout, a major turning point in the war. Seven agonizing weeks had passed since D day. All that time the terrain, the weather and the tenacious German troops had kept us bottled up in the Cotentin Peninsula. But now at last we were moving out at breath taking speed. One phase of the war on the Continent had ended, another had begun. [86]

REFERENCES

1. Simon Goodenough, *War Maps, World War II* (New York: St. Martin's Press, 1982) 124–27.

2. "The Army Air Forces in World War II, Combat Chronology 1941–1945," Kit C. Carter and Robert Mueller, compilers, 1973, Office of Air Force History, Simpson Historical Research Center, Maxwell Air Force Base, Alabama, 365.

3. Harry C. Butcher, USNR Captain, *My Three Years with Eisenhower* (New York: Simon and Schuster, 1946), 578.

4. "Eighth Air Force, History of Operations Analysis Section, October 1942–June 1945," Leslie H. Arps, 520.303-3, Archives, Simpson Historical Research Center, Maxwell Air Force Base, Alabama, appendix I, 116.

5. Leroy A. Brothers, *Operations Analysis in World War II, United States Army Air Forces* (Philadelphia: Stephenson-Brothers, 1948), 9–12.

6. "Combat Chronology," Eighth Air Force, June 1944, July 1944.

7. Ibid.

8. "Gunnery Subsection, Operational Analysis Section, Eighth Air Force, June 1943–January 1945," W. L. Ayres, 520.303-2, Archives, Simpson Historical Research Center, Maxwell Air Force Base, Alabama, 16.

9. Ibid., 17.

10. Porter Henry, in a tape recording, 1983.

11. "History of the Battle Damage Subsection, Operational Analysis Section, Eighth Air Force, December 1943–May 1945," 520.303-1, Archives, Simpson Historical Research Center, Maxwell Air Force Base, Alabama, 30.

12. Ibid., 31–32.

13. "Eighth Air Force," 83.

14. "Combat Chronology," Eighth Air Force, 21–25 June 1944.

15. Ibid., 26, 27 June 1944.

16. "Eighth Air Force," 148.

17. "Combat Chronology," Eighth Air Force, 5 July 1944.

18. Wesley Frank Craven and James Lea Cate of the USAF Historical Division, eds., *Europe: From Argument to V-E Day, January 1944 to May 1945*, vol. 3 of *The Army Air Forces in World War II* (Chicago: University of Chicago Press, 1951).

19. "Eighth Air Force," 128.

20. Ibid., 98.

21. Ibid.

22. Thomas Parrish and S. L. A. Marshall, eds., *The Simon and Schuster Encyclopedia of World War II* (New York, 1978), 429.

23. Operations Analysis Report, OAS, Third Air Division, Eighth Air Force, "A Report on the Micro-H Bombing Missions During November 1944," 15 December 1944, Angus Taylor, 527.310A, Simpson Historical Research Center, Maxwell Air Force Base, Alabama, 1.

24. "Eighth Air Force," 101–2.

25. G. Baley Price, *Gremlin Hunting in the Eighth Air Force, European Theater of Operations, 1943–1945*, 45.

26. Ibid., 56.

27. Ibid., 57.

28. "Eighth Air Force," 100.

29. *Gremlin Hunting*, 56.

30. Ibid., 64–65.

31. Ibid., 65.

32. Ibid., 71–72.

33. "Combat Chronology," Eighth Air Force, 6 June 1944.

34. Ibid., June 1944.

35. "Report for Colonel W. B. Leach on the History and Development of the Bombs and Fuzes Subsection of the Operational Analysis Sections, Headquarters Eighth Air Force," 10 April 1945, Bissell Alderman, 520.303-3, Archives, Simpson Historical Research Center, Maxwell Air Force Base, Alabama, 17.

36. Ibid., 17.

37. "Eighth Air Force," 136.

38. *Three Years with Eisenhower*, 583.

39. *Encyclopedia of World War II*, 661–62.

40. "Report for Colonel W. B. Leach," 21.

41. *Three Years with Eisenhower*, 588.

42. "Combat Chronology," Eighth Air Force, July 1944.

43. "Report for Colonel W. B. Leach," 21.

44. *Three Years with Eisenhower*," 629.

45. Lowell Thomas, *History as You Heard It* (Garden City, NY: Doubleday, 1957).

46. "Combat Chronology," Eighth Air Force, July 1944.

47. "Report for Colonel W. B. Leach," 22.

48. OAS Fifteenth Air Force, "Air Report on the Bombing of the Oil Refineries at Naples, Italy," December 1943, George Housner, Microfilm, Roll a1077, Index 2227, 131.504-B through 131.504-C N. D. Vol. 13, Simpson Historical Research Center, Maxwell Air Force Base, Alabama.

49. "Report for Colonel W. B. Leach," 39.

50. Bissell Alderman, "Bombs and Fuzes, Eighth Air Force, WW II," A4. This is Bissell Alderman's personal copy of "Report for Colonel W. B. Leach," which has been retyped and augmented with pictures, orders, awards, etc.

51. "Report for Colonel W. B. Leach," 39.

52. Ibid., 39–40.

53. "Combat Chronology." See index under Caen-Carpiquet (Eighth Air Force).

54. Ibid., Eighth Air Force, 6 June 1944.

55. "Eighth Air Force," 136.

56. "Report for Colonel W. B. Leach," 31.

57. *Gremlin Hunting*, 56.

58. "Report for Colonel W. B. Leach," 30.

59. "Eighth Air Force," 62.

60. *Europe: From Argument to V-E Day*, 20.

61. Solly Zuckerman, *From Apes to Warlords* (New York: Harper and Row, 1948), 281.

62. From the author's personal records.

63. *From Apes to Warlords*, 281.

64. *Europe: From Argument to V-E Day*, 209.

65. Ibid., 208.

66. Ibid., 209.

67. Ernie Pyle, *Brave Men* (New York: Holt, 1944), 295.

68. Ibid., 297.

69. *Europe: From Argument to V-E Day*, 231–33.

70. Ibid., 232–33.

71. Ibid.

72. Ibid., 234.

73. *Brave Men*, 297.

74. Ibid., 298.

75. Ibid.

76. Ibid.

77. Ibid., 299.

78. Ibid.

79. Ibid., 300–301.

80. *Europe: From Argument to V-E Day*, 235–36.

81. Ibid., 236.

82. General of the Army Omar N. Bradley and Clay Blair, *A General's Life, An Autobiography* (New York: Simon and Schuster, 1983), 280.

83. "Report for Colonel W. B. Leach," 39.

84. *A General's Life*, 280.

85. Ibid.

86. Ibid., 280–81.

8

Operations Analysis in the Eighth Air Force
August–December 1944, Part I

BACKGROUND

The war on the ground. During August and the first two weeks of September 1944, most of France, excluding certain key ports held by the Germans, was liberated by Allied troops. In late July and early August the Germans were cleared from Normandy. In August nearly 100,000 German troops were surrounded by Allied armies in an area just south of Caen called the Falaise pocket. Approximately 10,000 German troops were killed there. Another 50,000 were captured, and the rest escaped from the pocket, leaving behind most of their equipment, including 500 tanks and assault guns. [1]

On 20 August Patton's forces established a bridgehead across the Seine. Paris was liberated on 25 August. [2]

On 15 August the Allies staged a second invasion of France between Cannes and Toulon in the south. It was a spectacular success. Two days after the invasions began, Hitler ordered the general responsible for defending southern France to withdraw into the Vosges mountains of northern France. In two weeks the Allies opened two major ports in the south and took 57,000 prisoners at a cost of 4,000 French casualties and 2,700 American casualties. On 11 September patrols from the southern Allied armies met patrols of the northern Allied forces at Dijon. [3]

On 3 September the Allies captured the great port of Antwerp, Belgium, and on the next day, Brussels. However, Antwerp remained useless as a port until 26 November when the Scheldt Estuary, sixty miles long, leading from Antwerp to the sea, was cleared of German defenses and mines. [4]

On 5 September Hitler reinstated von Runstedt as commander in chief in the West and ordered him to hold firm along the Holland-Belgium border, along the West Wall of Germany (called the Siegfried Line by the Allies), and along the Moselle river in northeastern France. [5] And hold they did for the rest of 1944.

On 21 October the Allies succeeded in capturing Aachen, thus breaching the Siegfried Line in one place. They were preparing to advance to the Rhine, when on 16 December, 1944, the Germans, with eight Panzer divisions, attacked the American lines in the Ardennes. This was the beginning of the "Battle of the Bulge."[6]

The war from the air

Operation MARKET-GARDEN. On 17–18 September 1944, the Allies launched an attack, called Operation MARKET-GARDEN, which had been planned by British Field Marshal Montgomery. The plan called for air force power to drop three airborne divisions to seize the bridges north from Antwerp along the Eindhoven-Arnhem road. This would create a corridor along which British troops could advance and make an end run around the northern end of the Siegfried Line. The Siegfried Line was the name used by the Allied troops for the German West Wall, a series of fortifications along Germany's western frontier. (This name for the West Wall was made popular in Allied circles by a British music hall tune, "We're Going to Hang Out the Washing on the Siegfried Line.") The airborne attacks were successful at Eindhoven and Nijmegan, but after heroic efforts failed at Arnhem.[7]

The problem of the V-weapons. Once the V-1 attacks against England began in June, they continued unabated despite heavy Allied bombing of launching and supply sites. However, from 15 August on, launchings declined due to the overrunning of launching sites in France by Allied troops. The last V-1 fired from a launching site in France fell in Kent on the afternoon of 1 September 1944. From then on, the only V-1s launched against England were fired from the Netherlands or were air launched. However, on the evening of 8 September the first of more than a thousand ten-ton rockets (the V-2, traveling at more than five times the speed of sound) that were to strike England fell and exploded at Chiswick.[8] How would the Allies defend themselves against this new menace?

The oil offensive

THE GERMAN OIL INDUSTRY AS A STRATEGIC BOMBING TARGET SYSTEM. On 18 May 1943 the Allied Combined Chiefs of Staff approved a plan, known as the Combined Bomber Offensive, for the strategic bombardment of the Western Axis, which in its early stages had been formulated at the direction of General Arnold in Washington by a group of both military and civilian experts known as the Committee of Operations Analysts (COA). This committee had fifteen subcommittees—one for each major industry, such as petroleum and motor vehicles, for example. In its final report the COA listed nineteen target systems in priority. The first three were fighter aircraft, ball bearings, and petroleum. Ninth in priority was transportation.[9]

On 30 March 1944, General Spaatz had argued unsuccessfully to give oil targets higher priority than transportation targets. However, it was not until after the cross-channel invasion that Spaatz was allowed to place oil in a high priority. [10]

By 1943 Germany had to rely on the oil produced in Germany itself plus that from conquered and satellite countries—especially Rumania. Only 23 percent of the oil produced in Germany itself was crude oil. The remaining 77 percent came from synthetic oil plants. The mining of the Danube and the capture of the Rumanian oil fields by the Russians in August 1944 made Germany's dependence on her own synthetic oil plants acute. The synthetic plants were chiefly of two types: those using the Bergius hydrogenation process and those using the Fisher-Tropsch process. Almost all German aviation gasoline came from the hydrogenation plants. These were located at Merseburg-Leuna, Politz, Gelsenberg, Brux, Bohlen, Zeitz, Wesseling, Scholven, Magdeburg, Welheim, Moosbierbaum, Ludwigshaven, Lutzkendorf, Heydebreck, Blechammer-North, and Auschwitz. These sixteen plants are listed in order of volume of production of synthetic fuel with Merseburg-Leuna being the most productive.

The bombing of the synthetic oil plants had even more far-reaching consequences than the loss of oil production, because technically the plants were integrated with the chemical industry. Bombing them also crippled the munitions and explosives industries and hurt the synthetic rubber industries as well. Nitrogen and methanol were also produced in the synthetic oil plants, especially at Merseburg-Leuna and Ludwigshafen. These were the most important war chemicals. [11]

THE ATTACK ON OIL BEGINS. The first major attack on Western Axis oil had been on 1 August 1943 when the Ninth Bomber Command flew over 1,000 miles from Bengazi, Africa, to make its famous low-level attack on the oil refineries at Ploesti, Rumania. Then, in April 1944, the Mediterranean Allied Air Force (MAAF) began a series of high-level attacks against the Ploesti oil refineries. Twenty-four attacks were made on the Ploesti refineries between 5 April and 19 August 1944, twenty daylight attacks by the Fifteenth Air Force, and four night attacks by the RAF. When the Russians moved in on 22 August 1944, the great complex of refineries was in ruins. [12]

Although oil was not given first priority until June 1944, and only then with provisos, serious attacks on oil began earlier. The Eighth Air Force began systematic attacks on oil targets on 12 May by bombing the hydrogenation plants of Leuna, Bohlen, and Gelsenberg. On 28 and 29 May it attacked Magdeburg, Lutzkendorf, Zeitz, Leuna, and Politz. [13] The effect of bombing of German synthetic oil in May and June was immediate and profound. Speer's letter to Hitler dated 30 June 1944 describes the damage:

> Our aviation gasoline production was badly hit during May and June. The enemy has succeeded in increasing our losses of aviation gasoline up to 90 percent by June 22. Only through speedy recovery of damaged plants has it been possible to regain partly

some of the terrible losses. In spite of this, however, aviation gasoline production is completely insufficient at this time.

The already heavy losses in June and the estimated very low production for July and August, on account of increased air attack, will doubtless make us use up the greater part of our reserves in aviation gasoline as well as in other fuels. If it is not possible for us to protect these plants we will be forced to curtail the supplies to the Army in September, which will mean that from that time on there will be a terrible bottleneck which may lead to the most tragic consequences. I think it is my duty to call your attention again to the following:

a. The strictest orders will have to be issued to start limited flying. Every flight which is not absolutely necessary either for defensive action or for training has to be stopped.

b. The strictest measures in the consumption of motor and Diesel fuel on the part of the Army will have to be taken.

c. Fighter protection at the plants will have to be increased. The Luftwaffe should realize that with continued successful enemy air attacks only a small percentage of our fighter planes will be able to fly on account of aviation gas shortage.

d. A greatly increased use of smoke screens is necessary using smoke screens over dummy plants in addition to over the real plants.

e. More flak protection is necessary, even at the expense of protection of German cities.

I regret having to inform my Fuehrer of these tragic developments and beg you to issue all the necessary orders for this additional protection of these plants.[14]

Speer put Edmund Geilenberg in charge of the repair, rebuilding, and dispersal of the bombed oil plants. As many as 350,000 men worked day and night on this job. Plants that had been knocked out completely were brought back in production in relatively few weeks, necessitating renewed attacks.[15]

THE BATTLE OF MERSEBURG-LEUNA. The largest synthetic oil plant was the Leuna plant just south of Merseburg, a small German city about thirty miles due west of Leipzig.

Leuna was the most heavily protected plant in Central Europe. The defenses were such that the plant was most difficult to hit. The first large-scale daylight attack came on May 12 by the Eighth Air Force, with 220 bombers with fighter escort, and the famous battle of Leuna began. Before the end of the war, Leuna was raided 22 times, twice by the RAF and 20 times by the Eighth. Due to the urgency of keeping this plant out of production, some of these missions were dispatched in difficult bombing weather. Consequently, the order of bombing accuracy on Leuna was not high compared with other targets. A total of 6,552 bombers attacked this target with 18,328 tons of bombs. The battle of Leuna was one of the major battles of the war and, in spite of severe losses, the battle was won. [16]

SUMMARY OF OIL OFFENSIVE FOR 1944. According to the U.S. Strategic Bombing Survey, the Eighth Air Force, the Fifteenth Air Force, and the Royal Air Force dropped 137,000 tons of bombs on oil targets in the period June through December 1944. The greatest effort, 35,023 tons, came in November.

During the first two weeks in December bad weather enabled the Eighth to fly only two major oil missions, each against Merseburg-Leuna. It dropped approximately 1,000 tons of bombs each time. The German offense, launched on 16 December, put the Eighth Air Force out of the oil business and into ground support, when it could fly, until the last day of the month. However, the German oil position was desperate enough to allow the Allies to slacken their oil attacks for a while without paying too high a price.

The Ardennes offensive was made possible only by the German "collecting every drop of fuel he could find over a period of weeks, and even then his supply was no more than equal to the demands of five days of continuous operations. His last great gamble, in other words, depended for its ultimate success upon the capture of Allied stores." [17]

> [Despite some quibbles] the air offensive against German oil production was the pride of the U. S. Strategic Air Forces. Initiated through the insistence of its officers, effective immediately, and decisive within less than a year, the campaign proved to be a clear-cut illustration of strategic air-war doctrine. [18]

HARLAN LEAVES THE SECTION

Should operations research personnel be commissioned? In June and July 1943, Harlan, chief of the section, and Arps, his deputy, had been commissioned as officers in the army air force. However, with only a few other exceptions, the analysts of the section remained civilians. Being a commissioned officer and not a civilian implied some distinct disadvantages for operations analysts. This was demonstrated on 7 August 1944 when John Harlan left the section and the Eighth Air Force, under orders which reassigned him to the United States Strategic Air Forces (USSTAF), commanded by General Spaatz with headquarters in London. [19] This organization contained the Eighth Air Force as a component. We do not know what Harlan thought of this reassignment. However, Col. W. B. Leach, the chief of the headquarters section of Operations Analysis in Washington, D.C., discussed the pros and cons of commissioning analysts.

The Chief of the Operations Analysis Section at Eighth Air Force was commissioned in the belief that he would function more effectively as an officer; but the sequel to his commissioning was that at the height of the Eighth Air Force operations in the summer of 1944 he was transferred out of the section to a planning post in London. [20]

Harlan's reassignment came during a major reorganization of the command structure of the Eighth Air Force. A couple of months later when Arps, who was also commissioned, protested further sweeping changes that would have harmed the section, he too was threatened with reassignment. Thus Harlan, still in touch with the section, was ready and helped turn things around.

Harlan's leadership. John Marshall Harlan had been a distinguished chief of a distinguished operations analysis section. His deputy and successor, Leslie Arps, pays high tribute to Harlan with these words.

> As might be expected in the course of its history many obstacles were encountered not the least of which were involved at the very beginning in determining the Section's place in the military organization and its proper functions. Through Col. Harlan's exceptional ability and foresight the Section, early in its history, was placed in the proper military niche and was started along lines the soundness of which became increasingly evident with the passing of time. The importance of Col. Harlan's contributions cannot be over emphasized for to him more than to any other person must credit for the success of the Section be given. [21]

A few comments from the analysts who worked under Harlan illustrate how well he was regarded by his men. The mathematician Hewitt in his typically cryptic, forceful way says, "Col. Harlan was a superb commanding officer. Urbane and also humane, supremely intelligent, he did a wonderful job." [22]

Porter Henry, gunnery analyst and newspaperman, affectionately recalls Harlan in an oral history, as "one of the loveliest, loveliest gentlemen in the world with a mind like a buzz saw." [23]

We only know about the work of Harlan through the memoirs of his men— Arps, Hewitt, Alderman, Price, Henry. What we learn there is that Harlan was both respected and liked by his staff. We learn from them how, when Harlan was convinced of the soundness of their ideas, he backed them to the hilt and was a powerful and successful advocate of them.

John Marshall Harlan, operations analyst and chief of the operations analysis section of the Eighth Air Force from 16 October 1942 to 7 August 1944, was named for his famous grandfather, John Marshall Harlan, who served as associate justice of the U.S. Supreme Court from 1877 until 1911.[24] John Marshall Harlan, the operations analysis chief, was destined to follow in his grandfather's footsteps. He was later appointed to the U.S. Supreme Court by President Eisenhower.

LESLIE ARPS TAKES COMMAND OF THE SECTION
AND MEETS UNACCEPTABLE REORGANIZATION PROPOSALS

In August Leslie Arps assumed the duties of chief of the section. Henry B. Ashton served as his deputy. They were fortunate in having the assistance of Staff Sergeant Edna S. Boland, who had served as Harlan's secretary since 23 September 1943, and who would continue as Arps' secretary until the end of the war in Europe.[25]

Arps, of course, was a veteran of the section. He was one of the original six to arrive in London on 15 October 1942. The others were James W. Alexander, John M. Harlan, H. P. Robertson, W. Norris Tuttle, and W. J. Youden. Alexander and Robertson left the section early in January 1943 after just a little more than two and a half months, before the section even established itself. Youden left at the end of March 1944 to become an analyst with the air force in the China-Burma theater. Now Harlan's transfer to USSTAF left only Arps and Tuttle of the original six. Tuttle too would soon leave on 3 October 1944 to work as an analyst with the Twentieth Air Force in Washington, D.C. Arps, of course, could not have left if he had wanted to, for he was a commissioned officer.

At the beginning of August a radical reorganization, at least for the OAS, of the staff of the Eighth Air Force headquarters took place. The civilian OAS, originally requested by the military commanders, Generals Spaatz and Eaker, was to serve as an advisory body of analysts to them. Because individual civilian analysts were volunteers, they were free to leave whenever they chose. They seldom did leave, however, and when they did they almost invariably undertook another job where they could continue to serve their country.

Prior to August 1944 the Eighth Air Force headquarters was composed of the usual general and special staff sections. The ORS was a special staff section that reported to General Doolittle. The reorganization did away with the staff sections and created three deputy commanders; a deputy for operations, a deputy for administration, and a deputy for material maintenance. Under each deputy were certain directors.

The deputy for operations was Major General O. A. Anderson. The seven organizational commanders under him were deputy chief of staff for operations, director of operations, director of intelligence, director of plans and requirements, director of operational analysis and training, director of communications, and air force weather officer.

When Colonel Harlan was assigned to USSTAF, the ORS became part of the office of the director of Operational Analysis and Training, under Colonel W. C. Dolan. Leslie Arps reported to his director, Colonel Dolan. [26] Clearly, this reorganization was harmful for ORS as an advisory body because it put the section at a further organizational distance from the commander of the Eighth Air Force.

In his history of the section Arps gives an account of what happened.

> While this new organization multiplied the red tape with which the Section had to cope by a factor of two, at first it was not entirely unworkable. Colonel Dolan was primarily interested in training and the ORS was left pretty largely alone under Colonel Arps. Towards the end of September and the first of October, Colonel Dolan began to interest himself in the Section's activities and arrived at a startling decision. Colonel Dolan informed Colonel Arps that henceforth the Section was not to engage in any activity concerned with day by day operations and that the Gee-H and Micro-H calculation work was to be transferred from the Section. It was pointed out that almost 90 percent of the Section's activities in nearly every subsection was primarily concerned with operations and if this decision were adhered to the Section could not function. It seemed perfectly evident that if this decision was to be followed the Section was doomed. [27]

Thus, Arps vigorously objected to Colonel Dolan's plan. However, Arps, in bucking his immediate military superior in order to protect his men and their work, had taken a great personal risk as he soon found out. Without Arps's knowledge, Dolan had orders prepared at headquarters to send Arps back to the States. The orders completely surprised Arps. He says in a letter, "Around noon the day after I received my orders, Harlan arrived at the Headquarters and told me that I wasn't to return to the U. S. pending an investigation. [28]

The whole matter was then referred to General Doolittle, who promptly decided that the section was to continue functioning as it had in the past. Thus, after considerable investigation the section was reorganized as a directorate. On 10 November 1944 Colonel Arps was given the new title Director of Operational Analysis. The section became the Operational Analysis Section. [29]

General Doolittle had an outstanding OAS, and no doubt he knew it. But it was fragile. The key people in every subsection were civilian volunteers who could terminate their service whenever they wished. The proposed transfer of Arps, coming so soon after Harlan's transfer, plus other apparently planned changes by Dolan, would surely have alienated the civilian experts of the section.

Another independent account of Colonel Arps' struggle with Colonel Dolan over reorganization appears in Baley Price's memoir *Gremlin Hunting*. Unlike Arps, who was writing an official history of the section, Price is less restrained. Arps's memoir was written in 1945 for his OAS chief in Washington, D.C., Colonel Leach. Price's account is told from the point of view of the men of the section. It not only supports Arps's account, but provides additional information about Dolan's leadership. Price's version of the Arps-Dolan controversy is told in the context of problems the Bombing Accuracy Subsection was having with Colonel Dolan and Colonel Geerlings, the director of Radar Bombing for the Eighth Air Force. He writes,

> There was an interesting conclusion in the report on the Cologne (radar bombing) attack. The targets for these attacks were stated to be the five or so marshalling yards in the city, and aiming points were assigned in the individual yards. A careful check, however, showed that, with exactly the same aiming errors, more bombs would have fallen in the system of all marshalling yards if every bomb had been aimed at the very center of the city. This conclusion earned a loud haw-haw for Colonel Geerlings, who was now Director of Radar Bombing, from the operations staff of Eighth Air Force. The conclusion emphasizes that bombing contains many subtle problems, the answers to which are not obvious. It is not surprising that many of them cannot be answered by a person who has had only a general training. Colonel Geerlings took almost no advantage of the assistance that Bombing Accuracy could have given him. I can recall only one occasion—there may perhaps have been a second—when he visited the Bombing Accuracy hut to talk about problems of blind bombing.
>
> At this time, the Operational Research Section had been absorbed into a larger unit headed by Colonel Dolan, who had the title of Director of Operational Analysis and Training. The men in the Section were not happy over the arrangement from the beginning, and as time went on it became more and more evident that a change must be made. The difficulties were brought to a head partly as a result of a report on blind bombing: Colonel Dolan, with much encouragement from Colonel Geerlings and Dr. Murrell (civilian Radiation Laboratory advisor to Geerlings), refused to approve for distribution a report prepared by Bombing Accuracy. It seemed that they were afraid to have the facts published, although every Commander and crew in the Air Force knew what was happening on blind missions. Furthermore, it had always been our experience that a full knowledge of the facts was the beginning of improvement.
>
> The Section's fight with Colonel Dolan eventually broke into open rebellion. The desirability of a separation was urged upon

General Doolittle by Colonel Harlan. A thorough investigation was made by General Allard and Colonel Todd, during the course of which Colonel Todd called me in to discuss the situation. It seems that my activities in connection with the Oxford Experiment had brought me to his attention. I told Colonel Todd that Colonel Dolan was suppressing our reports, and that he knew nothing of the work that went on in the Section. I even added that Colonel Dolan had never spent ten minutes in the Bombing Accuracy hut in all the time he had been in charge of our work.

The final explosion came when Colonel Arps suddenly found orders on his desk one Sunday morning directing him to report to the Zone of the Interior (the United States) immediately. Colonel Dolan had sneaked a cablegram through Headquarters which resulted in Colonel Arps being recalled from Washington. The Command (General Allard and others) were embarrassed in the extreme when they found out what happened.

Eventually our Section was separated from Training and set up as the Operational Analysis Section, a separate unit. Colonel Arps' orders were rescinded, and he was made Acting Director of the new Section.

Colonel Dolan was pleasant enough, but he was utterly incompetent to direct the work of the Section.[30]

OPERATIONAL RESEARCH SECTIONS
AT THE BOMBARDMENT DIVISIONS

In a report called "The Operational Research Section at the Eighth Air Force" dated 18 July 1944, Harlan tells about the plan for operational research sections at the bombardment divisions. The report, completed just before Harlan left the section, is a sort of history without names. It describes the structure and functions of the section and its mode of operations. With regard to the operational research sections at the bombardment divisions Harlan says:

> Under date of 7 May 1944, the Commanding General, this Headquarters [General Doolittle] approved the request of the commanding Generals of the three Bombardment Divisions for the establishment of small Operational Research units at their respective commands. The initial set-up will be two analysts at each Division, and the required personnel is being recruited through the Operations Analysis Division at Headquarters AAF, and is expected to arrive shortly. It is contemplated that the work of these Division units will be closely integrated with that of the Section at this Headquarters.[31]

The six men Leach persuaded to undertake this new assignment were all of the highest caliber.

Assigned to the First Division were John B. Chamberlin and Robert P. Dilworth. Chamberlin had an A.B. from Dartmouth College (1931), a law degree from Northwestern University (1934), and an LL.M. from Yale University (1935). He left his job as assistant general counsel of the War Labor Board in Washington, D.C., to undertake this work. Dilworth had a B.S. (1936) and a Ph.D. (1939) from California Institute of Technology. He was an assistant professor of mathematics at Cal. Tech. when he accepted the job of operations analyst.

Assigned to the Second Division were S. Hazard Gillespie, Jr., and Harry C. Carver. Gillespie had an A.B. (1932) and an LL.B. (1936) from Yale University. He was an attorney with a law firm in New York City. Carver was a well-known professor of mathematics and statistics at the University of Michigan.

Assigned to the Third Division were Lawrence Pomeroy and Angus E. Taylor. Pomeroy had an A.B. (1934) from Yale and an LL.B. (1938) from Harvard. He was working as an attorney for the War Production Board in New York City when he accepted an assignment as operations analyst. Taylor had an S.B. (1933) from Harvard and a Ph.D. (1936) from California Institute of Technology. He was an associate professor of mathematics at University of California at Los Angeles when he accepted an appointment as operations analyst. [32]

All six served about the same amount of time—from August 1944 until the end of the war in Europe. They served under essentially the same conditions. Each, for example, served in a two-man civilian section at a bomb division of the Eighth Air Force. Furthermore, all six named as their primary duty bombing accuracy analysis—mostly of blind bombing. At Leach's request, one of them, Angus Taylor, wrote a memoir of his work.

The six new analysts arrived in London at slightly different times, ranging from Gillespie's arrival on 31 July to Pomeroy's on 30 August 1944. Taylor had two weeks of orientation at the headquarters section of Operations Analysis in Washington, D.C. After arriving in England he had another two weeks of orientation and indoctrination at the Eighth Air Force ORS. Taylor writes:

> I was instructed in the different subsections of the Operational Research Section at Eighth Air Force, principally about the methods which were being used in studying problems of bombing accuracy, battle damage and loss, gunnery, radar and radar countermeasures, and the selection of bombs and fuzes. On 29 August 1944 I was assigned to the 3d Bombardment Division, where I was at once introduced to Major General Partridge, the Commanding General, and to all the heads of Sections. [33]

Most likely, each of the other five new analysts had similar orientations and indoctrinations in Washington, ORS Eighth Air Force, and their respective bomb divisions.

Each of the three two-man sections had unique problems settling in and gaining acceptance. Unfortunately, only information from Taylor's section exists. For the first month and a half Taylor and Pomeroy were not really an OR section. They were attached to the Tactical Analysis Section of the Third Division. However, in the middle of October a separate ORS was established, consisting of Pomeroy and Taylor and headed by Lt. Colonel J. W. Fredericks. Fredericks was given the title of director of operational research and plans. He had finished a combat tour as pilot and had served as a divisional training officer. The section was given a WAC sergeant who served as secretary. Later on, Lt. W. M. Milner was added to help prepare daily bombing reports. The section was an independent staff section responsible to the deputy chief for operations.

We do not know how Pomeroy, or Leach in Washington for that matter, viewed the installation of an ex-pilot as chief of the section. Records show that Leach did not list Fredericks on the roster of operations analysts. He was, rather, considered part of the Eighth Air Force establishment. Taylor, in his memoir, views the situation positively. He says,

> In our experience at the 3rd Air Division, it was advantageous to the Operational Research Section to have as its Chief an officer with combat experience in the European theater of operations. Our Chief, Colonel Fredericks, was highly regarded in the headquarters; he had for a long time been interested in and sympathetic to operations analysis work, and his influence strengthened the position of the O. R. S. as well as improved its chances to exert an influence on the command. [34]

The ORS at Third Division was housed in a large room with the photographic interpreters,

> ... an arrangement deliberately planned to give us prompt and convenient access to the evidence of current bombing results. The function of the section was pretty well understood by the intelligence, operations, and training branches of the headquarters staff; as a result, cooperation with other sections in getting necessary information was smooth. [35]

Chamberlin served as director of the two-man ORS at the First Bomb Division. No record shows who served as the ORS director of the section at Second Division, though evidence points toward Gillespie.

Although analyzing bombing—especially blind bombing—became the principal duty of each divisional section, their availability and smallness required them to be generalists as well. They had to consider all problems presented to them. Among those given serious attention by Taylor before he concentrated on Micro-H bombing were:

1. a statistical study of difficulties encountered by lead crews on the bomb run,

2. a study of the Ninety-second Combat Wing's bombing accuracy records with B-24 and B-17 aircraft respectively to determine why the wing bombed more accurately with B-17s than it did with B-24s,

3. a study of the relative flak risk to a task force when bombing in group formation as compared with bombing in squadron formation.

In working on these problems Taylor consulted with Lieutenant Colonel Scott and Clarkson of the Bombing Accuracy Subsection of the Eighth Air Force. He also used flak analysis materials furnished him by the Loss and Battle Damage Subsection. He worked very closely too with the Micro-H computing section people at the ORS of the Eighth Air Force—particularly Dr. W. A. Mersman. [36]

The collaboration between the small sections at the division headquarters and the large ORS at Eighth Air Force headquarters was not a one-way affair. Pilat of the Loss and Battle Damage Subsection, for example, mentions in his memoir the help and information his subsection got from Hazard Gillespie on several occasions. [37]

BOMBING ACCURACY

Visual bombing—July–October 1944. Whereas visual bombing reports were made by the Bombing Accuracy Subsection and distributed to the groups, wings, and divisions monthly, the subsection made more comprehensive reports on bombing irregularly. One of these is a report titled "Report on Bombing Accuracy for the Months of September and October" dated 6 November 1944. The report was prepared by the veterans of the subsection, Scott and Clarkson, and the more recent arrivals, Katzenbach and Gilman. [38]

This report shows how profoundly the weather influenced bombing operations and how the air force was struggling to offset the influence of weather. In September the number of visual sightings evaluated by Bombing Accuracy was 581. That was 42 percent of the total sightings for that month. In October the number of visual sightings dropped to 325, or 21 percent of all sightings. Expressed explicitly in terms of blind bombing, 58 percent of the bombing done by the Eighth Air Force in September was blind bombing. This percentage rose to 79 percent in October.

Because of the vastly superior accuracy of visual bombing over blind bombing, the combat boxes tried to bomb visually even in poor weather, which caused a high proportion of "mission failures" in October—nearly one third. A mission failure was defined as a mission where bombing accuracy was negligible by visual bombing standards.

The analysts point out that in June, July, August, and September the Eighth Air Force did a lot of tactical bombing, whereas in October the Eighth Air Force engaged exclusively on strategic targets.

From July through October, 41.5 percent of the bombs dropped visually by the Eighth Air Force landed within 1,000 feet of the assigned mean point of impact. For July alone, the percentage was 37.4, for August, 44.5 percent, and for September and October combined, 37.6 percent.

The percentages for the period July through October for the three combat divisions were 47.1, 32.8, and 43.9 respectively. The variation among the thirteen combat wings in this four-month period ranged from a high of 53 percent to a low of 30 percent. Such extreme discrepancy in visual bombing performance, which is more severe if studied by group, explains why groups, wings, and divisions were sensitive about scores from the ORS.

In August 1944, probably in response to a request of the commanding general of the First Division, Chamberlin and Dilworth prepared a memorandum, "Comparative Analysis of Performance of Groups, Month of July, 1944." It was dated 12 August 1944. Evidently, the general found the results interesting, because the memorandum was expanded into a second memorandum, "Summary of Group Standings in Operational Performance June, July, August 1944." [39]

The report studied the twelve groups of the First Division. Each group was ranked from one to twelve with respect to each of the following categories:

1. percent of aircraft attacking target, of aircraft dispatched,
2. percent of bombs landing within 1,000 feet of assigned MPI,
3. tonnage on targets,
4. losses to sorties.

These were combined for an overall rank.

The group placing number one overall also ranked first with respect to percent of aircraft attacking of aircraft dispatched. It ranked second, however, with respect to percent of bombs landing within 1,000 feet of the assigned MPI (mean point of impact). It was first with respect to tonnage on target and fifth with respect to losses on sorties.

On the other hand, the group which was ranked first with respect to percent of bombs landing within 1,000 feet of the assigned MPI (mean point of impact) was ranked fourth with respect to percent of aircraft attacking of aircraft dispatched, fourth with respect to tonnage on target, tenth on losses to sorties, and fourth overall.

The Oxford Experiment in H2X bombing

Gathering the data. In the middle of July 1944, the Eighth Air Force set aside two B-17 airplanes and crews for experimental work to determine and measure factors affecting the accuracy of H2X bombing. The planes and crews were provided by the 333d Squadron of the Ninety-fourth Bombardment Group. Dr. G. Baley Price of the OAS of Eighth Air Force supervised the experiment. Since there were no H2X targets of the kind bombed by the Eighth Air Force in combat, it was necessary to simulate bombing. Price soon discovered that camera bombing could not feasibly simulate blind bombing. Price's search for a technique which would be both accurate and free from weather interference resulted in having the facilities of a British gun-laying unit, used for calibrating their blind bombing instruments, placed at his disposal. Because of its location, Ot Moor Bombing Range equipment was such that it could be used in simulated attacks on Oxford. Two targets were chosen in Oxford, and the experiment began (see pages 176–180).

On a practice run, the bombsight was set up by the bombardier with data supplied by the H2X operator. Bombs away was determined as the instant when the indices of the bombsight met. Because it was assumed that the bomb had no trail, the point directly below the plane at the instant when the sighting angle was zero was considered the position of strike.

The IP (initial point of the bomb run) was a point approximately twenty-eight miles from the target. The Mark II unit of the GL equipment picked up the plane and put the Mark III unit on it as soon as it came within the 30,000-yard range of the Mark III. At least during the last five minutes of the bombing run the plane was followed accurately by the Mark III. Photographs of its dials (on the ground) were automatically taken every five seconds. A special photograph of the dials was shot at the instant of bombs away and labeled number one fix. This photograph was taken on a signal given by the bombardier over VHF. The plane flew straight and level after bombs away. A second photograph of the dials (number two fix) was taken at the instant of strike (zero sighting angle on bombsight) on a sight given once more by the bombardier over VHF.

To interpret these data, the film was developed and projected. The coordinates of the plane on the last ten or twelve fixes, including the number one and number two fixes were recorded. Likewise, the time between the two fixes as indicated on a stopwatch in the photographs was recorded. With the data, points on the ground directly below the plane could be located. Though they could be calculated mathematically, it was quicker to plot the points graphically on grids supplied by Mr. Cornford, a British analyst at Stanmore. Thus, for each run, the position of bomb release, bomb strike, and at least four other points were located on the track of the plane on the ground.

In the experiment 320 runs were made, 285 of them assessable, against two targets. Target number one was the center of Oxford; target number two was a large industrial plant, the Morris Motor Works at Cowley, on the edge of Oxford. [40]

Setting up the experiment and making the runs took from the middle of July 1944 until 6 September, about seven weeks.

A typical day and week during the experiment. On a typical day Price would arrive at Squadron Operations at 8 A.M., check the status of planes and crews, and check the latest weather forecasts. Wind and clouds could give trouble. If the weather was favorable he checked to find out the take-off time of the day's combat mission. Then he sent word to the crews to let them know when they should report. Usually, 11 A.M. was convenient.

> The day's mission was gone by that time, and we could arrange for the crews to eat at the mess hall.
>
> Finally, the crews would arrive. I would walk out to the hardstands with them, wait while they warmed up motors, and wave goodbye when they left. I always tried to be there to talk over results when they returned five hours later—or whatever it was. I had no rank or authority, and close contact with the progress of the experiment and a genuine interest in the men was my best means of keeping everything under control. When the planes took off, I returned to Squadron Operations and put in a call to Captain George [in charge of the gun-laying equipment] to let him know when he should expect the first VHF contact. [41]

Price worked on this project six days each week at the base at Bury St. Edmund. Then, each Sunday he returned to Pinetree (Eighth Air Force headquarters) to check work there.

> Mr. Ashton maintained close contact with Captain George and handled a lot of the administrative details in connection with delivering and processing the film record from the GL equipment, getting a large number of copies of the grid, and so on. Dr. Youngs and Sgt. Farrington were busy projecting and reading the film, and making plots of the results. At the same time Bombing Accuracy was training several new men for our three divisions (Taylor and the others) as well as others for the Fourteenth and Twentieth Air Forces. I spent considerable time going over the blind bombing record with these men. When Sunday was over, I returned to Bury St. Edmund by car—frequently after supper. [42]

Problems during the experiment. While Price ran the experiment, he had two problems.

> There was constant and continual equipment trouble in Samerdyke's plane, 633M, and Smith's crew continued to complain and make trouble.
>
> The equipment troubles in 633M were one of those things that could not be foreseen or prevented. The H2X equipment was out of condition almost every other day—usually it failed just after the plane had completed the long climb to altitude. One day the wheels had to be lowered by hand when the plane returned to base.

On another day there were two fires... and if Samerdyke's crew borrowed a plane, their luck was no better. For whatever reason, whether it was the fault of the plane or something else, Captain Samerdyke's crew became a 'hard luck' outfit. They worked faithfully and put in twice the effort of the other crew but nothing ever changed their luck. [43]

As was mentioned earlier, Samerdyke and his crew had not completed a combat tour because Captain Samerdyke was taken off combat duty because of stress. Captain Smith and crew had, however, completed a combat tour. They were ready to go home. Price writes:

Smith's crew continued to complain so much that I finally agreed with Col. Riva that I would accept a second crew to make the runs that Smith's crew should have made on the second target; Windberg would continue as H2X operator. Captain Simon's crew was named to finish out the experiment. This crew had one mission to fly before most of its members finished their tour. Now this crew was unhappy to be designated for any such work. The Germans (in the later part of August) were on the run in France, and the war was over, it seemed. Crews were anxious to get out and go home before the Group was sent to India! Certainly there was no need to plan for blind bombing through another winter. [44]

At this point Colonel Castle, commander of the Fourth Bomb Wing, called Price in to find out how the work was going. Price told him all that had happened, including trouble he was having with Smith and Simon's crews.

Colonel Castle called in his chief of staff, Lieutenant Colonel Thorup and said, "Thorup, would you go over to the 333d Squadron and straighten things out? I want this work to go on without any interruption."

"Yes Sir," replied Thorup. [45]

Price devotes two pages of his memoir to the scene in the 333d Squadron Operations building in which Colonel Thorup "blew his top" at the men directly responsible for seeing to it that Price's crews did their job. Price concludes the episode by saying,

Colonel Thorup stood up and strode out of the room. He was a big man and a fighting man. He had 'ditched' his plane in the Channel and crash landed on the Cliffs of Dover. When he went on a mission, he hit the Jerries [Germans] hard; and he didn't take any foolishness from the men at home. They feared and respected him, and they would do anything for you just to keep him from being brought into the argument.

This incident and one other that followed soon afterward completely solved Price's troubles with crews.

We sent Captain Smith's and Captain Simon's crews over to visit Captain George's GL installation near Oxford. Captain George had a jolly outfit, and the men thoroughly enjoyed the day. Captain Smith's crew at least understood all that was going on, and they left for the United States in a thoroughly happy frame of mind. Captain Simon's crew, on the other hand, saw what was coming and they threw themselves into the work with real enthusiasm. [46]

Conclusions and recommendations. Price arrived at four main conclusions or recommendations.

1. On H2X as an effective bombing instrument

The order of accuracy obtainable with existing equipment is such as to give hope for a reasonable degree of success against appropriate targets, namely, city areas or isolated industrial complexes. The experiment emphasizes, however, that the chance of hitting a pre-assigned industrial target within the built-up areas of a city is extremely slight with any reasonable size force. [The Oxford Experiment and the above conclusion is explicitly referred to in the USAAF official history of WWII. [47]] It is recommended that studies be made of (i) the organization of H2X combat missions and of the tactics employed and of (ii) the selection of targets and aiming points for the purpose of finding ways to achieve in combat the good results of which the H2X equipment is capable.

The accuracy obtained on the simulated targets in the experiment was:

(i) Center of City. The average circular error, measured from a pre-assigned aiming point, was 5630 feet, and 82 percent of all strikes fell in built-up areas of Oxford.

(ii) Morris Motor Works. The average circular error was 3370 feet, and 54 percent of all strikes fell in built up areas of Oxford. Furthermore, 34 percent fell in the Morris Motor Works itself.

2. On errors caused by instruments

Many substantial errors are traceable to correctable difficulties in the maintenance, adjustment, and calibration of instruments. It is recommended that appropriate instructions be issued to maintenance personnel and H2X operators.

3. On training and target study

The need for an expanded training and practice program and the intensification of target study is apparent. It is recommended that

'A Program of Practice and Experimental H2X Bombing', recommended in an ORS memorandum dated 15 September 1944, be put into operation as quickly as possible, and that efforts be continued to provide better target materials and better briefings of crews for combat missions.

4. On the use of GL equipment

Radar anti-aircraft gun laying equipment provides an entirely satisfactory means, and indeed the only practicable means in England, for H2X practice and experimental operations: it is accurate and it can be operated in any weather. [48]

Price was well aware that the accuracy achieved in the Oxford Experiment was far from being achieved operationally. Indeed, the accuracy achieved through experimentation represented ideal results rather than operational results. Unlike actual operations, in the Oxford Experiment, the same three crews bombed the same two targets using the same IP over and over again. Furthermore, they *never* had flak, fighter opposition, or camouflage to distract them.

Price includes in his report the following statement on the estimated combat accuracy of H2X.

The accuracy of combat H2X bombing cannot be expected to be as good as that achieved in the experiment. The experience of the Eighth Air Force with the Norden bombsight in the early months of combat emphasizes this fact; the large average errors observed bore little relation to the inherent capability of the bomb sight .... The experience of the RAF with equipment similar to the H2X indicates that their combat errors are from 1.5 to 2 times those of practice. The information available indicates that H2X combat errors in the Eighth Air Force are at least twice the practice errors observed in this experiment. [49]

The Oxford Experiment, begun in mid-July, was carried out in August and early September. The data were analyzed, and the report was completed in late November 1944. Though numerous people contributed. Baley Price was the driving force behind the project. When the report was completed he was given a week's leave for a much-needed rest in Cambridge. [50]

Additional matters connected with the Oxford Experiment

THE WAR WAS CLOSER AT THE BASE AT BURY ST. EDMUND THAN AT PINETREE. Price's seven weeks at the B-17 base at Bury St. Edmund brought him much closer to the air war than he had been at Eighth Air Force headquarters at Pinetree. He lived in a visitor's hut at the Fourth Combat Wing, and he ate with the officers in the combat mess.

The food was plentiful, but it was not really good. Perhaps I was spoiled, because the mess at Pinetree gave us very good meals most of the time.

When I went to the photographic Section one day to check some of my photographs, I found them taking a picture of a flak helmet which had a hole, caused by a shell fragment, as clean as one that could be made with a punch. This helmet had just arrived from a mission on a dead crewman.

A young navigator—"he was so young he was really only a boy"—worked at the desk next to Price for several weeks. The young man had his leg in a cast because of a flak wound, and *he* complained of the awful odor.

Planes often returned to the base on three and even two motors.

And then there was the day the plane returned after a heavy flak shell had passed through it directly behind the pilots—passed through without exploding. It had caught the top turret gunner, however, and torn his leg off; he died just after the plane returned to base. [51]

PRICE INTRODUCES THE USE OF GUN-LAYING EQUIPMENT IN SIMULATED BLIND BOMBING INTO THE EIGHTH AIR FORCE. News of the Oxford Experiment soon spread around the air force. Many people began to arrive to observe the gun-laying equipment in use. One of the earliest visitors was Colonel Moore, commanding officer at Alconbury. Colonel Moore was commander of the 482d Bombardment Group whose duty was to train radar operators. Price says:

It seems that he had known of the use of the American SCR-584 for assessing the results of simulated blind bombing, but had felt that the plotting board (which took all the hard work out of plotting the runs) was too inaccurate to be satisfactory. As a result, he had vetoed a proposed installation at Alconbury. Now, however, as a result of what he saw us doing with inferior British equipment, he hastened to make a SCR-584 installation at Alconbury and put it into use for assessing blind bombing training. [52]

Thus, the Oxford Experiment introduced the use of GL equipment in simulated blind bombing into the Eighth Air Force.

Price, in his 15 September 1944 memorandum, "A Program of Practice and Experimental H2X Bombing," had recommended that at least one SCR-584 installation be made available for each division. Thus, after the flights of the Oxford Experiment were over, Price and Captain George were authorized to visit the headquarters of each division and locate suitable sites for the proposed installations. After the details had developed sufficiently the project was left in the hands of the division to complete. In brief what happened was this:

> Three SCR-584's were made available from Eighth Air Force
> sources of supply. The British supplied sites on some of their
> bases for the location of this equipment. In addition, they lent us
> Captain George to oversee the installation of the equipment and
> supervise its use. It is to be regretted that the whole program of
> setting up the SCR-584's for the assessment of practice bombing
> moved slowly. It is my recollection that not one of the stations
> was ready for use before about the first of February [1945]. [53]

A memorandum written by John Chamberlin, OAS chief of the First Division, explains to his commanding general how the installation would be set up in the First Division. [54]

In memoriam. After the experiment was over, the British continued to operate the GL station near Oxford to train crews in the Ninety-fourth Bomb Group. Price recalls:

> It was while this flying was going on that Colonel Castle called and
> asked me to bring a good staff car to Mount Farm on a certain day.
> He was bringing General Partridge, now commanding General of
> the 3rd Division, down to see Captain George's installation...
> Captain George, of course, was delighted with all the distinguished
> visitors we brought him, and he showed General Partridge the full
> details of the equipment and its operation with much pleasure.

When it came time to leave, General Partridge rode with Price back to Eighth Air Force headquarters at Pinetree.

> Colonel Castle climbed aboard the B-17 that had returned for him
> and flew away. Little did I realize that this would be the last time
> I would see him. [55]

On Christmas Eve 1944 the Eighth Air Force mounted the largest single operation ever flown by that air force. Since 16 December, the Battle of the Bulge had been under way. The vast overcast which had shrouded western Europe and protected German forces from air attack for over a week began to dissipate.

Over 2,000 Eighth Air Force bombers were dispatched on 24 December. This force was led by the Third Division (B-17s) followed by the First Division (B-17s). They were to attack eleven airfields east of the Rhine. The Second Division (B-24s) brought up the rear. They were briefed to bomb fourteen communication centers west of the Rhine. The planned route of the bombers was from Clacton, England, to Ostend, Belgium, to a point northeast of the Luxembourg border. They would turn into Germany near the battle lines.

Electing to make the trip and lead this force was Brigadier General Fred Castle, Commander of the 4th Wing, and a veteran of 29 missions. Riding in a 487th Group B-17 from Lavenham that morning, he found the weather much as predicted, but ground haze so restricted visibility that the take-off of fighters assigned to escort the forward bomber boxes was delayed, although it was expected that they would overhaul the bombers before crossing into hostile territory. The Luftwaffe, however, made an unprecedented move in bringing a fighter Gruppe over the Allied lines in the Liége area to meet the head of the bomber column. Before Mustangs arrived on the scene, four 487th B-17's were shot down and five so badly battered that they were abandoned after making emergency landings in Belgium. One victim was that carrying General Castle. Engine trouble had caused the Fortress to abandon its position in the formation at the time of the first surprise pass by Me-109's. While trying to join the rear box the Fortress was hit again, the navigator wounded and the engines set on fire. Castle took control and though the bomber was still under attack he would not jettison the bombs for fear of killing Allied troops or civilians below, nor would he take evasive action as it would endanger the crew while it parachuted. A further burst of cannon fire severed the burning wing and sent the Fortress spinning down, from which there was no escape for the General. His crew lived. [56]

General Castle was posthumously awarded the Medal of Honor.

Baley Price, in his memoir, gives a less detailed version of General Castle's last mission. He also gives the rest of the story on Captain Samerdyke's crew. After the end of the Oxford Experiment, in which they had participated without complaint from beginning to end, the crew was taken from Samerdyke. His health would not stand the strain of further combat missions. The crew, however, was ordered back to combat flying. In addition to Samerdyke, the officers on Captain Samerdyke's crew were Lieutenant Tjousland (co-pilot), Lt. Gunderson (bombardier), Lieutenant Ball (navigator) and Lieutenant Murphy (H2X operator). A person not mentioned before is Major Blount, who was commanding officer of the 333d Squadron (Radar Lead Crew Squadron of the Ninety-fourth Bomb Group) when Lt. Colonel Thorup "blew his top."

Baley Price tells of the last mission of Blount and most of Samerdyke's crew.

On a day in October a mission started out. Major Blount, Lt. Tjomsland, Lt. Gunderson, and several enlisted men from Samerdyke's crew were in one of the planes. Fortunately, Lt. Murphy had not been needed on this mission, and he had been left at the base. They reported over VH that they would have to abort because of mechanical troubles, and Division told them to go forty miles out to sea to drop their bombs—they were still too heavily loaded to land. But they did not succeed in getting back. Air-Sea Rescue watchers saw the plane hit the water about two miles from land—hit the water in forty foot waves! Some of the bodies were found. Lt. Gunderson's body was found a week or two later, and he was buried in Cambridge. [57]

REFERENCES

1. Thomas Parrish and S. L. A. Marshall, eds., *The Simon and Schuster Encyclopedia of World War II* (New York, 1948), 679.

2. Ibid.

3. Ibid.

4. Ibid.

5. Ibid., 680.

6. Ibid., 2.

7. Ibid., 391–92.

8. Wesley Frank Craven and James Lea Cate of the USAF Historical Division, eds., *Europe: From Argument to V-E Day, January 1944 to May 1945*, vol. 3 of *The Army Air Forces in World War II* (Chicago: University of Chicago Press, 1951), 541.

9. "History of the Organization and Operations of the Committee of Operations Analysts," 1942–1944, Guido Perera, 118.01, Simpson Historical Research Center, Maxwell Air Force Base, Alabama.

10. Harry C. Butcher, USNR captain, *My Three Years with Eisenhower* (New York: Simon and Schuster, 1946), 507–10.

11. "The United States Strategic Bombing Survey, Overall Report (European War)," 30 September 1945, Florida State University Library, 39–58.

12. Headquarters Fifteenth Air Force, "The Air Battle of Ploesti," 5 April 1945, National Archives, Washington, D. C.

13. "Strategic Bombing Survey."

14. Ibid., 41–42.

15. "Strategic Bombing Survey."

16. Ibid., 42.

17. *Europe: From Argument to V-E Day*, 646.

18. Ibid, 794.

19. "Eighth Air Force, History of Operations Analysis Section, October 1942–June 1950," Leslie H. Arps, 520.303-3, Archives, Simpson Historical Research Center, Maxwell Air Force Base, Alabama, 113.

20. "Operations Analysis, Headquarters, Army Air Forces, December 1942–June 1950," 143.504, Simpson Historical Research Center, Maxwell Air Force Base, Alabama.

21. "Eighth Air Force," 2–3.

22. Hewitt, in a letter to the author, 20 April 1982.

23. Porter Henry, in a tape recording to the author, 1983.

24. *Encyclopedia Brittanica*, 1958 ed., s.v. "Harlan, John Marshall."

25. "Eighth Air Force," preface.

26. Ibid., 112.

27. Ibid., 113–14.

28. Leslie Arps, in a letter to the author, 14 December 1982.

29. "Eighth Air Force," 29.

30. G. Baley Price, *Gremlin Hunting in the Eighth Air Force, European Theater of Operations, 1943-1945*.

31. "The Operational Research Section at the Eighth Air Force, 20 March 1943–17 July 1944," 17 July 1944, 520.303-1, Simpson Historical Research Center, Maxwell Air Force Base, Alabama.

32. Leroy A. Brothers, *Operations Analysis in World War II, United States Army Air Forces* (Philadelphia: Stephenson-Brothers, 1948), 12.

33. Angus Taylor, "Personal Narrative of an Operations Analyst," 1945.

34. Ibid.

35. Ibid.

36. Ibid.

37. "History of the Battle Damage Subsection, Operational Analysis Section, Eighth Air Force, December 1943–May 1945," 520.303-1, Archives, Simpson Historical Research Center, Maxwell Air Force Base, Alabama, 42

38. Operational Analysis Section, Eighth Air Force, "Report on Bombing Accuracy for the Months of September and October," 6 November 1944, Simpson Historical Research Center, Maxwell Air Force Base, Alabama.

39. Operations Research Section, Headquarters, First Bombing Division, "Summary of Group Standings in Operational Performance, June, July, and August 1944," John Byrne Chamberlin and Robert P. Dilworth.

40. Operational Analysis Section, Eighth Air Force, "The Oxford Experiment in H2X Bombing," 30 November 1944, G. Baley Price and J. W. T. Youngs, 520.310-4, Maxwell Air Force Base, Alabama.

41. *Gremlin Hunting*, 72–73.

42. Ibid., 73–74.

43. Ibid., 74–75.

44. Ibid., 75.

45. Ibid.

46. Ibid., 77–8.

47. *Europe: From Argument to V-E Day*, 666.

48. "The Oxford Experiment," 5–6.

49. Ibid., 8–9.

50. *Gremlin Hunting*, 88.

51. Ibid., 79.

52. Ibid., 86.

53. Ibid., 86–87.

54. Headquarters, First Bombardment Division, Operations Research Section, "Practice and Experimental H2X Bombing," 30 September 1944, John Byrne Chamberlin, 525.310, Maxwell Air Force Base, Alabama.

55. *Gremlin Hunting*, 84.

56. Roger Freeman, *The Mighty Eighth, A History of the U. S. Eighth Army Air Force* (London: Macdonald, 1970), 201.

57. *Gremlin Hunting*, 84–85.

9

Operations Analysis in the Eighth Air Force
August–December 1944, Part II

Four Ground Support Missions of the Eighth Air Force

The early stages of the Falaise Pocket: Operation TOTALIZE. On 7 August, two full months after the Normandy landings, the German lines were still holding at the Caen Hinge. However, Montgomery advanced toward Falaise while Patton swerved north toward Argentan in an operation which was to trap 100,000 German troops. The slowness of the Allies to close the pincer allowed many of the German troops to escape—perhaps 35,000 of them—through the "Falaise Gap." To strengthen his attack, the British general requested direct support from the heavy bombers. On the night of 7 August, 637 RAF bombers attacked areas flanking the projected assault. On the following day the Eighth Air Force was to bomb four areas in formations flying parallel to the front lines. They were to deliver their attacks progressively, from north to south, in the general manner of a creeping barrage. This plan, involving a long flight over enemy territory, greatly magnified the problems of flying in heavy traffic. Special precautions were taken to prevent bombing errors. Artillery was to smoke the edges of target areas which were also to be marked by dropped flares. Scouting aircraft were to give information on weather over the targets and to check on the target markers, while troops were withdrawn nearly a mile from the area to be bombed.

The American heavies attacked at about 1300 hours on the 8th, flying straight and level through intense and accurate flak. Good concentrations were effected on three areas; the fourth was not bombed because it proved impossible to make positive identification of the target. Of the 678 bombers dispatched, 492 attacked. In spite of precautions taken, there were errors which resulted in the bombing of the points outside the target areas but within enemy lines. Shortbombing within friendly lines resulted from gross

225

errors on the part of two twelve-plane groups. In one case, faulty identification of target by the lead bombardier led him to drop near Caen .... In the second instance a badly hit lead bomber salvoed short and the rest of the formation followed in regular routine. Canadian troops were thereby in some measure disorganized, and suffered casualties amounting to 25 killed and 131 wounded. Eighth Air Force losses were counted at 9 heavies destroyed by flak and over 200 [40 percent of the attacking bombers] damaged. [1]

The five minutes allowed between the end of the bombing and the beginning of the attack, plus the one-mile withdrawal of the Canadian forces from the bomb line, may have given the Germans time to recover from the initial shock of the air attack. Progress of the Canadians on the ground was slow. Three days later, on 11 August, they had gained eight miles. Falaise, however, was still at least eight miles away. They reached Falaise on 16 August.

The above account of the action is based on "8th AF, Special Report on Operation, 8 August, 1944." [2] It, in turn, was partially based on another report, the ORS "Bombfall Analysis of Close Support Operations (8 August 1944)." [3]

Operation MARKET-GARDEN.   After the Falaise gap was finally closed, Allied armies advanced rapidly to the German Siegfried line. On 17 September the Allies began another battle—MARKET-GARDEN, a two-phase airborne and armored operation planned by Field Marshal Montgomery. It called for the British Second Army to outflank the German West Wall (Siegfried Line) at Arnhem. The ground phase of the operation, with the code name GARDEN, called for Allied airborne troops to support it by seizing key waterways and railheads in advance of Montgomery's tank column. The ground advance was to be along a narrow front from the Dutch-Belgian border in the direction of Eindhoven, Veghel, Grave, Nijmegen, Arnhem, and Apeldoorn.

To facilitate and expedite the advance of the ground troops, General Brereton's newly organized Allied Airborne Command undertook the largest airborne operation attempted up to that time. It was given the name MARKET. The U.S. 101st Airborne Division was to seize the city of Eindhoven and the bridges (river and canal) near Veghel, St. Odenrode, and Zon; the U.S. Eighty-second Division was to capture several bridges at Nijmegen and Grosbeck. The British First Airborne Division, supported by Polish paratroopers, was to gain control of road, rail, and pontoon bridges at Arnhem.

The available airlift was not adequate to deliver all the 20,000 airborne troops at once. Thus, the schedule called for delivery of about half the strength of the three airborne divisions on D day for this operation and the rest on D plus one and D plus two days. Two air routes were used to transport the troops from England to the Netherlands, the Northern Route and the Southern Route. The main task of the Eighth Air Force was to bomb and neutralize strong points, mostly antiaircraft defensive positions, along the selected airborne routes and the drop and landing zones. This had to be done just in advance of the airborne troops. [4]

Early Sunday morning on 17 September 1944, our crew—I was bombardier—was awakened to go on a mission. We were one of the crews of the 493d Bomb Group base near Ipswich, England. At the morning's briefing we were told that our group would fly in six flights of six, each to a separate target in the Rotterdam area. Furthermore, we were told that as soon as we dropped our bombs we were to get back to the base as quickly as possible, land, park, get out, and wait by our plane. We would see something interesting, we were told.

One hundred seventeen targets were bombed by the Eighth Air Force along the MARKET-GARDEN air routes that day. Around mid-morning we bombed ours from a medium altitude. The experience was unique.

Ordinarily, we were part of a large formation. On this particular morning we were a small six-plane flight; we felt all alone over enemy territory. Usually we bombed at an altitude of 22,000 feet or higher and were shot at by many guns, none of which we were aiming at. This morning we aimed at and bombed an isolated antiaircraft installation from a relatively low altitude while its gunners were explicitly shooting at us. This "them against us" kind of "shoot-out," though not as dangerous as our usual mission against industrial targets, was more personal and psychologically different for the crew. Although I do not recall our plane sustaining damage, the record shows that one fighter and two B-17s were lost to flak. One hundred twelve B-17s sustained battle damage from flak. [5] Thus, on the average, about one plane was hit by each of the 117 targets bombed.

As instructed, we quickly got back to our base, landed, and stood beside our plane. We watched the skies for something interesting to happen. Our base was right on the route taken by most of the planes and gliders going the Northern Route. Not long after we had landed a seemingly never-ending stream of planes, many of them pulling gliders, flew over our heads at what seemed like, in retrospect, 1,000 to 2,000 feet, low enough that we waved at them again and again. It was a thrilling and terrible sight, for we knew that thousands of men would be leaping into battle from these planes within the hour.

> The vast fleets of carrier aircraft and gliders which had taken off from their English bases carrying approximately half the strength of the British 1st and US 82nd and 101st Airborne Divisions converged on their designated drop and landing zones during the noon hour. Of the 1,546 aircraft and 478 gliders dispatched, 1,481 of the former and 425 of the latter were highly successful in their drops and landings. [In the airlift of the next day] 1,306 aircraft

and 1,152 gliders accomplished their assigned missions at a cost of 22 aircraft and 21 gliders destroyed or missing. [6]

Despite heroic efforts and many temporary successes by the airborne troops, MARKET-GARDEN, after over a week of desperate fighting, failed. Montgomery's main advance never developed enough strength to push through effective relief for the increasingly exhausted paratroopers. [7]

The ORS put out a report on the mission of 17 September against the 117 strong points in Holland. It is titled "Report on Operation by Eighth Air Force Heavy Bombers in Support of Nijmegen and Arnhem Operations—17 September 1944." [8] The report, dated 10 October 1944, was prepared by Lt. Col. P. C. Scott, Major Charles R. Darwin, and Dr. James A. Clarkson. Its purpose was to assess bombing accuracy.

The report states that on 17 September the Eighth Air Force dispatched 150 formations of B-17 aircraft to attack strong points, mostly gun positions, immediately preceding the airborne operations in the Nijmegen and Arnhem areas. Of these formations, 136 were composed of six aircraft and fourteen of four aircraft. One hundred and seventeen different points were assigned. All attacks were made with 260-pound fragmentation bombs. The altitudes of attack varied from 10,000 feet to 23,000 feet. The average was approximately 18,000 feet. Bombing was visual.

Strike photographs were available from 112 of the 150 formations that were dispatched. Bombfalls of all of these were located and plotted.

The pattern centers of twenty-three of the 112 identified falls (20 percent) were 2,000 feet or more from assigned aiming points. The average circular error of the pattern centers of the remaining eighty nine falls was 950 feet. Expressed in terms of the proportion of bombs which fell within 1,000 feet of assigned points—exclusive of patterns with errors of over 2,000 feet—approximately 45 percent of all bombs dropped fell within this standard distance.

The bombing accuracy on this special operation was considerably below that which the Eighth Air Force achieved on ordinary missions. The report says,

> On a comparable altitude, in our recent attacks with 12 aircraft formations on our normal strategic targets, we have averaged approximately 62% of bombs dropped within 1000 feet of pre-assigned aiming points, while the average circular error of pattern centers has been of the order of 725 feet.

The analysts were at loss to explain the lower bombing accuracy. They did, however, offer three probable causes:

(1) More difficult problems of target identification.
(2) A lowering of the average proficiency of lead crews with the

substantial increase in the numbers required.

(3) Tactical problems associated with the size of the operation.[9]

Operation MADISON. On 8 November 1944 General Patton's Third Army opened an attack against the southern and northern flanks of the fortifications around the city of Metz on the Moselle River. On 9 November Patton's Twentieth Corps was to cross the Moselle in the vicinity of Thionville. They were also to cross the Moselle twenty miles north of Metz, take Metz by encirclement and infiltration, and gradually reduce forts. To assist the advance of the two-pronged attack, and especially to help bypass the Metz-Thionville defenses, the heavy bombers of the Eighth Air Force, the medium bombers of the Ninth Air Force, and the fighter-bombers of Nineteenth Tactical Air Command (TAC) were to execute large-scale attacks on 9 November. The heavies were to attack seven forts south and southeast of Metz and a number of targets at Thionville, Saarbrücken, and Saarlautern. The mediums were to strike four forts and numerous other targets in the Metz vicinity. Fighter bombers were to carry out low-altitude missions against nine enemy headquarters and command posts. Fighters of the Eighth were to bomb and strafe a number of airfields east of the Rhine. There was to be no withdrawal of American troops from their existing positions before the bombing. However, in order to avoid shortfalls, General Patton insisted that all bombing must be at least four miles from the nearest friendly troops.

> The air operations took place as scheduled. Preceded by a chaff-dropping force of 10 bombers, 1,120 heavies out of a total of 1,295 dispatched attacked primary and secondary targets in the battle zone. The first force of heavy bombers, sent to the Thionville area, found visual bombing impossible. As a result, only 37 of them dropped 104 tons of bombs in the assigned tactical area while 308 dropped 964 tons by H2X on their secondary target, the marshalling yard at Saarbrücken. The primary targets of the second and third forces were in the vicinity of Metz. Here a total of 689 bombers succeeded in dropping 2,386 tons on targets in the tactical area, and 86 unloaded their 336 tons on various targets of opportunity. Bombing was both visual and by Gee-H."[10]

The Eighth Air Force ORS made a report on this operation, "Report on Attacks by Eighth Air Force Heavy Bombers against Fortifications in the Metz-Thionville Areas (9 November 1944)."[11]

Bombing accuracy was low in both the Thionville and Metz areas; only a few of the forts sustained any real damage. However, the intensity of the air attacks effected excellent results. The density of the defenses was such that bombs dropped anywhere within the tactical area were bound, inevitably, to hit some vital installation.[12]

By 15 November the battle had moved eastward along a sixty-mile front. Metz was encircled and bypassed on 19 November. By the end of November resistance ended in all but four forts. [13]

Operation QUEEN. Operation QUEEN was the code name of WWII's heaviest aerial bombardment in direct support of ground troops. It was mounted on 16 November 1944 to help the U.S. First and Ninth Armies break through to the Roer River east of Aachen, Germany. [14]

In this operation on 16 November 1944 a total of 1,191 Eighth Air Force heavy bombers reached their target areas between 1113 and 1248 o'clock—their bombs were dropped over a period of one hour and thirty-five minutes—and dropped 4,120 tons of fragmentation bombs on Eschweiler, Langewehe, Weisweiler, Durwiss, and Hehlrath. RAF Bomber Command's 1,188 heavies unloaded 5,640 tons of bombs on Düren, Jülich, and Heinsberg. Because weather at their bases was bad, only eighty Ninth Air Force mediums were able to attack four assigned targets with fifteen tons of bombs. Because of fog at their bases, the Ninth and Twenty-ninth TACs permitted their fighter bombers to fly only some 350 sorties in which 187 tons of bombs were dropped. [15]

The Eighth Air Force ORS produced a bombing accuracy report on this mission titled "Report on Operations by Eighth Air Force Heavy Bombers against Enemy Positions in the Eschweiler-Düren Area near Aachen, Germany" dated 8 December 1944. [16]

The bombing accuracy is summarized in the statement, "The accuracy of the bombing operations in the entire battle zone did not measure up to expectations because clouds, haze, smoke, and snow in some of the areas obscured a great many of the targets." [17] Most of the bombing was done by radar. In fact, all but one of the groups of the Third Division bombed using the Micro-H technique. This will be reported on in the next section.

That mission was the last ground support mission for our crew. By this time we were veterans of major ground support missions. We had been in on the unsuccessful breakthrough attempt of the British on 18 July at Caen. We had been part of the successful 25 July breakthrough at St-Lô. We had done our part in the 17 September MARKET-GARDEN operation. Now on 16 November we were approaching the German lines once more.

Our mood was one of excitement and cautious optimism. By this time we realized that what we were to do, although important, would not necessarily determine the outcome of the overall operation. The air force was only one component in a complex situation. The timing and force of the attack made by our ground troups was, of course, another factor, and the quality and depth of the resistance of the Germans was yet another. The breakthrough attempts at Caen, St-Lô, and Thionville-Metz were all on French soil. The end-run attempt of MARKET-GARDEN had been in Holland. This mission was in support of the first breakthrough attempt of the Allies on German soil. The

Germans were now defending their Fatherland. Furthermore, the Eschweiler-Düren area was near where the great German counterattack, the Battle of the Bulge, would take place exactly one month later. As we approached the target area, at low altitude for us, around 15,000 feet, my clearest memory of the mission forty-one years later is seeing, through breaks in the clouds, heavy snow on the ground. The mission was otherwise uneventful with meager flak and no fighter attacks.

The overall analysis of the attack gives this summary:

> Effectiveness of bombing operations was further reduced by the reluctance of the air forces to bomb 'short'; as a consequence, the defenses directly in front of the ground troops were not sufficiently softened. Moreover, withdrawal of the troops for their protection at points delayed their advance until the psychological effects of the bombing carpet had been lost.
>
> Nevertheless, the destruction wrought by the 10,000 tons of bombs dropped over a relatively small area was enormous. Jülich was almost completely destroyed. In Düren and Eschweiler the results were similar. Several fortified villages were virtually obliterated.
>
> Enemy (i.e. military enemy) casualties from bombing appear to have been relatively light, since the number of prepared shelters was so large that protection for troops caught in the open was within fairly easy reach. Strafing by the escorting fighters, according to enemy statements, was ineffective, because the strafing planes... went too far beyond the front line. [18]

How successful was the operation?

> By 30 November, which marked the end of operation QUEEN, a dozen villages had been captured and the VII Corps front had been pushed forward from four to ten miles. Elsewhere on First Army's front no important changes had taken place. [Also] in Ninth Army's zone small gains [only] were made. [19]

MICRO-H BECOMES OPERATIONAL

Angus Taylor is assigned Micro-H bombing analysis. By November 1944 the way was finally clear for Micro-H to go operational. One transmitting station had been set up at Namur, Belgium, and another at Verdun, France. Like other beam radars, range was affected by the curvature of the earth. Thus, its range was limited to about 180 miles for a bomber at 25,000 feet. [20] This, however, was sufficient to put a good deal of Germany's West Wall within range. On 1 November 1944 the first operational mission using Micro-H was flown when a bridge at Rudesheim, Germany, was attacked. Micro-H, developed for the Eighth Air Force, was employed almost solely by the Third Air Division, which specialized in Micro-H to the exclusion of Gee-H. From the beginning of Micro-H bombing, the Third Air Division ORS kept close watch over the progress of the new method of radar bombing.

Colonel Fredericks, ORS chief, assigned Dr. Angus Taylor the task of studying all phases of the use of Micro-H in the Third Division. [21]

Taylor describes his Micro-H training.

> My first task was to learn as much about the system as I could. I began by going to the Micro-H computing Section in the Operational Analysis Section at Eighth Air Force Headquarters. This section was in charge of Dr. W. A. Mersman, of the British branch of the M.I.T. Radiation Laboratory (BBRL-MIT). From Dr. Mersman I learned the fundamentals of the laying out of a course so that an aircraft flying the course could hit the assigned target, as well as the method whereby the proper release point could be determined. I learned about the radar equipment and the duties of the radar navigator from the divisional officer in charge of radar navigation, and by visiting the Groups, examining training equipment, and talking to various radar navigators. Later on I flew in the radar navigator's compartment on some training flights. After I had pretty thoroughly learned the theory of Micro-H bombing I frequently discussed training problems with the divisional Radar Navigator, and went with him to meetings at the Groups or Wings or at Division Headquarters. [22]

Each month Taylor reported on Micro-H bombing. The reports analyzed bombing accuracy to the extent that evidence was available. The reports also described any difficulties with equipment performance or operator use, and recommended changes based on ORS studies of Micro-H bombing. Because these reports provided useful information, they were circulated throughout the command.

Taylor reports on his relationships with BBRL-MIT.

> In checking up on difficulties with the equipment I was aided by various representatives of BBRL-MIT from Alconbury. They visited a great many of the airfields and checked up on individual cases in which something went wrong and hindered the successful use of Micro-H on a particular mission. The cooperation between this group of men, the Division Radar Navigator, and the Operational Research Section was always close and mutually beneficial. [23]

The November report on Micro-H. [24] In November 1944 seven missions were flown in which targets were attacked using the Micro-H technique of radar bombing. One hundred seventeen squadrons, each of twelve or thirteen aircraft, were dispatched. Of these 117 squadrons, eighty-six actually attacked their assigned targets by the Micro-H technique, eight did not bomb at all, and the rest attacked either their primary or secondary targets by means of H2X or in some instances with visual aid. Thus 73.5 percent of the forces assigned to bomb by the Micro-H technique carried out the assignment.

On three of the seven missions, photographs permitted reasonably accurate determination of the results. These three missions included eighteen aiming operations; fourteen of the resulting patterns were identified. Of these, eight aimings were by Micro-H alone. Six were aimed by Micro-H with some visual assistance, usually consisting of a very short opportunity to correct for rate and range. See Table 9.1.

Table 9.1. Average Aiming Errors with Micro-H

	Range	Deflection	Circular
Pure Micro-H	0.4 mile	1.0 mile	1.2 mile
Micro-H and Visual	0.4	0.6	0.8
Both types	0.4	0.8	1.0

Table 9.2 provides a rough estimate of the percentages of bombs dropped within specified distances of the assigned mean point of impact (MPI). Accuracy is within 5 or 10 percent.

Table 9.2.

	$\frac{1}{2}$ mile	1 mile	2 miles	3 miles
Pure Micro-H	25%	45%	75%	95%
Micro-H and visual	15	50	100	100
Both types	20	45	85	95

One of the three missions for which Taylor got photographic coverage of the bombfalls was the 16 November Düren ground support mission. All thirteen of the Third Division groups went on the mission. There was one sighting for each group. Seven of the sightings were made by Micro-H alone. Unfortunately, four of the bombfalls of these seven Micro-H sightings were not identified. Five Micro-H sightings assisted by visual sighting were made; all five bombfalls were identified. One group, the 493d Bomb Group, may have lost its Micro-H beam, for it bombed using H2X alone.

Table 9.3 shows the results in average aiming errors in miles.

Table 9.3.

Type of aiming	Range	Deflection	Circular
Pure Micro-H (3 sightings)	0.4 long	1.3	1.4
Micro-H with visual assistance (5 sightings)	0.5 long	0.6	0.9
Pure H2X (1 sighting)	1.2 short	2.2	2.5

Table 9.4 shows the estimates Taylor made of the percentages of bombs falling within specified distances of MPI.

Table 9.4.

Type of aiming	Bombs That Fell Within			
	$\frac{1}{2}$ mile	1 mile	2 miles	3 miles
Pure Micro-H	5–10%	30–35%	85–90%	100%
Micro-H with visual assistance	10–15	45–50	100	100

Assuming that the accuracy of the four groups whose bomb patterns were not identified was similar to that of the other eight—Taylor thought this likely—the above gives a reasonable picture of the bombing accuracy of the Third Bomb Division on the 16 November ground support mission in the Düren area. Such poor accuracy may seem shocking. Nevertheless, it was much, much more accurate than the average H2X bombing.

TUTTLE LEAVES THE SECTION FOR THE UNITED STATES

In the summer of 1944 Dr. W. Norris Tuttle recommended to the command that Gee-H be used on tactical support missions. He and Major Bales had worked out an alternative technique for Gee-H bombing which was adopted by the Second Division.

During the month of September, when Gee-H beacons were moved to the continent, it became evident that Gee-H would continue to play an important role in operations. When Tuttle was convinced that the Gee-H program was salvaged he felt free to leave the command.

On 3 October 1944 Dr. Tuttle left for Washington. He then served as a radar analyst with the Twentieth Air Force until V-J Day, 15 August 1945.[25] Tuttle's departure left Leslie Arps as the last of the original six.

Dr. Tuttle's main contribution was introducing Gee-H to the Eighth Air Force. Gee-H was very important. Arps points out that in December 1944 alone, Gee-H attacks were made against 100 targets.[26] Its importance to the bombing effort of the Eighth Air Force becomes evident when it is compared with visual and H2X bombing in the period 1 September 1944 to 31 December 1944. See Table 9.4.

Table 9.4. Visual Bombing Versus Gee-H Bombing
1 September 1944 to 31 December 1944

	Visual bombing	Gee-H bombing
Percentage of all bombing	24	15
Bombs dropped on primary targets	33,209 tons	20,220 tons
Bombs dropped within		
1,000 feet of aiming point	7,430	1,030
half mile of aiming point	17,462	5,260
one mile of aiming point	24,364	11,320

A more startling comparison is that only 15 percent of all bombs in the period were dropped by Gee-H; 11,320 tons fell within one mile of the AP. By contrast 58 percent of all bombs of the period were dropped by H2X; only 13,444 tons landed within one mile of the AP. [27]

Of course, these figures do not tell the whole story about the role of the three methods. Each method had its limitations and its important uses. Visual bombing, the most accurate, was limited by weather and smoke screens. Beacon-based radar bombing like Gee-H and Micro-H were limited by range. H2X was used when blind bombing had to be done (as in the oil campaign) beyond the range of Gee-H or Micro-H.

COLONEL SCOTT DEVOTES HIS EFFORTS TO H2X BOMBING

Colonel Scott was the chief and veteran of the Bombing Accuracy Subsection. Up until the last quarter of 1944 he had devoted most of his efforts and attention to visual bombing. Beginning in September 1944 blind bombing missions constituted a major portion of all missions. Thus, in October when the pressure of work on visual missions slackened Colonel Scott was able to devote his efforts to the analysis of blind bombing. Furthermore, he brought with him more help from photographic interpreters and other personnel in the subsection than had been available before. [28]

On 25 October Scott released "Report on H2X Operations during September against Targets in Ludwigshaven and Mannheim." On 21 November he released "Memorandum on H2X Operations against Cologne in September and October 1944 and Plots." He also prepared "18 Bombfall Plots of H2X Missions in September and October." [29] Targets for the Cologne attacks were the five or so marshalling yards in the city. Aiming points were in the individual yards. The report concluded with the observation that with exactly the same aiming errors, more bombs would have fallen in the system of *all* marshalling yards if every bomb had been aimed at the very center of the city. [30] Thus, in terms of tactics, low-order accuracy of H2X radar bombing proved most effective when aiming at city centers. Interestingly, bombing city centers, while routine for the RAF, had been rejected by the Eighth Air Force.

My crew and I went on the 14 October 1944 mission to Cologne. Before leaving, I remember how we were admonished at briefing not to hit the cathedral. After the war the great cathedral still stood, surrounded by rubble, with only minor damage. The naive attributed this to bombing accuracy. Many a worldly-wise airman, however, recognized it for what it was—a miracle.

Beginning with the Ludwigshaven attacks, Colonel Scott used PRU (photographic reconnaissance unit) strike photographs, many showing cloud breaks and some ground detail, to determine the location of the bombfalls. This technique was discovered and used by Price as early as his analysis of the 11 April attack on Politz. Price notes.

> The use of PRU photographs with strike photographs that show some ground detail is a thoroughly satisfactory means of locating accurately the position of a bombfall that would otherwise be known only approximately. The use of PRU photographs as the sole basis of information for plotting the position of bombfalls dropped blind turned out to be thoroughly unsatisfactory. After many such plots had been made we found that they gave biased results. The reason is obvious: PRU photographs are made to show the condition of the target; hence, they show bombfalls near the target but seldom those far away. A great deal of effort had been expended on the analysis of PRU photographs alone, and then we had to expend a lot more effort to remove the results from our records and calculations. [31]

I remember well the September Ludwigshafen missions reported by Scott. I went on the 13 and 15 September missions. Ludwigshafen was a high-priority target for two reasons. It had a synthetic oil refinery, and by-products of the refinery were nitrogen and methanol. Ludwigshafen-Oppau was one of two plants—the other was at Merseburg-Leuna—which produced 60 percent of Germany's nitrogen and 40 percent of its methanol. [32] Ludwigshafen was defended accordingly.

My third mission to Ludwigshafen on 5 November was the most memorable. We ran into intense flak over the target, which was covered by a smoke screen. Two bombers from our group were simultaneously and fatally hit by bursts of flak, evidently from the same battery, at about 26,000 feet. One of the bombers, its number 2 engine on fire, descended to about 17,000 feet and blew up. We saw several chutes drop from this plane. The other plane also descended to about 17,000 feet, turned over, and exploded. We saw seven or eight chutes from this plane. [33] The group bombardier was flying as an observer in one of the planes which went down.

While my crew and I were flying our first twenty-one missions during June through September 1944 the Eighth Air Force had the policy of taking its flying crews off combat status at the end of twenty-five missions. As we passed the twenty-mission mark we were at first sustained by the expectation of going home after twenty-five missions. However, somewhere between our twentieth and twenty-fifth missions we experienced what became known in the air force as Catch 22. The Eighth Air Force decreed that a combat tour would consist of thirty missions instead of twenty-five. Since there was no alternative we accepted this as best we could. However, as we approached our thirtieth mission we were subjected to Catch 22 a second time. We were told that our tour would consist of thirty-five missions. By this time we needed a rest cure. Instead, between 16 November and 6 December we flew to six major German targets, three of them being the number one oil target of Merseburg-Leuna. The term flak happy began to take on personal meaning for us.

SYNTHETIC OIL, MERSEBURG-LEUNA

Merseburg, the number one target.   In late 1944 Merseburg was the dominant synthetic oil target for the Eighth Air Force strategists. To the aircrewmen, however, Merseburg was synonymous with flak. Roger Freeman expresses the sentiment.

> It [Merseburg] was what Schweinfurt had been to their predecessors in the autumn of 1943, for it became the most heavily defended place in Hitler's crumbling empire, with more guns than Berlin. There were over a thousand flak guns defending the Leipzig area oil plants by late November [Merseburg was 20 miles or so west of Leipzig] and Merseburg had 506 of these in 39 sites at its peak. This underlined the importance of the large I. G. Farbenindustrie plant at Leuna three miles south of the town, which produced an estimated 10% of Reich oil, half the ammonia, plus other chemical by products. The Eighth ran a score of missions to Merseburg and it became, in the eyes of the combatants at least, the No. 1 target. [34]

Price makes a study of the Merseburg-Leuna target.   When, early in December, Price returned from his week's leave after the Oxford Experiment, he found a job waiting for him. The Third Division requested a special study of the missions against Leuna. Sixteen missions had been flown against this target up to 30 November, and two more were flown by the middle of December. Price writes:

> Some of these missions had been outstanding failures, and there was some reason to believe that a careful analysis of them would indicate some of the causes. The study seemed to offer unusual

opportunities. One variable had been controlled: there was a large number of attacks against a single target. [35]

Price and Scott selected for study the sixteen attacks, beginning with the first one on 12 May and ending with the famous mission of 30 November. Much additional photographic analysis was required. Price continues:

> We plotted every bombfall that could be observed directly or whose position could be calculated from a bombs-away photograph showing ground detail. We read the many volumes of mission reports in order to learn the details of the execution of these missions. When the data was all assembled, Colonel Scott turned it over to me for analysis. [Price reached a disappointing conclusion.] There were so many variables that the sixteen missions did not constitute a controlled experiment in any respect. It was possible to indicate a large number of factors which had influenced the performance, but it was not possible to single out and measure the influence of any one of them. [36]

Price's report was completed on Christmas Day 1944, ten days after the Battle of the Bulge began. It was dated 2 January 1945.

The report of the Combined Strategic Targets Committee on oil tactics.   At the end of October 1944 the oil experts of the Combined Strategic Targets Committee estimated that German oil production had risen seven points in October to 30 percent of the preattack level. The following conclusions were drawn:

1. Heavy bombers were not effective in attacks on tiny storage facilities. This task would be turned over to medium and fighter bombers.

2. Benzol plants were very difficult to hit because they were small and hidden away in urban centers.

3. AAF blind bombing was not as accurate as hoped. "A visual attack with 250 tons was usually more profitable than a radar mission involving 1000 tons."

4. Reconnaissance could not keep up with the bombing missions. In mid-October it had become a settled policy to attack and reattack regardless of reconnaissance data.

5. "The Allies had much to learn about the size of type of bombs that would produce maximum damage." [37]

The race between production and destruction at Merseburg-Leuna.   The U.S. Strategic Bombing Survey report sketches the struggle between the bombers trying to stop production at Leuna and the Geilenberg crews trying to keep it going.

> The first attack on May 12 knocked out production completely. Geilenberg put several thousand additional men in the plant and

partial production was resumed 10 days later. The raid of May 28 again knocked out the plant, but production was resumed on June 3 and reached approximately 75% of capacity by the early part of July. The July 7 raid once again shut down the plant, but production started two days later and reached 53% of capacity by July 19. A raid on July 20 again caused a shut-down, but only for 3 days and by July 27 production was back to 35%. Two raids on the 28th and 29th closed down operations once more, and continuing raids on August 24, September 11, 13, 28, and October 7 prevented any production. In spite of this pounding and the accumulation of vast damage, operations were resumed on October 14, and while interrupted by a minor raid on November 2, production reached 28% by November 20. In spite of six additional heavy raids in late November and December (largely ineffective because of adverse weather), production came back to 15% in the middle of January, 1945, and was maintained at an average of 15% capacity during March and April. [38]

The 2 November battle at Merseburg-Leuna

The strategic bombing survey view. The U.S. Strategic Bombing Survey report states "in spite of this pounding and the accumulation of vast damage, operations (at Leuna) were assumed on October 14, and while interrupted by a minor raid on November 2, production reached 28% by November 20." [39] Now the Bombing Survey people, understandably, viewed the mission of 2 November from the point of view of damage to the plant. It was, evidently, minor. However, from the point of view of the Eighth Air Force the mission was far from minor.

The USAAF view of the operation. In the last three weeks of October 1944 the Eighth's flyers seldom saw a fighter and made no claims of damage or destruction against the GAF. However,

> Having hoarded sufficient gasoline the Nazis rose on 2 November 400 strong, the largest number that had been able to get into the air at one time since early June. One combat force from the Eighth about to bomb the synthetic oil plant at Merseburg-Leuna was shielded effectively by its escorts but another force was less fortunate. Before its protecting Mustangs could interfere, some sixty German fighters closed in to shoot into the rear bomber formations. But for a lucky chain of circumstances and almost perfect fighter cover, Spaatz wrote Arnold, many more bombers would have been lost (to the GAF) than the 26 that fell to the Nazis." [40]

"Combat Chronology" reports that in all Eighth Air Force missions on 2 November, an estimated 500 GAF fighters were encountered (approximately

400 of them at Merseburg-Leuna). Forty bombers were lost, and twenty-eight United States fighters were lost. [41]

The Me-163, German rocket airplane. The Me-163 was an interceptor-fighter powered by a rocket motor. It was also known as the Komet. Its first operational use was in July 1944 against B-17s. It was a single-plane, target-defense interceptor powered by a 3,750-pound-thrust rocket engine. It flew 596 miles per hour maximum speed and climbed at a rate of 16,000 feet per minute. Climbing to 30,000 feet took 2.6 minutes. The plane carried two 30-mm cannon and twenty-four underwing rockets or four rockets in each wing mounted to fire upward. [42]

The Me-163 could maintain powered flight for only eight minutes, limiting it to target interceptor work. It appeared fairly regularly to defend targets in the Leipzig area. Its incredible speed allowed it to climb or dive away from U.S. fighters with ease. Because its fuel capacity was limited, the Me-163 could only operate in visibility good enough for spotting bombers instantly. It could not waste time and gasoline searching. [43]

My view of the 2 November Merseburg-Leuna mission. My twenty-sixth mission was to Merseburg on 2 November 1944. Our crew made return trips to this number one flak target on 25 and 30 November. My last mission, the thirty-fifth, was to Merseburg on 6 December. This personal account explains why bombing accuracy was low at this target in the fall of 1944.

The small city of Merseburg is located about twenty miles due west of Leipzig. About ten miles due north of Merseburg is the city of Halle. Approximately twenty-five miles southeast of Merseburg is the city of Zeitz. Then Jena is about thirty miles southwest of Merseburg followed by Weimar and Erfurt a little farther to the west of Jena. All of these were part of the big stage of the 2 November Merseburg mission.

After forty-five years my memory of the 2 November mission consists of a number of disconnected yet vivid mental pictures. The following account of our group's action is based on notes taken from the group's report of the mission plus my recollections. [44]

Our group was led by the 863d Squadron (A-squadron) under the command of Lt. Col. George B. Whitlock. It consisted of twelve planes, eleven squadron planes plus a Pathfinder leader from the Thirty-fourth Group. B-squadron consisted of thirteen planes, twelve squadron planes (either 860 or 862) plus a Pathfinder leader. Our squadron, the 861st Squadron (C-squadron) brought up the rear and consisted of thirteen planes, one of which had to turn back before we reached the target.

We approached the target area at an altitude of 26,000 feet. Beneath us at 15,000 feet was an undercast which covered from five- to seven-tenths of the sky.

As we approached the target area, though breaks in the clouds we could see a large smoke screen. We had been warned to beware of dummy targets complete with smoke screens. I wonder now whether what we saw was the real thing or a decoy.

The PFF (Pathfinder) plane of B-squadron took a direct hit and was unable to function as a Pathfinder. Consequently, none of its twelve planes bombed the briefed target. Seven dropped their bombs in the area, and the other five returned to the base with their bombs.

We followed A-squadron led by its PFF plane into the target area. On the bomb run (on a heading of 116°) we encountered, beginning at 12:12, an intense, accurate barrage of flak. When A-squadron dropped its bombs, we dropped ours. We learned later we bombed at Halle, ten miles north of Merseburg, and our bombs fell two miles east of Halle next to an autobahn. The lead ship of A-squadron stayed on course two whole minutes after dropping its bombs. It took a direct flak hit eight minutes after bombs away. Lt. Colonel Whitlock went down over the Merseburg area in the aircraft piloted by Captain Alexander. The deputy then assumed the lead and led us out of the flak at 12:26. We had been in flak continuously for fourteen minutes and sporadically for another six. The group narrative states that we overshot and probably got flak from Leipzig and Zeitz, and then in leaving we skirted the northern edges of Jena, Weimar, and Erfurt, picking up flak from these.

The group report on the mission states that our fighter escort was good going into the target area and coming out of it, but was absent over the target. At any rate while we were still in the target area and under fire (we were now on a heading of 236°) I looked down. At about two o'clock low I saw a plane climbing at an incredible speed and angle toward us from the white undercast below. It was an Me-163. I announced over our intercom that we were under attack. The report states that our group was attacked at 12:23 by six Me-163s. We were under attack for six minutes. Our squadron was attacked by two of them. The Me-163s came up singly and attacked singly. Our squadron claimed one of these as destroyed and another as probably destroyed.

A gunner in our squadron was given credit for destroying one Me-163. The official report is as follows:

> The Me-163 was first seen in the Merseburg area about 3000 feet below the Squadron coming up in an almost vertical climb. The jet plane climbed to about 4000 feet above the formation where it flew to a level position off 9 o'clock about 400 yards out. The jet plane flew a parallel course at the formation for a few seconds and was then fired upon by the top turret. The jet plane at once broke away to the left completing a quarter circle, and began an attack at 6:30 o'clock. Top turret opened fire at about 800 yards firing 50 rounds until the jet plane reached a point about 400 yards from the tail of the B-17 where it blew up. There was little left of

the plane and the explosion and aftermath resembled a large flak burst. [45]

Two gunners of another plane of our squadron received credit for a probably destroyed Me-163. The story was:

The Me-163 attacked from high at 4 o'clock closing to about 800 yards. Top turret started at about 950 yards, expending 40 to 50 rounds, before the jet plane peeled off and dove downwards. Tail gunner was also firing until the jet plane dove away. Claimant was sure that he was getting strikes on the jet plane which broke off the attack quite suddenly. [46]

Probably every plane in our squadron got in shots at the Me-163s. Our plane, in the rear of the squadron, shuddered from the recoil of our guns as they fired. Even I, in the nose of our plane, got in a few bursts at the second plane as it flew over us from behind. I can still see a flying wing pass over us. Our tracers seemed to go right through it. We grumbled and marveled that we didn't get some credit. This experience, however, made me realize why Eighth Air Force claims of downed enemy fighters were greatly inflated in earlier combat.

On 2 November 1944, in the vicinity of Merseburg, our fighters and bombers claimed over 160 German planes destroyed. [47] Our group lost two planes—both to flak. In all, forty bombers were lost.

Above the 15,000 foot undercast the sunshine was bright over Merseburg on 2 November 1944. I remember looking around the horizon through the bright haze and seeing planes, near and far, bombers and fighters, friend and foe, falling. To the USSBS that mission was a "minor raid." To the airmen it was a major battle. Furthermore, it was no victory for the Germans. Despite a supreme effort, they were unable to stop the oil campaign against them.

The number one cause for inaccuracy on the mission was the inability to bomb visually. For example, the H2X Pathfinder led two of our squadrons to the wrong target—Halle instead of Merseburg. Though this case seems extreme, it is by no means unprecedented. The number two cause for inaccuracy by our group that day was flak. By eliminating the lead crew of one squadron before bombs away, the squadron was rendered ineffective. Half bombed individually in the general target area; the other half did not bomb at all. Though American fighter cover prevented the GAF from seriously affecting the accuracy of the mission, twenty-six bombers were downed by the GAF.

In 1944 German resistance, including flak, fighters, and camouflage, was a big factor in decreasing the fourth quarter bombing accuracy of the Eighth Air Force. An even greater factor, though, was bombing overcast targets. Merseburg, for example, had to be bombed but could not be bombed visually. Furthermore, it was too far away for Gee-H or Micro-H.

The problem of the best bombs and fuzes for synthetic oil plants. A good deal of debate arose over the right weapon to use on oil targets. In a letter to General Spaatz dated 3 November 1944, General Eaker, commander of the Mediterranean Allied Air Force, said that much opinion but little factual knowledge was available ~~to help~~ calculate correct mixtures of bombs and fuzes.[48]

When the Eighth Air Force began bombing oil plants the Bombs and Fuzes Subsection recommended 100-pound GP bombs aimed at the gas generator units. On 12 May, the very first raid on Leuna, carried out with the relatively small force of 220 planes, shut down the plant for ten days. Assuming that 100-pound bombs were used on this raid, this seems impressive in light of subsequent experience. Nevertheless, the remarkably swift repair work of Geilenberg's crews raised the question of whether larger bombs might cause more permanent damage.

About the first period of attacks on oil targets:

> During the first period the 100-lb GP was used when it was available. There was considerable opposition to this weapon on the part of some officers in A-2 and A-3. Most of this stemmed from the same source, namely, the photo-interpreter for the Eighth Air Force. Whenever small bombs were used on any target, the photo-interpreter invariably objected. He objected most strenuously on these targets [oil plants] for the reason that he could seldom see any visible damage and lacked the imagination and understanding to appreciate the extent of the damage to the contents [of buildings] and equipment damage which could not and was not expected to be visible in aerial cover. It was surprising that he was as influential as he was in view of the work that had been done in explaining the reasons for the use of the 100-lb bomb, and in view of the fact that General O. A. Anderson and others had agreed with the reasons for its use. Part of his regular job was to interpret the damage as seen in strike photographs and to brief the Commanding General in a special morning conference which we did not attend.[49]

However, to improve bombing accuracy in the fall quarter the Bombs and Fuzes Subsection recommended for oil targets the next larger bomb, the 250-pound GP. This recommendation, prepared by Alderman, Kring, and Clarkson, appeared because it soon became impossible to use gas generators as aiming points. Alderman's explanation illustrates how closely the work of the Bombing Accuracy Subsection related to that of Bombs and Fuzes.

> The attacks on Synthetic Oil Plants in the first period must have hurt the enemy. They increased several fold the flak defenses and forced our aircraft to attack at higher altitudes. This caused substantial reductions in our bombing accuracy. The enemy also

increased its use of smoke screens and became expert in maintaining a constant smoke screen over the plants well in advance of the time our bombers arrived. This also reduced the accuracy. It became impossible for bombardiers to single out special aiming points or vital installations which were often located at the edges or corners of target areas. Aiming points had been selected on boiler houses and refinery units as well as the gas generators.

It was decided that because of the reduced probability of getting bomb patterns on target, a single aiming point would be used near the center of the effective target area. This meant that all bombs in patterns which were well aimed would be within the target area and have a chance of hitting some installation. It also meant that fewer bombs would be wasted in fields outside the target area. This was agreed upon by the Bombing Accuracy Subsection and was strongly recommended by them. This accepted, it then became necessary to select a weapon which would be the most effective against the majority of the installations in the target area. [50]

Alderman's analysis explains why the Air Force was compelled to treat German oil plants as area targets rather than precision targets.

The analysts of the Bombs and Fuzes Subsection decided to direct the attack on the oil plants against the contents of the buildings and the many installations in the open. Thus, the 250-pound GP was selected because

> ... it was large enough to be effective against the various stalls, apparatus and general equipment in the buildings as well as against the installations in the open. Because of the many individual cells of equipment covering practically the entire target area and because these could be easily repaired and reconnected after an attack by by-passing the destroyed units, it became important to use a bomb which could be carried in large numbers to obtain as many hits as possible with a bomb of sufficient size to knock out the typical installation. [51]

The critics of small bombs finally prevailed, at least temporarily, with General Doolittle. Alderman writes:

> Most of the Operations Officers were inclined to agree with scientific reasons for using smaller bombs on certain targets, but there were those who were not, and they were influenced by the quick and unprofound judgements of the photo-interpreter. His comments nevertheless were so convincing that General Doolittle prohibited the use of any bombs smaller than 500-lb GP without his special permission. This seemed to us unfortunate. General O. A. Anderson immediately requested a personal memorandum

be submitted to him summarizing all our reasons for our past recommendations of bombs smaller than 500-lb GP's. Our report [prepared by Alderman and Hedefine] included our reasons for 100-lb GP's on: Marshalling yards, airfield post-holing attacks, city areas, and special tactical targets; and our reasons for 250-lb GP's on Synthetic Oil Plants, Oil Refineries, Modified Sites, and certain special targets."

Alderman makes the final comment, On some of the attacks on Synthetic Oil Targets it was necessary to use 500 and 1000-lb GP's because of bomb shortages or because of the ban on the use of smaller bombs. [52]

In the chapter "Autumn Assault on Germany," John E. Fagg writes that "a study of the Ploesti refineries had indicated that small bombs were probably best, but postwar surveys (USSBS) concluded that larger bombs and a higher percentage of incendiaries should have been used." [53] He writes again in the chapter "Mission Accomplished," that "the Americans used too many small bombs, too few incendiaries, and too many (about 14 percent) defective bombs." [54]

George Housner, an operations analyst with the Ninth Bomber Command and the Fifteenth Air Force, helped plan the 1 August 1943 low-level attack on Ploesti. He also completed extensive ground survey work in the Naples area right after it was captured in the autumn of 1943. In his "Report on the Bombing of the Oil Refinery at Naples, Italy," [55] he made relevant judgments on the issues of fire bombs and proper bomb sizes for oil plants and made several conclusions on the use of incendiaries and small bombs. He also analyzed oil refineries, not synthetic oil plants, though the similarity is great. Alderman recommended the 250-pound bomb for both.

Though the Naples refinery (the Raffineria di Napoli S. A. I.–Socony Vacuum) suffered extensive damage by fire, Housner recommended against incendiary bombs as the primary weapon against oil targets for the following reasons:

1. The contents of storage tanks are ignited by high explosive bombs, such as the ordinary general purpose bombs.

2. Refinery installations themselves are not combustible. Intense heat from burning petroleum products causes damage to the installations.

3. Small fires, such as the burning of a single installation, can be controlled with equipment kept at the refinery.

4. Large uncontrolled fires are likely to happen only when storage tanks receive direct hits or near misses by high explosive bombs. If there is a drainage and dyking system, it must also be damaged by high explosive bombs to render it inoperative.

Housner's rationale for the use of small bombs was,

> It has been shown that in order to seriously damage the vital installations of an unprotected refinery, it is necessary to obtain a direct hit or a near miss. If the refinery is adequately protected with blast walls, etc., then it is necessary to obtain a direct hit on a vital installation in order to cause serious damage. With these facts in mind, it appears that the smaller H.E. bombs would be more suitable than larger bombs. By carrying smaller bombs, more can be carried by a given number of sorties thus obtaining a larger number of hits on the refinery grounds. A direct hit on a vital installation or a storage tank by a 250-lb or 500-lb bomb would certainly cause sufficient damage. [56]

After the Russians captured the Ploesti refineries, a team of analysts including the chief of the OAS of MAAF conducted a ground survey in August and September 1944. [57] They appear to have concluded that "small bombs were (probably) best." Understandably, in his official USAAF history, Fagg adopts the view of the larger and more prestigious USSBS. [58]

After the carefully made arguments of Alderman and Housner, the dogmatic statement, "The Americans used too many small bombs [and] too few incendiaries [on oil targets]" is a proposition that is not beyond argument. Suppose on every mission against Merseburg we did everything the same except use bigger bombs, say 500- or 2,000-pound bombs instead of 100- or 250-pound bombs. One B-17 can carry forty to fifty 100-pound bombs, sixteen to twenty 250-pound bombs, eight to ten 500-pound bombs, or four to six 1,000-pound bombs. Using bombs weighing 500 pounds or more on all missions would have produced less than half the hits obtained with the smaller bombs. Because a direct hit by a small bomb would destroy many of the plant components just as thoroughly as a direct hit by a 1,000-pound bomb, it is not clear why the bigger bombs would have been better.

The following quotation from Craven and Cate probably contains the basis of the USSBS's conclusion that more large bombs should have been used.

> Early in November a USSTAF general had hinted to Air Marshal Bottomley that the RAF was not carrying its share of the oil offensive, even though it had enjoyed more clear nights for such missions than the Eighth Air Force had clear days. Before the month was out, however Bomber Command was exceeding the American Air Forces in the tonnage dropped on oil targets. Gigantic night missions and occasional daylight attacks by this force brought ruin to the synthetic oil plants and benzol works of the Ruhr... by the last of November all of the RAF's synthetic oil targets were suspended because they were no longer operating. Whereupon Air Chief Marshal Portal demanded that the British share the losses

the Eighth had been taking by assuming responsibility for two of the largest and most distant targets, Politz and Merseburg-Leuna. The crippling of Germany's warning system in the west as a result of the Allied victory in France and the increased efficiency of blind-bombing techniques made such RAF missions possible, and they proved generally successful. Indeed Speer subsequently reported to Hitler that the night attacks were more effective than the daylight missions, because heavier bombs were used and greater accuracy had been attained. On the average British operation against oil targets during the autumn, 660 tons fell as compared with 388 tons for a USSTAF mission. [59]

The USSBS placed great weight on Speer's judgments—as it should have. However, Speer's reported judgment that "night attacks were more effective than the daylight missions, because heavier bombs were used and greater accuracy had been attained" warrants comment.

The RAF bombing should have been more accurate. In November and December of 1944 the Eighth Air Force and the RAF were both using area bombing of oil targets. The RAF had been using area bombing from the beginning of its operations against Germany and was expert at it. The Eighth Air Force, on the other hand, had only begun to bomb oil plants as area targets in November.

It was not the heavier bombs that caused the RAF to be more effective on these targets. It was their greater accuracy coupled with their much larger bomb loads—660 tons per average mission for the RAF compared with 388 for the Eighth.

References

1. Wesley Frank Craven and James Lea Cate of the USAF Historical Division, eds., *Europe: From Argument to V-E Day, January 1944 to May 1945*, vol. 3 of *The Army Air Forces in World War II* (Chicago: University of Chicago Press, 1951), 250–51.

2. Ibid., 834.

3. "Bombfall Analysis of Close Support Operations (8 August 1944)," 14 August 1944, John Byrne Chamberlin, ORS of First Division, 525.310, Simpson Historical Research Center, Maxwell Air Force Base, Alabama. This memorandum was to the commanding general of First Division. Chamberlin lists all items in the ORS library of First Division.

4. *Europe: From Argument to V-E Day*, 600–601.

5. Ibid., 602.

6. Ibid., 604, 606.

7. Ibid., 607.

8. Headquarters, Eighth Air Force, ORS, "Report on Operations by Eighth Air Force Heavy Bombers in Support of Nijmegen and Arnhem Operations—17 September 1944," 10 October 1944, Simpson Historical Research Center, Maxwell Air Force Base, Alabama.

9. Ibid.

10. *Europe: From Argument to V-E Day*, 626–27.

11. Eighth Air Force ORS, "Report on Attacks by Eighth Air Force Heavy Bombers Against Fortifications in the Metz-Thionville Areas (9 November 1944)," 29 November 1944. Listed in "Eighth Air Force, History of Operational Research Section," Leslie Arps, 520.303-3, Simpson Historical Research Center, Maxwell Air Force Base, Alabama.

12. *Europe: From Argument to V-E Day*, 627.

13. Ibid., 628.

14. Thomas Parrish and S. L. A. Marshall, eds., *The Simon and Schuster Encyclopedia of World War II* (New York, 1978), 511.

15. *Europe: From Argument to V-E Day*, 631–33.

16. "Attacks . . . in the Metz-Thionville Areas," 128.

17. *Europe: From Argument to V-E Day*," 632.

18. Ibid.

19. Ibid., 633.

20. Roger Freeman, "Mighty Eighth War Manual" (London: Janes, 1984), 51.

21. Angus Taylor, "Personal Narrative of an Operations Analyst," Eighth Air Force, 1944, 1945.

22. Ibid.

23. Ibid.

24. Headquarters, Third Bombardment Division, Operational Research Section, Eighth Air Force, "A Report on a Micro-H Bombing Missions During November 1944," 15 December 1944, Angus E. Taylor, 527.310-4 (November 1944), Simpson Historical Research Section, Maxwell Air Force Base, Alabama.

25. Leroy A. Brothers, *Operations Analysis in World War II, United States Army Air Forces* (Philadelphia: Stephenson-Brothers, 1948), 22.

26. "Attacks . . . in the Metz-Thionville Areas," 99.

27. "Report on Bombing Accuracy, Eighth Air Force, 1 September 1944–31 December 1944," 20 April 1945, Archives, Simpson Historical Research Center, Maxwell Air Force Base, Alabama.

28. G. Baley Price, *Gremlin Hunting in the Eighth Air Force, European Theater of Operations, 1943–1945*, 90.

29. "Attacks . . . in the Metz-Thionville Areas," 128.

30. *Gremlin Hunting*, 91.

31. Ibid., 90–91.

32. "The United States Strategic Bombing Survey, Overall Report (European War)," 30 September 1945, 50.

33. "Mission Report," 493d Bomb Group, Simpson Historical Research Center, Maxwell Air Force Base, Alabama.

34. Roger Freeman, *The Mighty Eighth, A History of the U.S. 8th Army Air Force* (London: Macdonald, 1970), 177.

35. *Gremlin Hunting*, 93.

36. Ibid., 93–94.

37. *Europe: From Argument to V-E Day*, 643.

38. "Strategic Bombing Survey," 42.

39. Ibid.

40. *Europe: From Argument to V-E Day*, 660.

41. "The Army Air Forces in World War II, Combat Chronology 1941–1945," 1973, Office of Air Force History, Simpson Historical Research Center, Maxwell Air Force Base, Alabama. See 2 November 1944, Eighth Air Force.

42. *Encyclopedia of World War II*, 193.

43. *The Mighty Eighth*, 193.

44. 493d Bomb Group Records, Microfilm, Simpson Historical Research Center, Maxwell Air Force Base, Alabama.

45. Ibid.

46. Ibid.

47. "Combat Chronology."

48. *Europe: From Argument to V-E Day*, 643.

49. "Report for Colonel W. B. Leach on the History and Development of the Bombs and Fuzes Subsection of the Operational Analysis Section, Headquarters Eighth Air Force," 10 April 1945, Bissell Alderman, 520.303-3, Archives, Simpson Historical Research Center, Maxwell Air Force Base, Alabama, 23.

50. Ibid.

51. Ibid., 24.

52. Ibid., 23–24.

53. *Europe: From Argument to V-E Day*, 643.

54. Ibid., 795.

55. OAS, Fifteenth Air Force, "A Report on the Bombing of the Oil Refineries at Naples, Italy," December 1943, George Housner, Simpson Historical Research Center, Maxwell Air Force Base, Alabama.

56. Ibid.

57. "Report of the Operations Analysis Section, Mediterranean Allied Air Forces, July 1943–July 1945," I. H. Crowne, section chief, 622.303, Simpson Historical Research Center, Maxwell Air Force Base, Alabama.

58. *Europe: From Argument to V-E Day*, 643.

59. Ibid., 649.

10

Operations Analysis in the Eighth Air Force
August–December 1944, Part III

Major Changes in Personnel

Seven analysts leave the section. In the last four months of 1944 there were major changes in the personnel of the section. During a reorganization of the staff of the Eighth Air Force headquarters in August, the section lost its original chief, John Harlan. He moved to SHAEF in London and was replaced by his deputy, Leslie Arps. Furthermore, Dr. Tuttle, one of the original six men of the section, the man who introduced Gee-H radar bombing into the Eighth Air Force, returned to the States early in October.

Other key members of the section were also lost during this period. Edwin Hewitt, pioneer of the zone system of firing in the Eighth Air Force and founder of the Gunnery Analysis Subsection, began to show signs of exhaustion from work-related stress, including voluntary missions. Hewitt was sent back to the States early in August. After a brief rest he resumed duties as a trouble-shooting gunnery analyst for the Twentieth Air Force with headquarters at the Pentagon.

At the end of August, Kenneth A. Norton returned to the States, where he served as an analyst with the Twentieth Air Force. Norton had served as the civilian analyst on radio countermeasures for over sixteen months with the Eighth Air Force ORS. Arps says:

> At the time Norton left the Section there was no one to take his place. For awhile it looked very much as though the ORS, which until then had held a prominent position in RCM matters, would have to retire from that field. [1]

The main project of the General Mission Analysis Subsection had become fuel consumption studies. This work essentially came to an end in July with the publication of the pamphlet "More Miles Per Gallon." The final report on this project was titled "The Prediction of the Fuel Consumed by B-17G Aircraft on Combined Missions," and dated 1 November 1944. The analysts working on the project were Louis Lusky, Frank M. Stewart, and George W. Mackey. When the project ended Lusky returned to the States in August, Mackey returned to the States in September, and the versatile Frank Stewart continued as an analyst with the Bombing Accuracy Subsection.

The final member of the section to leave in this period was Dr. Forrest R. Immer who left Bombing Accuracy analysis and returned to the States in November. [2]

Thirteen new analysts work for the section.   Of the six new analysts who joined the section in August, two were assigned, according to plan, to the headquarters of each of the three bomb divisions. The remaining seven new analysts were, in effect, replacements.

The first to arrive was James L. Morrisson. Morrisson had an A.B. from Harvard, 1938, and an LL.B. from Columbia University, 1941. He was employed as a law clerk to Chief Justice Harlan F. Stone of the United States Supreme Court in Washington, D.C., before he began his operations research work in August 1944. Morrisson worked as an analyst in the Loss and Battle Damage Subsection until 1 June 1945.

Next to sign up for operations research work was Dr. John W. Odle. Odle was an assistant professor of mathematics at Pennsylvania State College when he officially entered operations research work on 15 September 1944. Odle had a B.S., M.S., and Ph.D., all from University of Michigan. He worked as a specialist in flexible gunnery with the OAS of the Eighth Air Force until 22 July 1945.

Captain Robert Kessler joined the section on 22 September to assume the duties of the second in charge, after Major Bales, of Gee-H calculations. Kessler received his university training at Purdue.

Finally, the biggest influx of personnel was in the RCM (Radio Countermeasures) Subsection. First was Dr. Eugene G. Fubini, who took charge of the subsection on 1 September 1944. Dr. Fubini had been technical observer and engineer at the American-British Laboratory at Malvern. He earned a doctorate in physics from the University of Rome, 1933. Dr. Fubini served until 19 April 1945.

Next was Dr. Gerard P. Kuiper, who served two months in the RCM subsection from 25 September 1944 until 28 November 1944.

Dr. David B. Langmuir served nearly three months in the RCM Subsection from 1 November 1944 until 20 January 1945. Dr. Langmuir, a member of the London Mission, OSRD, was on loan to the section.

Finally, David Park served with the RCM Subsection from 1 November 1944 until 1 June 1945. He had been a research associate at the Radio Research Laboratory at Cambridge, Massachusetts. Park worked both for the RCM and the Loss and Battle Damage Subsections. [3]

RADIO COUNTERMEASURES OF THE EIGHTH AIR FORCE

Arps appeals for help from ABL-15.   The new chief of the section, Leslie Arps, realized the importance of the RCM program to the air force. When Kenneth Norton, head of the section's RCM Subsection, returned to the States, Arps appealed to Dr. John Dyer of the American-British Laboratory-15 (ABL-15) for help. Dyer responded by making Dr. Eugene Fubini available. Though he remained on the ABL-15 payroll, Fubini became an ORS consultant. Arps says:

> Never has a relationship been more satisfactory or gratifying. Two very desirable results were accomplished by this move: First, the Eighth Air Force acquired a man highly skilled in his field, well qualified to advise on the operational employment of RCM equipment; and second, ABL-15 secured first hand knowledge of operating conditions and problems. One of the consequences was that Eighth Air Force had available to it the resources of ABL-15 and as the occasion demanded personnel from ABL-15 (such as Drs. Kuiper and Langmuir) were placed on temporary duty with ORS so that the RCM commitments could be expeditiously handled. [4]

Carpet and Window (Chaff).   Flak had always been the major cause of damage to the bombers of the Eighth Air Force. By June 1944 the statistics of the Loss and Battle Damage Subsection showed that flak, rather than GAF planes, had also become the major cause of loss of the bombers. [5] Accordingly, efforts to minimize loss and battle damage due to flak were intensified. The Eighth Air Force became even more committed to radio countermeasures.

Carpet. The first use of Carpet by the Eighth Air Force had been on the 8 October 1943 mission to Bremen. [6] Airborne transmitters, Carpet I, were used to jam German radar. Carpet I was a "barrage jammer" which transmitted a continuous signal on a preset frequency range when in operation. In order to jam the frequency the enemy was using, at least half the bombers in the formation needed to be equipped with Carpet.

By the second half of 1944 a more sophisticated Carpet jammer became available, Carpet III. Carpet III was a selective spot jammer. "It consisted of a transmitter, receiver set, and indicator unit. The receiver, via a short aerial, 'swept' automatically for Würzburg transmissions. On receipt of a signal the automatic sweep stopped and a noise-modulated transmission was made to jam it." [7]

The Eighth Air Force embarked on an ambitious Carpet jamming program. Twelve planes of each group were to carry the new Carpet III jammer, and the remaining planes were to carry two sets of Carpet I each. The installations were made, group by group, and the job was accomplished by late autumn 1944.

Window (Chaff). Window, called Chaff by the Americans, was first used by the British. It was the simplest of the radio countermeasures. It consisted of metallic strips, cut to various lengths, that reflected radar waves, producing clutter on the radar scopes. This prevented ground controllers from pinpointing the approaching bombers. The first use of Chaff by the Eighth Air Force had been on the 20 December 1943 mission to the port area at Bremen. [8]

At first, bundles of Chaff, each containing 2,000 strips, were thrown out of waist gun windows. Later, special dispensing chutes were manufactured and installed in the radio operator's room on the B-17 and near a waist window in the B-24. By December 1944 all operational Eighth Air Force bombers had these dispenser chutes. One bundle of Chaff produced a response on enemy radar equivalent to a single bomber. Each bomber assigned to dispensing Chaff carried two to four cartons, each containing seventy-two bundles of Chaff. Chaff did not protect the bombers releasing it, only those which followed. Therefore, only the leading combat wings or groups carried it.

The use of Chaff varied according to attack altitudes, weather, types of radars, and the target itself. In general, a formation approaching a gun-defended target area began dispensing Chaff several minutes before the target and continued to release it until clear of the target area. The rate of discharge of the Chaff was prescribed at the briefing for the mission. It was usually fifteen bundles per minute. As the German flak defenses were strengthened Chaff was scattered over larger areas and in greater density in the vicinity of the targets.

From October 1944 on, special Chaff-dispensing formations of from six to twelve heavy bombers, B-17s and B-24s, were sent ahead of the main force on missions to screen the leading formations. Soon the faster, and hence less vulnerable Mosquito was also used for this purpose. [9]

The RCM Squadron—its RAF origins and activities. On 28 December 1943, the Eighth Bomber Command was charged with forming and training a special organization, the Radio Countermeasure Unit, to use radio countermeasures against enemy defenses. [10] The directive states that twenty-four specially equipped heavy bombers contributed by both American and British forces would operate in support of night and day raids. The RAF, already advanced in the use of RCM, had dedicated an entire group of planes, the 100th Group, to the use of RCM by November 1943. The Eighth Air Force met the 28 December 1943 directive by setting up, on 19 January 1944, an RCM squadron in the British 100th Group. This detachment trained with the British until mid-May 1944 when it moved from Great Britain's Sculthorpe base to Oulton, also British, to become operational. By June 1944 the squadron had a number, the 803d Bombardment Squadron (P), and it had twelve operational planes—mostly well-worn B-17s.

The planes of 803d Squadron were equipped with a mix of jammers. They either had Mandrel, a jammer designed for work against the German long-range early warning ground radars, Carpet, Rug (a variation of Carpet), Jackal (a new American device), or a combination of all of them.

The first operational jamming mission of the squadron was on the night of June 5/6 (D day). Four planes joined the RAF RCM aircraft in putting up a Mandrel screen to jam enemy radars that might otherwise have detected the Allied invasion fleet. During the rest of June and July, the RCM Squadron helped the RAF with night screens or in converting the squadron from a B-17 to a B-24 outfit. Early in August the squadron was given a new number, 36 Squadron, and moved to an American base—Cheddington. During August, September, and most of October, the squadron continued to assist the RAF with RCM work. During November 1944, however, it began to primarily support the Eighth Air Force on daylight missions. [11]

Spoofs and screens for the Eighth Air Force. By October 1944 the RCM Squadron had developed capabilities which were put to use regularly by the Eighth Air Force. Roger Freeman recounts:

> On 19 October 1944, when there was no daylight heavy bomber mission, six RCM B-24's attempted to simulate an assembling bomber force by spoof electronics and VHF radio traffic, a task they had previously practised for the RAF. The success of this operation and an increase in the RAF's own RCM capability were influential in an arrangement whereby 36 Bomb Squadron would be used to screen for 8th Air Force operations but still support Bomber Command on request. [12]

"Combat Chronology" gives 25 November 1944 as the date the Thirty-sixth Bomb Squadron began daily operations as a screening force for the bombardment divisions. It was assigned the task of protecting the Eighth's primary VHF and fighter-to-bomber communications from interception during assembly. Other activities included occasional spoof jamming of enemy VHF and electronic intelligence sorties. The squadron remained on this assignment until the end of the war in Europe.

Freeman gives a good description of a typical screening operation:

> VHF screening was usually conducted by four to eight aircraft taking off about 30 minutes before the bombers to position singly, about ten miles apart, in an arc 50 miles east of the bombers' assembly area. Each RCM B-24 flew a race track circuit and began jamming transmissions as altitude was increased for two to three hours, until the bomber formations were about to penetrate enemy airspace. During this period the jamming screen would gradually be advanced towards enemy territory. ... Spoof operations were conducted along the same lines but included VHF radio exchanges to simulate the usual radio telephone transmissions associated with bomber assembly. [13]

The ORS role in RCM work

Under Norton. The section had played a leadership role in the development and use of RCM. Norton, on 31 May 1943 (less than a month after his arrival in the theater), had recommended using a jammer against the German radar system by Eighth Air Force bombers. Furthermore, on 4 June 1943 he submitted a design for such a jammer (Carpet) which was then manufactured in the United States and became operational in the Eighth Air Force on 8 October 1943.

On 19 September and 3 October 1943 Norton had written memoranda on the possible use of Window in the Eighth Air Force for "the confusion of the enemy gunlaying radar sets in the immediate vicinity of the target." Window subsequently became operational in the Eighth Air Force on 20 December 1943. The importance of both of these programs increased as the air force grew, bombing became more frequent, and the Germans began to strengthen their antiaircraft defenses. Norton had kept busy analyzing the effectiveness of Carpet, its relatives, and Chaff. He served as a liaison between the Eighth Air Force, the RAF, and scientific agencies in England and the United States on RCM matters. He helped promote the use of the RCM Squadron for screening our rendezvous for missions from enemy radar. He wrote his first memorandum on this subject on 13 January 1944, six days before the RCM Squadron was officially formed. He wrote a second memorandum on the subject to Colonel Sullivan, the Eighth Air Force signal officer, on 21 February 1944, and a third on 7 March 1944.

Norton's last report was on "The Operational Effectiveness of the Radio Countermeasures Window and Carpet." [14]

Beginning late spring and early summer there was a large build-up of staff in the RCM Subsection. In August when Norton left the section, two officers and five enlisted personnel (one WAAF) worked full or part time on RCM matters.

Under Fubini. From September through December 1944 the RCM Subsection underwent its largest expansion. In addition to the three analysts (Dr. Kuiper, Dr. Langmuir, and David Park), two officers, an enlisted man, and Miss Katherine E. Mumford joined the subsection. Leslie Arps points out,

> Countermeasures are ever changing; for as the enemy takes steps to vitiate the effectiveness of RCM equipment so must the equipment or tactics be changed to offset the enemy action. To meet this situation, Dr. Fubini established close relationships with all intelligence sources on enemy radar both British and American. As a result the ORS became a clearing house for such information. The number of carpet installations on each aircraft, their frequency, and the type of spot jamming all were determined by Fubini, his ORS assistants and the ABL-15. [15]

From October on, special Chaff dispensing bombers preceded the main force on missions to screen the leading formations. Fubini's first recorded memorandum, dated September 1944, suggested that the swift British Mosquito Mark XVI, a fighter bomber, would be useful for dispensing Window (Chaff) and ought to be equipped for this purpose. This recommendation was put into effect by the air force. [16]

On 11 October Fubini issued a memorandum, "Recommendations for RCM Program," one day after RCM Squadron's 10 October spoof. As a result of that rendezvous, screening became part of the Eighth's RCM program on 25 November.

On 20 October Fubini issued a report "Analysis of Window Protection for the Month of September." On 30 November the subsection released another report, "Analysis of Window and Carpet Protection for the Month of October."

On 13 December 1944 Fubini's subsection issued another memorandum on "The Use of VHF and Radar Screens." [17]

Clearly Fubini had regained any momentum that may have been lost when Norton left the section.

GUNNERY, AUGUST–DECEMBER 1944

The resurgence of the German Air Force in the last four months of 1944 was an unprecedented turn of events. During the late spring and summer of 1944 American bomber fleets had met interference on some of their missions against the most vital targets, but most often they encountered no enemy air opposition.

Some thought strategic bombing of the German aircraft industry of the POINTBLANK campaign of early 1944 had shattered the industry beyond hope of recovery. This was not the case.

> Speer's ministry had worked its usual magic. Skillfully mobilizing materiel and manpower, it concentrated on the Me-109 and FW-190 types and effectively dispersed aircraft production from 27 main plants to 729 smaller ones, some of which were located in quarries, caves, mines, forests, or just in villages. In doing this, the Germans abandoned mass production methods and greatly increased their costs, but they also concealed most of their production centers from both the bombardiers and intelligence officers of their enemy. In the long run, the effort defeated itself, particularly when the transportation chaos of early 1945 paralyzed so much of the Reich, but the immediate effects were spectacular. The number of single-engine fighters accepted by the German Air Force rose from 1,016 in February, 1944, at a steady rate month by month until it reached 3,013 in September, after which a slow decline set in.

The total number of fighters of all types produced in September, 1944, Germany's peak month of the war in this respect, amounted to 4,103, which compared favorably with Speer's schedule calling for 5,372. It was altogether an amazing feat of industrial planning and management, but fortunately the gasoline and pilot shortage forbade the use of fighters in any such numbers.[18]

German single-engine fighters, such as the Me-109 and the FW-190, were the real menace during this period. The Eighth Air Force, however, still had to be greatly concerned about the German jet fighters. They began appearing more frequently and in greater numbers.

The first Allied combat with a German jet fighter took place on 29 July 1944. An American pilot, Captain Arthur Jeffrey, on the way home from escort work to Merseburg in a P-38, attacked an Me-163 that was stalking a straggling B-17. The Me-163 was awarded to Jeffrey as "destroyed" after the combat film was examined. One month later, on 29 August 1944, Major Joe Myers in a P-47 near Brussells, Belgium, dived down on a low-flying Me-262, causing it to crash. Myers and a crew member were credited with this first Me-262 "kill."[19]

Gunnery matters in August

Ayres' memorandum on the Me-163 and Me-262. On 9 August, just ten days after the first Allied encounter with the Me-163, Dr. W. L. Ayres of the ORS wrote a "Memorandum on Defensive Fire Against the German Fighters Me-163 and Me-262." These two encounters warranted a re-examination of the aiming rules used for defensive fire from bombers. Ayres wrote, "The problem is to determine the changes in the present Zone and Position firing rules necessary to hit these fighters at higher airspeeds."[20]

Because intelligence reports "seem[ed] to indicate a figure of 500 to 550 miles per hour" as the speed of the new planes, Ayres computed separate figures for speeds of 500, 550, and 600 miles per hour. He also assumed the bombers were flying a straight course at 155 mph. Separate computations were made for 20,000 and 25,000 feet.

Ayres found, fortunately, that "no change need be made in the aiming rules for attacks within 45 degrees of the nose or tail. On attacks nearer the beam the present aiming rules must be reduced by 1/2 rad." Ayres correctly anticipated that most of the attacks from the jets would be from the tail quarter, and hence there would be little change in the defensive fire except that the length of the attack would be shorter and the gunner would have to "be more alert to begin his fire the instant the attacking fighter comes within range."[21]

The view from Short Bursts. Porter Henry's monthly magazine for gunners, *Short Bursts*, and the German jets both made their debuts in July 1944. *Short Bursts* did an extremely effective job of communicating vital information to the combat crews—especially the gunners—in time enough to do plenty of good.

> A monthly magazine for aerial gunners...founded in July, 1944, in order to furnish information concerning new gunnery equipment, German fighter tactics, etc., to combat crews and gunnery officers of the 8th AF. The magazine attempts to dress up this dry technical material by the use of 'gag' style of writing and abundant cartoon and art drawings so that it will be read by all gunners.... The magazine is written by J. Porter Henry, and the art work and cartooning is done by Cpl. John Faulkner." [22]

Though 1,100 copies of the first issue were printed, this number was soon raised to 2,600 because Eighth Air Force groups, the Ninth Air Force, the Fifteenth Air Force, and the RAF all requested more copies.

The leading article of the August issue was on "The German Jet Fighter." September's leading article was, "The 163, It's Poison!" Each issue contained an article on the encounters of the previous month between Eighth Air Force bombers and German fighters. The issue included a monthly boxscore of enemy aircraft destroyed, classified by groups and gun positions. By September Henry had plenty to write about.

In August, fifteen of the approximately forty operational groups of Eighth Air Force heavies had encounters with the GAF. The heavies were credited with twenty-nine fighters destroyed, eleven probably destroyed, and thirty-eight damaged. Although most of these attacks were by 109s and 190s, two different groups, on 16 and 24 August, had been attacked by Me-163s.

The article on jets in the September issue begins with this statement:

> Jet Propelled [actually rocket propelled] Me-163s went into action against our bomber formations last month—and the score didn't make our gunnery look any too sharp. The jetties shot down at least three B-17s, with the gunners chalking up a record of only one damaged and four no-claims. Escorting fighters destroyed two of the 163s. [23]

Porter Henry held special gunner critiques at the groups. With the cooperation of the division gunnery and intelligence officers as well as the group gunnery officers, he printed the following advice in *Short Bursts*.

> 1. YOU CAN TRACK THEM. Don't pay any attention to the intelligence reports that say the 163s attack so fast it's impossible to track them. On tail attacks, they go no faster, and maybe a little slower, than a 109 or 190. The 163s make climbing and diving attacks at very high speed, but it's still possible to track them. Of course, when the 163s are flying through the formation, or breaking away at close range, that's something else again.

2. KEEP A SHARP SEARCH. These babies are small and have a very thin wing—they're hard to see. You can't rely on spotting their contrail, because most of their attacks are made in a dive with the jet off—they'll catch you with your electrically heated pants down.

3. BE SURE TO SEARCH HIGH AND LOW. The jetties often make diving attacks from very high—almost straight up. Or they may attack from very low in a steep climb. One 163 sneaked up under a formation, knocked out the 17 in Purple Heart corner, and flew out right over the low squadron without a single shot being fired at it from any bomber in the box.

4. WATCH FOR JETTIES NEAR THE TARGET. Except for isolated attacks on stragglers, the jetties made their attacks around the I.P. [i.e., just before the bomb run] or right after the bomb run. They drilled right in through their own flak, hitting the B-17s at a time when plenty of gunners had their heads behind the armor instead of behind their sights. All jet fighter attacks last month were in the LEIPZIG area, but you may run into them farther west. If Me-262s hit us, it'll probably be somewhere around MUNICH. But you can never tell...

5. OPEN FIRE AT LONG RANGE. The jetty usually closes plenty fast, and there's not much time for shooting. Use your Position Firing rules, and smack him while he's way out there.

6. BE ALERT FOR BREAKAWAY SHOTS. In several cases, a 163 attacked the low squadron from 5 o'clock very low, rolling out about level with the high squadron and breaking away toward 9 o'clock. This gave the high squadron's gunners a momentary no-deflection shot. Plenty of lead was thrown around and some strikes were seen but the jetties got away. Watch for this chance— if the 163 seems to hang in the air like a sitting duck for an instant while making its breakaway, dish it to him pointblank.[24]

Henry's analysis of the GAF attacks on the bombers in August pointed up a number of facts. First, 90 percent of the attacks were from the tail. Second, attacks by the conventional German fighters were made when there were gaps in the fighter escort. Third, in several GAF attacks the number of bombers shot down was twice as high as the number of fighters destroyed by bomber gunners. Needless to say, this was very disturbing to Eighth Air Force gunnery officers.

New waist gun sights. At the end of August 1944 and the beginning of September, Allied armies had advanced to the German West Wall—the Siegfried Line. There was a general feeling among the Allies that the war would soon be over. This attitude is reflected in the first sentence of an article on "The K-13, Its Care and Feeding" in the September issue of *Short Bursts.*

Henry says, "Now that the war in the ETO is about over, we're finally beginning to get a decent waist gun sight—the K-13 compensating sight, produced by that noble old Brookline institution, the Sperry Corporation."

By September 1944 each group in the command had at least one of the new sights for training. A lot more were supposed to be coming soon. The K-13 was a compensating sight, not a computing sight. It was actually a sort of mechanical position firing machine. Thus, it gave the correct deflection only for a fighter making a pursuit curve attack on a bomber. In order to use the sight it was necessary to set the plane's indicated air speed and altitude into the computing dials at the front of the sight. The computer on the sight then gave a number which was the bomber's true air speed minus the allowance for the fighter's motion. This number then had to be set into a dial on the sight, and then all the gunner had to do was to put the bead on the fighter and fire the gun.

Acknowledgment. The September 1944 issue of *Short Bursts* bore this acknowledgment:

> *Short Bursts* is put together approximately once a month by a feather merchant named Henry in the Operational Research Section in cooperation with the Air Force Gunnery Officer (Maj. John H. Stark). Art work this month by Pfc. John (Rembrandt) Faulkner. All suggestions, contributions, and advance payments on subscriptions may be sent to Headquarters Eighth Air Force, ATTN. ORS.

Gunnery matters in September and October

The company front attack. The lead article of the October issue of *Short Bursts* was titled "Company Front." [25] Straight from the pen of Porter Henry, it begins:

> If there's anybody around the ETO still giving out with that stuff about gunnery training not being important, we have a fine sack set aside for him in Section 8 [the Army outfit for mental patients].
>
> The brass boys as usual, have a two-dollar word for it—the company front attack. In simple English, 109's and 190's, concentrating on one wing or one group as usual, are making mass tail attacks with anywhere from six to 30 fighters in line abreast formation, and usually with three or four waves coming in one right after the other. The 190's carry two 30 mms, two 20 mms, and two machine guns.
>
> The GAF has been damn successful with this stunt—so far. In one case he caught a combat wing [three groups] that had wandered off by itself and practically wiped it out—only four bombers came back.
>
> On another mission, the company front rubbed out the entire

low box from a wing formation. Twice he succeeded in shooting down all but a few planes out of a 12-ship box.

Specific GAF attacks in September

11 SEPTEMBER. The strongest GAF response to Eighth Air Force attacks since 28 May occurred on 11 September, when 850 heavy bombers escorted by fourteen fighter groups bombed oil and other targets in Germany. An estimated 525 fighters attacked the formation or were engaged by Eighth Air Force planes. A total of fifty-two heavy bombers (all causes) and thirty-two American fighters were lost. The heavy bombers claimed seventeen fighters and the American fighters claimed 116 in the air and forty-two on the ground. [26]

In *Short Bursts* Porter Henry tells us:

> The remaining Division, dispersing to attack Chemnitz, Ruhland, Brux, and Bohlen, was hit by the eastward concentration of 100 fighters. The enemy aircraft swamped the light escort and went to work on one wing headed for Ruhland.
>
> Here for the first time the GAF unleashed its company front. Popping up through 5/10 cumulus clouds, the fighters slammed into the trailing low box of the wing in waves reported as high as 30 abreast, hitting from 6 o'clock level slightly high and breaking away underneath. All 12 Fortresses were knocked out. [27]

All of these planes were from the 100th Group. On the same day in another encounter with the GAF, the Ninety-second Group suffered eight bombers missing. Four others were so badly damaged they landed on the Continent. [28]

12 SEPTEMBER. On 12 September over 800 of the Eighth's heavy bombers, escorted by fifteen fighter groups, attacked four synthetic oil plants, two oil refineries, an oil depot, and several targets of opportunity in Germany. The Eighth Air Force was opposed by 400 to 450 German fighters. The bombers lost forty-five (all causes) and claimed destruction of twenty-seven fighters. Thirteen P-51s were lost. American fighters claimed sixty-three air victories plus twenty-six on the ground. [29]

Twenty-three of the bombers were lost on 12 September to the GAF. The 493d Bomb Group, which had become operational on 6 June, a little over three months earlier, had a squadron which was flying low box of a combat wing headed for Magdeburg. It was attacked by Me-109s which came in singly from the nose and tail. This was the first encounter of the 493d with the GAF. It cost them seven B-17s. [30] The 493d Bomb Group had been a B-24 group until the middle of August when it was taken off operations for three weeks to convert to B-17s. Thus, the 493d was attacked by the GAF for the first time after about two months of actual operations. [31]

Porter Henry's version of this in *Short Bursts* is:

Over Magdeburg, 20 109s made aggressive tail attacks on the low group of one combat wing, bagging seven of the 12 forts. A jab by a 163 against another element of this Division resulted in the first "probable" scored against the jets by a bomber gunner. [32]

27 SEPTEMBER. On 27 September the Second Division sent 315 B-24s over solid undercast to the Henschel engine and vehicle plants at Kassel with thirty-seven aircraft of the 445 Group leading the Second Combat Wing. They were navigating with Gee-H. At the IP the group took a wrong heading and moved away from the bomber column. The group made a Pathfinder attack on what it thought was Kassel, but the bombs fell just outside Göttingen, twenty miles away. [33] The GAF saw its opportunity with this isolated group. Porter Henry tells what happened:

> First were the decoys—a couple of enemy aircraft doing acrobatics to the side and rear to divert the gunner's attention. Then the company front (FW-190s), hitting from 6 o'clock level in three waves of 30 each. Each wave was divided into three sections of 10 each, flying line-abreast or a flat V, with each section concentrating on one box. The first two waves swept through the formation and broke downward; the third pulled up and was reforming for another attack when the fighter escort arrived. In 3 minutes 26 bombers were lost. [34]

28 SEPTEMBER. On 28 September the Eighth Air Force sent 1,000 bombers to attack two synthetic oil plants, a motor plant, and a city area in or near Magdeburg. Fifteen supporting fighter groups claimed twenty-six enemy aircraft. However, over thirty heavy bombers failed to return. [35] According to Porter Henry, eighteen bombers were lost to enemy aircraft which came up through the undercast. Six abreast, they attacked low boxes.

The "Box Score for September of Enemy Aircraft Destroyed, by Groups," which appeared in the October issue of *Short Bursts*, shows that eight groups in the First Bomb Division, two groups in the Second Bomb Division, and eight groups in the Third Bomb Division were attacked by the GAF in September. The three divisions were credited with a total of seventy-one enemy aircraft destroyed, thirty-seven probably destroyed, and thirty-nine damaged.

Major Stark's grim memorandum. The command and especially the gunnery officers were shaken by the loss statistics for September. In a "Memorandum to Pilots" printed in the October issue, Major Stark, the Eighth Air Force officer, made the statement:

> In September, 1943, B-17 and B-24 gunners were destroying 18.8 enemy aircraft for each bomber lost to enemy aircraft. In September 1944, our gunners were destroying 0.61 enemy aircraft for

each bomber lost to enemy fighters—less than one for one." One bomber for one fighter was a very unequal exchange. It meant, for one thing, that we lost nine or ten men for every one of theirs.

What could change this ratio from 18.8 to one in September 1943 to 0.61 to one in September 1944? Major Stark zeroed in on one cause. Throughout late spring and summer of 1944 not only individual crews but also entire groups went months without encountering the GAF. Gunnery discipline had grown lax. Stark wrote:

> There seems now to be an everyday problem of getting some gunners, commissioned and non-commissioned, to stay at their combat stations, take along adequate ammunition, load their guns, fight off attacks, lend support fire, and even to open or return fire when attacked by enemy fighters."

Stark then proceeds to cite some actual cases:

> 1. Recently two bombers, each in the No. 3 position, were shot down by fighters attacking from about 5 o'clock, a little high of level—not out of the sun or clouds. Neither bomber opened fire, nor was there any fire from the No. 1 or No. 2 ships.
>
> 2. In another September case, an attacking 109 almost crashed a bomber from 6 o'clock level. There was no fire from the tail gunner. When the ship returned to base the tail gunner was found dead at his gun station—both boxes were full of ammunition, but the guns weren't loaded.
>
> 3. Another gunner explained why he had not fired at a sure kill—he was up in the waist and couldn't get back to his turret in time. [36]

Although discipline needed to be improved—and was—the above cases were extreme. Therefore, they could not explain the radical decline in the ratio of fighters downed to bombers from September 1943 to September 1944. Part of the explanation lay in improved German tactics, such as the company front attack.

The company front attack from the rear was ingenious. It was relatively easy to execute and utilized even inadequately trained pilots effectively. When a single plane attacked a bomber squadron from the rear the guns of a number of the bombers could be concentrated on the single attacker. When a squadron was attacked by a number of planes flying line abreast, the defensive fire of the squadron was dispersed.

Roger Freeman, with the benefit of postwar knowledge, explains some things about the company front attack that helped make it so deadly and so resistant to our fire:

The success of the Sturmgruppe tactics, perfected by Moritz with IV/J.G.3, encouraged General Galland to propose the formation of like units in each Jagdeschwader. In August 1944 J.G.4 had been reorganized along these lines and Gruppe II equipped with the 'heavy fighter.' This was the FW-190A-8, specially modified to give the pilot extra protection against defensive fire when attacking the rear of the bomber formation. A 60 mm sheet of armoured glass was placed inside the cockpit canopy to protect the head; and to shield legs and body against lateral fire, armour plates were fixed on either side of the front cockpit extending down to the wing roots. However accurate a bomber gunner's aim, the Sturm pilot was well protected from .50 bullets; only serious hits on some vital part of his aircraft could deflect his own aim; and in any case a rear gunner faced a very small target in a FW-190 approaching from dead astern. The full armament of the FW-190 used by II/J.G.4 was two 13 mm and two 20 mm guns plus wing-mounted 30 mm cannon. The tactics employed by J.G.4 were modelled on those of J.G.3 although the new Sturm organization made almost all its interceptions from the rear when it was a 'company front' (line abreast) saturation formation occasion. [37]

6 OCTOBER. In an attack on Berlin on 6 October the company front hit the last group of the last wing which was lagging slightly after the turn at the IP. The GAF sent out decoys at four o'clock and eight o'clock just before the attack. The main force achieved surprise by breaking through an overcast about 1,000 feet above the formation and catching the high box. About seventy fighters made a level attack in waves of six to eight, wiping out eleven bombers.

7 OCTOBER. On 7 October, the Eighth Air Force sent 1,300 heavy bombers to strike five synthetic oil plants and other targets in central and northeast Germany. The nineteen escorting fighter groups claimed twenty-two enemy aircraft, including four jets. However, both air opposition and ground fire took their toll—fifty-two bombers and fifteen fighters were lost. [38] Porter Henry tells us in *Short Bursts*:

> After a sideshow by a couple of 163s, 100 single engine fighters, mostly 190s, shoved its company front into a lightly escorted wing, most of them concentrating on the low box—nine bombers were shot out of the low box and three out of other boxes. [39]

8 OCTOBER–1 NOVEMBER. Throughout the rest of October, Eighth Air Force flyers seldom saw a German fighter. No claims whatsoever were made in this period by our airmen. What was the GAF up to?

Odle reports for duty. Dr. John W. Odle reported for duty as a gunnery analyst with the Eighth Air Force ORS on 2 October 1944. In addition to having earned a Ph.D. in mathematics, Odle had spent three weeks completing basic gunnery instruction at Laredo Army Air Field, a month with the Applied Mathematics Group at Columbia University, and several days at the Ballistics Research Laboratory at Aberdeen, Maryland. [40]

When Odle arrived the Gunnery Subsection was headed by Dr. W. L. Ayres, on leave from his headship of the mathematics department at Purdue. Porter Henry was the other civilian analyst with the section. With Odle the section consisted of three civilian analysts. In addition, on the staff was Lt. J. S. Jillson, a former B-17 gunner, and Corporal John F. Faulkner, draftsman and artist for *Short Bursts* and other projects requiring illustrations.

Drs. Ayres and Odle handled all the mathematical and technical work of the section. Lt. Jillson assisted as a computer expert, field man, and advisor on practical aspects of gunnery. Porter Henry and Corporal Faulkner wrote and illustrated *Short Bursts* and prepared posters and informational material to update gunners on the latest gunnery equipment, procedures, and Luftwaffe tactics.

Harmonization. Odle arrived just in time to participate in three major projects begun by Ayres. Odle writes:

> The first [of these] consisted of a series of firing tests of operational B-17 and B-24 gun positions and a lengthy set of ballistic computations, to determine the best possible sight harmonization patterns. I helped with some of the firing tests and did part of the ballistic computations.
>
> The harmonization schemes recommended in these reports were adopted by all the 8th Air Force groups, and this study was considered to be one of the most valuable contributions to gunnery ever made by our section. Major John Stark, 8th Air Force gunnery officer, opposed the study at its inception, but Dr. Ayres went ahead with it anyway, and eventually Major Stark became an enthusiastic exponent of the methods we recommended. [41]

FIRING TESTS. In studying aiming, the size of the bullet pattern of a burst is important. Yet Ayres found that there was no available data on the size of the pattern *under usual operating conditions*. Available figures were based on clamped guns or other optimum conditions, such as new guns and perfectly serviced equipment. Furthermore, the climb of a gun during the burst was discussed continually, but no figures were available. Also, the harmonization of the equipment made no allowance for this.

In order to get answers Ayres conducted an extensive series of firings during the summer of 1944 with the cooperation of the 389th, 452d, and 486th Bomb Groups. Nearly 700 patterns of twelve-round bursts were fired from the various gun positions of B-17 and B-24 airplanes. Under the limitations of ground firing, the test was designed to determine the average pattern fired by combat gunners with operational equipment under field conditions. The planes used were operational planes. In most cases they were flown on combat missions the day before or the day after the firing tests. The equipment was not serviced or adjusted in any way for the firing tests. Many planes and combat gunners were used to assure a random sample. The results represented average firings under combat conditions. [42]

The results appeared in a report titled "Gun Climb, Harmonization and Bullet Pattern," dated 12 November 1944. The Eighth Air Force used these results to harmonize its guns.

HARMONIZATION OF GUNS. The October issue of *Short Bursts* includes an article, "Harmonization in One Easy Lesson," which exemplifies Porter Henry's technical writing. Under the word "Harmonizing" appears a trio of singers. The little guy in the center has a head which is unmistakably a machine gun sight. The tall guys on each end have machine gun barrels for heads. As art the cartoon is questionable, though it does catch the reader's attention.

The article is prefaced by the following:

> Armament and Gunnery Officers of the 1st Division recently got together with all the latest poop on ballistics and the results of the Eighth Air Force gun climb tests, and worked out an up-to-date harmonization procedure. The result was an Armament Sergeant's dream—a simple system of harmonizing every gun position, accurately allowing for gravity drop and gun climb, without using a single pattern stand.

About gravity-drop harmonization, Henry writes,

> Let's begin by reviewing the general idea of gravity-drop harmonization. Roll up your pants, gents, here we go again: As you learned back in basic gunnery school, the bullet starts dropping as soon as it leaves the barrel, and drops faster and faster the farther out it goes. If you lined up your sights exactly parallel with the gun bore and fired at zero elevation, the bullet would drop farther and farther below the line of sight like this:

line of sight

bullet drop

> (We're talking only about guns with iron and optical sights—not computing sights.)
> Natcherly, it would be smart to raise the gun barrel just a little

bit with respect to the line of sight. The result would be this:

600 yards

Now, the path of the bullet is a little above the line of sight part of the way, and a little below it the rest of the way, but it's pretty close to it all the way out.

In that diagram, the sights are harmonized for 600 yards—that is, the bullet comes back down across the line of sight at 600 yards. By raising the gun a little more, we could harmonize for 800 yards, or 1,000 yards, or whatever.

But what about gun climb? Let's say you sight at a target and pull the trigger. If your sighting is perfect, your first bullet will go where you aimed it. But the recoil raises the barrel just a little and holds it there, so that all your shots after the first one go a little higher than your original aiming point. And that, as even a bombardier can plainly see, is going to have some effect on our harmonization S.O.P. There's no sense in raising the gun barrel to allow for gravity drop if gun climb is going to raise the gun barrel anyway.

People have been talking about gun climb for a long time, but nobody got around to studying it until last summer when Doc Ayres of the Operational Research Section (We compute 'em— you shoot 'em) conducted a flock of firing tests—these tests showed that on hand-held guns, the effect of gun climb just about cancelled out the effect of gravity drop. On the Bendix chin [nose gun turret in the B-17], the gun climb was less than the gravity drop, so some allowance for gravity drop seemed necessary.

So here's the new harmonization S.O.P. (we give it for the Bendix chin only): field harmonize by boresighting on an object more than 1,000 yards away, disconnect the sight, raise the guns 3 mils, and reconnect the sight. [43]

That sample was an important part of Henry's work—making complex technical matters simple and plain for the aircrew men.

Gunnery matters in November and December

The four air battles in November. These are the barebones statistics of the four November air battles between the Eighth Air Force and the GAF as they are found in "Combat Chronology" or other sources. [44,45]

2 NOVEMBER. The Eighth Air Force sent 1,100 heavy bombers in five separate forces to attack synthetic oil plants at Merseburg-Leuna and other targets

in Germany. Two main forces, 683 B-17s, went to the Merseburg plants. Opposition was heavy with an estimated 500 GAF fighters in all, an estimated 400 at Merseburg. Forty heavy bombers were lost at Merseburg, twenty-six to the GAF. The seventeen escorting fighter groups lost twenty-eight planes, perhaps eight to the GAF. The Eighth Air Force claimed 160 German fighters in all with 134 due to the Eighth's fighters. Nine of an estimated fifteen Me-163s penetrated the escort to make single attacks on the bombers.

21 NOVEMBER. Over 1,100 heavy bombers attacked the synthetic oil refinery at Merseburg-Leuna, two oil refineries at Hamburg, and a number of other targets in Germany. An estimated 400 German fighters were in the air. Thirty four American fighters and bombers were lost. American fighters claimed over seventy German fighters destroyed.

26 NOVEMBER. The Eighth Air Force sent 1,000 heavy bombers to bomb a mix of targets in Germany including the Misburg oil refinery. About 550 German fighters were encountered. Over thirty-five heavy bombers were lost, twenty-five to German fighters. United States fighters claimed over 100 German fighters destroyed. The German attacks were unusually vicious. The dangerous line-abreast (company front) attack proved deadly to one entire bomber squadron. [46]

27 NOVEMBER. More than 450 bombers attacked the Bingen and Offenburg marshalling yards and five targets of opportunity with five fighter groups flying escort. Ten groups of fighters, two of them fighter bomber groups, were sent to oil targets in north central Germany but failed to locate their primary targets. Eight of these fighter groups were jumped by about 750 German fighters (the largest sighting to date) in the Magdeburg, Münster, and Hannover areas when the hapless Germans mistook them for heavy bomber formations. American fighters claimed ninety-six destroyed against eleven losses.

The November air battles were significant defeats for the GAF. Germany had concentrated its gasoline and forces for big efforts against the strategic air forces with the objective of knocking down hundreds of big bombers at one time. This, however, had been prevented by the Eighth Air Force and by the Germans themselves whose battle plans for their fighter arm were incompatible.

Throughout this period Generals Spaatz and Doolittle, concerned about the obvious buildup of the GAF, wondered if the Eighth Air Force was following the best strategy. Should they scale down the oil campaign and go after the GAF in a more direct way? They wisely decided to continue the oil campaign.

The ORS gunnery posters. The resurgence of the GAF in July 1944 called for new Allied tactics and activities each month. The section needed a way to quickly communicate major GAF actions between monthly issues of *Short Bursts*. Porter Henry, Ayres, gunnery officers, and intelligence officers discussed ways to best inform combat crews of GAF attacks and tactics. They decided the section would issue a GAF tactics poster after each mission which encountered sizable enemy opposition. The first poster covered the 2 November air battle. By the end of December six posters had been issued.

Each poster displayed a diagram of the attack with the routes of all three divisions, a description of the type of attacks flown, and general observations and comments. The material was assembled from intelligence sources and information from critiques of the returning gunners. By working a twenty-four-hour shift in the section, staff distributed the poster to the bomber flying stations within forty-eight hours after the mission was completed. They were posted in crew libraries and briefing rooms. The posters were very effective in swiftly getting their message to the combat crews. Ayres wrote:

> The Commanding General of one Division considered the posters of such urgency that special courier runs are scheduled so that the posters may reach his stations without delay. [47]

By request the distribution of these posters was extended to include the bomber stations of the Ninth and Fifteenth Air Forces and the fighter stations of the Eighth Air Force.

The two German plans for the use of the GAF in November and December. The GAF had two plans in November and December 1944. One was the plan of General Galland, commanding general of the German Fighter Forces. The other was the plan of Adolf Hitler, kept secret from Galland. Hitler's plan called for using the GAF as a tactical air force in the Ardennes offensive.

GALLAND'S PLAN FOR "THE GREAT BLOW." Adolf Galland's book, *The First And The Last,* [48] provides a history of the air war in the West from the perspective of a German fighter pilot. Galland saw action from the conquest of Poland, at which time he was promoted to captain, until the end of the war in Europe when he was a lieutenant general. In mid-1941 Galland was promoted to general of the Fighter Arm, becoming, at twenty-nine, the youngest general in the German services. In 1944, at thirty-two, Galland was both a fighter ace and commander of the Fighter Forces in the West. Galland consistently advocated emphasizing the Fighter Arm, but often found himself overruled by Hermann Göring, the chief of the Luftwaffe, and by Hitler, who favored bombers.

General Galland and Albert Speer, chief of German war production, knew that the oil campaign of the Allies had to be stopped or the war would be lost. Galland wrote, "If it were impossible to stop the destruction from the air, then productively, technically, and militarily, it would be impossible to continue with the conduct of the war."

Thus Speer, despite Allied bombing, had managed to increase the production of aircraft, and Galland, with the support of Göring and Hitler, was allowed to build up the Fighter Arm of the Luftwaffe in the West. Galland describes his plan to stop the strategic bombing of the Eighth Air Force.

> The Great Blow had been carefully planned and worked out in all details. All commodores and commanders were called together for a rehearsal at the 1st Fighter Corps in Treuenbrietzen, during which four or five different action and approach flights were practiced with all variations. It was wholly agreed that in the frame of the planned action the following points had to be achieved:
>
> 1. In the first action at least 2000 fighters in 11 combat formations of the 1st Fighter Corps were to be brought into contact with the approaching bomber formation.
>
> 2. During the fly-in and the return of the enemy about another 150 fighters of the Luftwaffe Command, West, were to be sent up.
>
> 3. In the second action another 500 fighters were to be brought into contact with the enemy.
>
> 4. About 100 night fighters were to screen the borders toward Sweden and Switzerland to catch damaged or straggling single bombers.
>
> 5. To shoot down an approximate total of 400–500 four-engine bombers against a loss of about 400 aircraft and about 100–150 pilots.
>
> This was going to be the largest and most decisive air battle of the war. On November 12, 1944, the entire fighter arm was ready for action: 18 fighter wings with 3,700 aircraft and pilots—a fighting force such as the Luftwaffe had never possessed before. More than 3000 of these were expecting the Great Blow. [49]

This was just the kind of action that Generals Spaatz and Doolittle were concerned might happen. However, the plan was never implemented.

HITLER'S PLANS FOR A GREAT BLOW. While waiting for favorable weather to deliver the Great Blow, Galland, in the middle of November 1944, received "an alarming order—the fighter reserves were to be prepared for action on the front where a great land battle was expected in the West." Galland explains his alarm:

> The whole training had been aimed at action in defense of the Reich. All new pilots should have had some training in the totally different conditions at the front, but petrol shortage forbade this. With regard to the supply situation it would have been irresponsible to use the stores accumulated for the Great Blow for training purposes. Moreover the internal organization of the units, the tactics, the armament, the equipment, were only suited for the special task of the defense of the Reich. A readjustment within a fortnight, as had been ordered, could not be undertaken. The experience and standard of the unit leaders and pilots could be re-

garded as just passable for the defense of the Reich, but for action at the front they were absolutely out of the question. [50]

On 20 November the order for the transfer of Galland's forces to the West was given—over his objections. Only two fighter wings remained behind. For months Galland had been engaged in mobilizing a fighter force for the defense of the Reich, which all along Hitler planned to use as a tactical force in the Ardennes counteroffensive (Battle of the Bulge).

Galland says:

> Until the very last I was kept in the dark, and only a few days before the start of the offensive in the Ardennes was I informed of the plan. Only then did I realize that the High Command from the beginning had understood something quite different by the Great Blow, and that the intention to go over to the offensive in the west already existed at the end of July.

The formation of a fighter reserve sufficient to stop the strategic bombing of the Eighth Air Force was Galland's last major task as general of the Fighter Arm. He concludes, "The reserve was there; then it was taken away from me. For me any sense in continuing the struggle collapsed at this moment." [51]

Thus, the Eighth Air Force was not put to the test of the great air battle for which Galland had been planning.

December

MILITARY ACTION. Hitler's great gamble, the Ardennes counteroffensive or Battle of the Bulge, began on 16 December 1944 and was over by 28 January 1945. It was the largest pitched battle ever fought by American arms. The Germans suffered about 100,000 casualties and the Americans, 81,000. Both sides lost as many as 800 tanks each, and the Germans lost over 1,000 planes. [52]

On nine of the fifteen days from 1 December through 15 December, before the beginning of the German offensive, the Eighth Air Force could fly strategic missions. It was opposed by the GAF only twice, on 2 December and on 5 December. On 2 December the Germans made their first serious effort in months to defend targets west of the Rhine, sending about 150 fighters to intercept the big bombers. Evidently, some of Galland's reserve had reached the western front. On 5 December when the Eighth Air Force bombed Berlin, some 300 German fighters attempted to interfere. The escort claimed ninety fighters destroyed.

The Eighth Air Force did its best to help with the ground battle during December. Bad weather on four of the last sixteen days of December made it impossible to send out any bombers. On six of the sixteen days weather permitted an average of only 250 bombers to be sent out. Eleven of the twelve missions flown from 16 to 31 December were exclusively against tactical targets in the battle area—marshalling yards, bridges, road junctions, etc.

The GAF managed to oppose five of the twelve missions.

On 23 December, Eighth Air Force fighters encountered an estimated 450 fighters and claimed sixty-nine. On 24 December, Eighth Air Force fighters encountered 200 fighters and claimed seventy. On 25 December our fighters encountered 300 fighters and claimed forty—quite a way to celebrate Christmas.

I myself was at Stone, England, eating turkey and waiting for orders to return to the States, having finished my combat tour with my thirty-fifth mission to Merseburg-Leuna on 6 December.

On 27 December 200 fighters were encountered and thirty claimed. On 31 December, 150 fighters were engaged and sixty enemy craft claimed. On this day, though fourteen heavy bombers were lost, our bombers claimed twenty-six fighters. [53]

THE GUNNERY SECTION CARRIES ON. In this exceptional month, December 1944, in which the Battle of the Bulge was started and decided, the Gunnery Subsection was very active. Porter Henry and Faulkner had their hands full with *Short Bursts* and the air battle posters. Ayres and Odle were busy completing Ayres' projects before he returned to the States in January.

One of the studies under way when Odle joined the section in October was about offset guns in German fighter planes. Early in 1944 the Luftwaffe experimented with guns that fired at an angle rather than straight ahead. The GAF did not make extensive use of such planes, but the section wanted to be prepared to meet the threat if it became serious. Odle completed the mathematical analysis of the aiming and flying problems such equipment would entail, and Ayres and Odle collaborated on a final report, "Fighter Attacks with Offset Guns" which was completed on 28 December 1944. [54]

Another area of concern was support-fire problems. How a gunner should aim in order to deliver effective aid to a nearby bomber under attack was important. Ayres and Odle performed lengthy computations to calculate the theoretically correct deflections for a variety of attack positions. This resulted in a list of aiming rules for all situations much too long for gunners to learn. Hence, they concentrated on waist positions only. They formulated rules for the K-13 compensating sight which automatically took care of a large part of the deflections. This work was written up in "Support Fire with the K-13 Sight on the Waist Guns," dated 27 December 1944. [55]

THE FIRST REAL GERMAN JET PLANE BECOMES OPERATIONAL IN SEPTEMBER 1944. The command's concern over the emergence of the German jet fighters in the last part of 1944 has been reflected in the activities of the Gunnery Subsection above. One of the missed opportunities of the German high command was its failure to develop the Me-262 sooner. The first flight of the Me-262 was in July 1942, but "owing to official indifference, production was not begun until the end of 1943." [56]

Although Eighth Air Force encounters with the Me-262 began as early as

July 1944, it was not until September that the first Me-262 fighter unit, the Kommando Nowotny, named after its commander, Major Walter Nowotny, was formed and established near Osnabruch, Germany. It began with an assignment of thirty aircraft.

The Me-262, a superior aircraft for its time, had a twin-engine turbo-jet which ran on diesel fuel. Thus, it was not vulnerable, as was the Me-109 and the FW-190, to oil shortages.

In level flight the Me-262 was seventy-five to one hundred miles per hour faster than the P-51. It could easily pull away from the American fighter in a climb. Unlike the Me-163, the Me-262 had a respectable endurance of ninety minutes. It had the armament of four 30-mm cannon.[57] The Me-262 was a formidable opponent. American pilots had to dive down on it in order to overhaul it. Since American and British jets would not be operational for some time yet, the command was seriously concerned about the threat of increased numbers of the Me-262.

REFERENCES

1. "Eighth Air Force, History of Operations Analysis Section, October 1942–June 1945," Leslie H. Arps, 520.303-3, Archives, Simpson Historical Research Center, Maxwell Air Force Base, Alabama, 108.

2. Leroy A. Brothers, *Operations Analysis in World War II*, *United States Army Air Forces* (Philadelphia: Stephenson-Brothers, 1948), 9.

3. Ibid.

4. "Eighth Air Force, History," 141.

5. "History of the Battle Damage Subsection, Operational Analysis Section, Eighth Air Force, December 1943–May 1945," 520.303-1, Archives, Simpson Historical Research Center, Maxwell Air Force Base, Alabama.

6. The Army Air Forces in World War II, "Combat Chronology 1941–1945," 1973, Office of Air Force History, Simpson Historical Research Center, Maxwell Air Force Base, Alabama. See 2 November 1944, Eighth Air Force.

7. Roger Freeman, *Mighty Eighth War Manual* (London: Janes, 1984), 97.

8. "Combat Chronology."

9. *Mighty Eighth War Manual*, 97, 98.

10. "Combat Chronology."

11. *Mighty Eighth War Manual*, 99.

12. Ibid.

13. Ibid.

14. "Eighth Air Force, History," 103–4.

15. Ibid., 107.

16. Ibid., 116.

17. Ibid., 145.

18. Wesley Frank Craven and James Lea Cate of the USAF Historical Division, eds., *Europe: From Argument to V-E Day, January 1944 to May 1945*, vol. 3 of *The Army Air Forces in World War* II, (Chicago: University of Chicago Press, 1951), 658.

19. Roger Freeman, *The Mighty Eighth, A History of the U.S. 8th Army Air Force* (London: Macdonald, 1970), 184, 188.

20. Operations Analysis Report, OAS, Eighth Air Force, "Memorandum on Defensive Fire Damage against the German Fighters Me-163 and Me-262," 9 August

1944, Simpson Historical Research Center, Maxwell Air Force Base, Alabama.

21. "Gunnery Subsection, Operational Analysis Section, Eighth Air Force, June 1943–January 1945," W. L. Ayres, Simpson Historical Research Center, Maxwell Air Force Base, Alabama, 16.

22. *Short Bursts*, September 1944, Headquarters, Eighth Air Force, Simpson Historical Research Center, Maxwell Air Force Base, Alabama.

23. Ibid.

24. Ibid., October 1944.

25. Ibid.

26. "Combat Chronology."

27. *Short Bursts*, October 1944.

28. *The Mighty Eighth*, 178.

29. "Combat Chronology."

30. *The Mighty Eighth*, 178.

31. Charles W. McArthur, bombardier, 861st Squadron, 493d Bomb Group.

32. *Short Bursts*, October 1944.

33. *The Mighty Eighth*, 179.

34. *Short Bursts*, October 1944.

35. "Combat Chronology."

36. *Short Bursts*, October 1944.

37. *The Mighty Eighth*, 178.

38. "Combat Chronology."

39. *Short Bursts*, November 1944.

40. Eighth Air Force, "Activities Report of Dr. John W. Odle, Operations Analyst," Simpson Historical Research Center, Maxwell Air Fore Base, Alabama.

41. Ibid.

42. "Gunnery Subsection."

43. *Short Bursts*, October 1944.

44. Ibid.

45. "Combat Chronology."

46. Ibid.

47. "Gunnery Subsection."

48. Adolf Galland, *The First and the Last* (Harrisburg, VA: Bantam, 1979), 259.

49. Ibid.

50. Ibid., 260.

51. Ibid., 260–61.

52. Thomas Parrish and S. L. A. Marshall, eds., *The Simon and Schuster Encyclopedia of World War* II (New York, 1978), 86–91.

53. "Combat Chronology."

54. "Activities Report of Dr. John W. Odle."

55. Ibid.

56. *Encyclopedia of World War II*, Me-262.

57. *The Mighty Eighth*, 193, 194.

11

Operations Analysis in the Eighth Air Force
August–December 1944, Part IV

BOMBS AND FUZES

The V-weapons. Although all of the subsections were involved in the CROSSBOW targets, that is, any targets connected with the program of attacks against V-weapons, the Bombs and Fuzes Subsection seems to have been involved in less routine ways. The Bombs and Fuzes men, Alderman, Hedefine, and Kring, worked very closely with Operations in mission planning. Thus, Alderman notes that the command at one point requested the subsection to make an analysis of all of the CROSSBOW committee's data and "best guesses." Hedefine prepared and submitted this analysis to General O. A. Anderson. [1]

July and August 1944 were critical for the CROSSBOW campaign. During this period the V-1 (buzz bomb) offensive against England reached its climax. After August the gains of the Allied armies forced the Germans back far enough so that it was no longer possible for them to maintain their V-1 attacks across the channel.

> During this two-month period, the Eighth had made 164 attacks in operations against a total of 67 Crossbow targets (75 attacks in July and 89 in August—operating continuously the first 11 days in August). The U.S. heavy bombers had attacked modified sites (V-1) 116 times, storage depots (or fuel dumps) 15 times, strategic targets in Germany 9 times, 6 liquid-oxygen plants in France and Belgium 1 time each, airfields in France and Holland 6 times, supply sites 4 times, 1 ski site 6 times, and 1 marshalling yard 1 time. For its attacks against targets in the Pas-de-Calais the Eighth had used visual sighting 117 times and Gee-H bombing 24 times (in contrast to 64 visual-sighting and 49 Gee-H attacks in the second half of June); in all Crossbow operations outside the Pas-de-Calais visual sighting was used. [2]

The subsection's recommendations. The V-1 launching sites in this period, the modified sites, were extremely hard to find because of superior camouflage work. They were hard to hit because they were small and well defended. When they were hit, they were quickly replaced by another modified site. On 24 July 1944 the subsection released a report, "Recommended Bombs and Fuzes to be Used against Noball Targets." Their recommendation for the modified sites that consisted primarily of the launching ramp was the 250-pound general purpose bomb.[3] Big enough to destroy the launching ramp, it could be carried in large enough numbers to significantly increase the probability of hits.

The success of the CROSSBOW operation. Military historians have judged the first phase of CROSSBOW—from December 1943 to April 1944—a success. The great network of ski-sites lay in ruins, and the seven large sites had been damaged.[4] The U.S. Strategic Bombing Survey concluded that the first phase of CROSSBOW had delayed the launching of the buzz-bombs three to four months. Other Allied studies give the initial phase of CROSSBOW credit for a six-month delay in the launchings.[5]

The assessment of the second phase of CROSSBOW is quite different.

> The Crossbow campaign of the summer of 1944 must be regarded generally as having failed to achieve its objectives. It is apparent from the record of V-1 launchings during the summer of 1944 (6,716 missiles were plotted between 12/13 June and 1 September), as measured against the magnitude of Allied efforts to neutralize them by offensive air power, that the Germans had found in their improvised modified sites a launching method that was impervious to conventional attacks by heavy bombers. Though the Allies did neutralize or destroy a fair number of the modified sites, the Germans could build new ones faster than they could be destroyed by the air power committed to their attack.[6]

The Germans suspended the V-1 offensive by early September because its armies were defeated and withdrew, not because of CROSSBOW.

Generals Spaatz and Arnold warned that the heavy bomber was not the right weapon for the V-1 sites. Furthermore, they argued, committing the Eighth to this campaign would divert bombers from other targets where they were clearly effective. However, General Eisenhower's orders to give the buzz-bomb sites top priority in July and August prevailed. Generals Spaatz and Arnold were, of course, technically right. However, from a public relations point of view, Eisenhower's decision to bomb the buzz sites in July and August is quite defensible. The British people could see and hear the flying bombs. Approximately 100 civilians a day were being killed by them with many more being wounded. People were tired of "keeping a stiff upper lip."

The heavy sites and the V-2. Allied intelligence assumed that the seven heavy sites were part of the V-weapon complex and were V-2 launching sites. Thus, the Allies were eager to capture them before they could begin operation. Indeed, they were captured before they could be used. This caused some to wrongly conclude that the V-2 threat was over.

"The last V-1 fired from a launching site in France fell in Kent on the afternoon of 1 September 1944."[7] On that date the British civil defense halted its planning of precautionary measures in case of V-2 attack. On 3 September all operational air commands in the ETO were informed that every type of CROSSBOW offensive countermeasure was to be suspended. On 5 September the chief of the British air staff advised abandonment of bombing attacks on the V-2 storage depot and transportation system. The next day British chiefs of staff, convinced that "there should be no further danger" from either ground-launched V-1s or from the as yet unheard from V-2, agreed that all bombing attacks against CROSSBOW targets should cease, except for occasional strikes against airfields that might be used for air launching V-1s.[8]

England's respite from V-weapon attacks was brief. On 8 September 1944 the first of more than a thousand ten-ton rockets traveling five times the speed of sound fell and exploded at Chiswick. A few seconds later a second struck at Parndon Wood, Epping.

The Allies had no defense against this weapon except to prevent its launching. Fortunately for the Allies, it came too late for the Germans to develop its potential.

Although heavy sites were regularly bombed for months—Watten was bombed on thirteen occasions by the Eighth Air Force[9]—air attacks did not prevent their construction. In October 1944 Alderman and Kring of the Bombs and Fuzes Subsection were able to inspect the V-weapon sites in the Pas-de-Calais area. They had been especially requested by the command to survey the four heavy sites at Watten, Marquise-Mimoyeques, Wizernes, and Siracourt to determine which of these would be the most suitable for bombing tests. An earlier inspection ruled out Sotte-vaste for this purpose.

Alderman and Kring found that each heavy site they inspected had roofs with concrete slabs about five meters thick. They recommended the heavy site at Watten for the bombing tests because it had the largest interior area already excavated, and because it was further from nearby towns.[10]

The tests planned for Watten were for a 4,500 pound bomb, the Disney rocket bomb. The largest bomb normally carried by the B-17 or B-24 was the 2,000-pound general purpose bomb. In line with the dictum of using the smallest bomb large enough to do the job, the Eighth Air Force used larger bombs sparingly. However, by October 1944 the Allies were encountering obstacles for which their bombs were inadequate. Forts on the Siegfried line, for example, forts and U-boat and E-boat pens of port cities like Brest,

France, were held by German garrisons who refused to surrender. The German strategy of holding port cities as long as possible denied the Allies the facilities they sorely needed for delivering supplies to their troops.

The Disney rocket bomb, developed by the British navy for penetrating and destroying U-boat and E-boat pens, weighed 4,500 pounds and was fourteen feet long. No suitable British aircraft could deliver it. Thus, the Eighth Air Force was asked to help. [11] Alderman gives an account of this development.

> [A] special weapon was the 4,500 lb. rocket-assisted armor piercing bomb which was developed by the British. This weapon had an extremely small charge. It had to be carried externally, two per B-17. The rocket was provided to increase the striking velocity up to approximately 1,300 feet per second when dropped from 25,000 feet. The bomb was tested on the target at Watten on 3 February 1945 and results inspected (by Hedefine). One hit was scored over the wall section, and nothing could be determined about its penetration in the five meter thick concrete slab. It was used operationally on 10 February 1945 on a mission against submarine pens at Ijmuiden. Movies of this operation revealed nothing about its effectiveness. The smoke of the rocket was observed, and the detonations of near misses were seen to be very small indeed. No hits were to be seen scored on the concrete pens. [12]

Despite these discouraging results, the air force, assisted by the subsection, continued the experiments. The bomb was used operationally by several Eighth Air Force groups in March 1945. According to Freeman, eventually "a penetration of 20 feet was recorded before detonation." [13]

Bridge busting. In the interdiction bridge bombing before D day, the Eighth Air Force had been assigned bridges along the Loire at or beyond the limits of range of the Ninth Air Force bombers. Thus, in early August Hedefine and Kring inspected the damage done to some of these targets. They found that in some instances the bridges had been repaired by the Germans, and in others they had been further demolished by the Germans in their retreat. Some of the Loire bridges could not be inspected then because the Germans still held positions on the south side of the river. This information was used for their next bridge assignments.

Not long after D day Alderman and Kring had begun studying and working on plans to attack and neutralize the Rhine River bridges. Their basic estimates of force requirements were submitted to General O. A. Anderson.

This report was prepared by Kring of Bombs and Fuzes and Clarkson of Bombing Accuracy. It was titled "Estimates of Overall Force Required for the Destruction of 57 Rhine Bridges (Memorandum for General O. A. Anderson)" and dated 14 October 1944. [14]

More damage assessment by Alderman and Kring.   In addition to the heavy sites in the Pas-de-Calais area, in October Alderman and Kring made damage assessments of bombed-out towns, airfields, and marshalling yards at targets from the Paris area up to the vicinity of Brussels and Eindhoven.   They were prevented from making a study of the effect of fragmentation bombs in the vicinity of Eindhoven, where they had been used in the ground support missions (MARKET-GARDEN) in September, because their jeep was stolen in Brussels. They had to return to Paris to borrow another. [15]

Alderman writes regarding the effects of fragmentation of bombs:

> We saw much evidence of successful bomb fragmentation damage. We were told in Paris that the bombs which exploded high in the structures of the buildings raised more havoc than those which cratered, and the inspections we made verified this and substantiated our earlier beliefs and interpretations of damage in aerial photographs. We found there had been a marked tendency to universally underestimate the extent of damage in photo interpretation work, that, for example, machinery was often damaged well beyond the limits of structural and superficial damage visible in post-raid photographs.
>
> We noted one instance of a bomb which had failed to blast out a thin tile wall yet its fragments had perforated the wall and had knocked out heat treatment furnaces behind it. We saw evidence of serious damage to structural members caused by fragmentation alone. We examined targets which had been hit by bombs of various sizes and compared the effectiveness of each weapon insofar as it was possible to identify them. We had one single purpose on these trips: to obtain accurate data on bomb and fuze effectiveness to apply to the daily operations of the Eighth Air Force. [16]

The section's work with bomb survey groups.   In 1944, the headquarters of the army air force sent a small group of officers, called an air force evaluation board, to each theater of operations. An individual operations analyst was assigned to each air force evaluation board where he helped the board determine the scope of the directive, organize its efforts, and write its report. The civilian assigned to the evaluation board concerned with assessing the effects of bombing the Axis forces in northern Europe was George W. Ball. Before undertaking this assignment, Ball, a lawyer, had been serving as associate general counsel of the Foreign Economic Administration in Washington, D.C. [17]

Ball was asked by General Arnold, commanding general of the United States Army Air Force, to be the civilian member of the board of air force officers being established in London to study the effectiveness of the Allied air offensive.

Ball left the United States for London on 4 September 1944 to join his fellow members on the Air Force Evaluation Board. The board was chaired by Major General Jacob Fickel. General Fickel, sixty-one, claimed to be the first to shoot a firearm from a flying airplane. He gave Ball a picture of the historic event. However, Ball felt that Fickel's evaluation board was inadequately prepared to assess the damage bombing inflicted on the enemy's total war-making capacity. Furthermore, Ball felt the air force would have trouble appraising its own achievements objectively. Thus, when the evaluation board moved its office from Grosvenor Square to Paris in September, Ball stayed behind in London. With the help and advice of friends, he drew up an organization chart for a competent study, responsible not to the air force but to the secretary of war. He got permission from General Spaatz to return to Washington, to recruit, as he told Fickel, civilian experts for an evaluation board survey of the effect of Allied bombing on the French railroads.

Back in Washington Ball's plan was amplified and modified by the War Department and became the plan for the United States Strategic Bombing Survey.

Ball flew back to London on 4 November 1944 to "set about turning a blueprint into an organization." Before leaving Washington, Ball persuaded his friend, Adlai Stevenson, to return with him and work on the bomb survey.

Ball's first job was to delimit the tasks of the USSBS and the evaluation board. The USSBS was given the task of appraising the whole strategic air offensive. The evaluation board was given the limited task of "appraising the achievements of the tactical air effort in France that had been conducted by the British and our Ninth Air Force in connection with the Normandy invasion."[18] Stevenson worked on this project with his headquarters staff in Paris.

Alderman writes of the ground survey groups:

> At one time or another we were visited by the Chiefs of the Ground Survey Committees: General Fickel of the Evaluation Board; Colonel Koenig and Colonel Zierdt of the U.S. Strategic Bombing Research Mission (USSBRM), and members of their staffs.
>
> The very first of these meetings was with Colonel Ames who was making preliminary investigations for General Fred Anderson. He outlined the work he had been doing for setting up the USSBRM. Soon a London office opened and a staff assembled to begin operations. The development of this group was sluggish. We tried to be of assistance, but our advice and good intentions seemed to have little effect. As soon as Colonel Zierdt joined the Mission, progress was made. We had been asked if we would be interested in joining the mission, but, in addition to our not being available we were not enthusiastic about post mortem surveys of damage on the Continent. Colonel Zierdt, knowing that we could not be

taken out of our O.A.S. jobs, asked if one of us could collaborate with him to the extent of meeting once a week to help organize their staff and make future plans. Mr. Hedefine volunteered and in the next few months helped them to get their preliminary plans formed. Later he refused an offer to become head of their Damage Analysis Section.

We helped them to get complete basic data on bombs and fuzes, and they eventually sent out men to type certain of our records. We helped them select targets for survey, and made recommendations continually for targets which would produce good information on ground surveys. On one occasion with Major Ness, Architect, of our A-2 Section, we went through a list of all the industrial targets which had been attacked by the Eighth Air Force. Colonel Zierdt and Captain Weimar attended this meeting and took notes on those we considered best for analysis. Those which had been attacked with a single weapon on a single attack of reasonably good accuracy received the highest priority. [19]

LOSS AND BATTLE DAMAGE

Flak had always been the principal cause of damage to the Eighth Air Force bombers. From June 1944 onward, flak was also the principal cause of loss as well. In the last half of 1944 the Eighth Air Force bombed industrial targets in Germany at every opportunity. These were heavily defended by antiaircraft and by fighters when possible. It was not a static situation. The Germans were continually strengthening their flak defenses around vital industrial targets. At the same time, the Eighth Air Force took every measure to reduce flak risk and damage. Despite its efforts to reduce flak damage, the Loss and Battle Damage Subsection noted that on the 30 November mission to Merseburg-Leuna, the Eighth Air Force lost thirty bombers to flak alone—a loss rate of about 5 percent.

The efforts of the Loss and Battle Damage Subsection to reduce flak damage in the target area by experimenting with different maneuvers over the target had the full backing of the command as well as the cooperation of the groups and wings.

According to Pilat, "not only did the basic concepts of flak risk reduction as enunciated by us gain general acceptance about the command, but to a considerable extent they were in fact realized. Chief progress was made in reducing the size of bombing units and in closing up their intervals in trail." [20]

The Ninety-third Wing. In the "Reduction of Flak Risk" memorandum of July, ORS had suggested two maneuvers "to illustrate how we might be able to close up in trail and thus cut our flak risks sharply." In discussing these maneuvers with the Third Division and its combat wing commanders, two of the wing commanders expressed willingness to try out the "javelin" maneuver. The Fourth Combat Wing abandoned the experiment after concluding that the maneuver, as outlined in the memorandum, was not feasible. The Ninety-third Wing, however, under the command of Brigadier General Gerhardt, set to work to modify the maneuver to make it more flyable. ORS personnel, visiting the wing in July 1944 to discuss progress, found that the maneuver, with several modifications, had been flown successfully on combat missions. The wing, however, was not yet fully satisfied. On 23 September when Pilat and Shettle again visited the wing, they found that the maneuver, with modifications, had been flown on six to eight practice missions and a number of combat missions. The wing was convinced that it could practically be flown so as to achieve spacing between six successive squadrons of from a quarter to a half mile in trail without fear of collision or self bombing. The wing wanted to verify that enough reduction in flak risk was achieved to warrant the effort involved.

The section studied the comparative loss and damage rates of the Third Division wings, which proved inconclusive because too many variables were involved. The wing agreed to proceed with the maneuver and decided to run a test flight over a captured German radar. ORS personnel would join the flight as observers to verify spacing, to determine whether close spacing affects radio countermeasures, and to note whether German radar could identify such close formations.

Details of the mission were reviewed very thoroughly with Dr. Fubini of the RCM Subsection at wing headquarters on 28 November. ORS made arrangements with the 325th Photo-Reconnaissance Wing to film and photograph the mission. Major Darwin of ORS would go along to supervise the photography. Advance copies of the field order for the mission were sent to the section. Parts of the order were revised as a result of ORS suggestions.

Meanwhile, command approval for the practice mission had not yet been obtained. Pressure of operations was such that the suggestion to "stand down" seventy-six aircraft for one day met with little enthusiasm. Though the wing had persuaded the division, Eighth Air Force consent was necessary. Fortunately, because General O. A. Anderson was interested, the plan was approved.

Finally, on 1 February 1945 the combination of proper flying weather and relaxed operational demands enabled the practice mission to fly. The mission, on which all members of the Battle Damage Subsection flew alongside the formation as observers, clearly proved that the maneuver could be flown with squadrons close together. Eyewitness and photographic evidence showed that six squadrons flew within a total airspace of 3.6 miles. The average spacing between squadrons was slightly less than half a mile. Unfortunately, radar results were inconclusive because the ground equipment malfunctioned. As a result of this test, the Ninety-third Wing continued to fly the precision maneuver on selected missions, primarily to targets with the heaviest flak defenses, until the close of the war. [21]

The Ninety-sixth Wing of the Second Division.   The ORS hoped that the success of the Ninety-third Wing's maneuver would stimulate similar experimentation by other Third Division wings. A concerted effort to conduct similar experiments in another division seemed opportune. The Second Division (B-24s) had been willing to experiment with flying six-ship squadrons over Cologne in October. Furthermore, it reduced its formation size from twelve to nine. The Second Division seemed the logical choice. After discussions with Hazard Gillespie, one of the two ORS men at Second Division headquarters, Pilat visited the Ninety-sixth Wing on 30 December 1944. He discussed with officers of that wing the basic principles and advantages of precision flying at the target and the maneuvers being flown by the Ninety-third Wing. He, in effect, challenged them to do as well with B-24s as the Ninety-third had done with B-17s. The operations officers believed they could do better. They proceeded to develop a precision maneuver radically different from the Ninety-third Wing's vertical stack, the original "javelin" proposal, or anything previously flown by the Eighth Air Force.

The maneuver was described in a "Report on the 96 Combat Wing Integrated Formation," dated 30 April 1945, which was prepared and distributed by ORS. It involved a route formation in which the squadrons of a group, instead of flying abreast, flew in trail echeloned downward, while groups of the wing flew substantially abreast of each other and echeloned upward. Thus, no squadron uncovery was necessary at the IP. Though groups had to swing into trail, vertical spacing was such that they had ample room to swing over each other, while still keeping the overall spacing in altitude to a minimum. Spacings in trail at the IP were so designed that with differential true air speeds resulting from uniform indicated air speeds flown at different altitudes, intervals of the order of one quarter mile between squadrons at the bomb release line could be achieved. [22]

This formation was consistently flown on all combat missions from 28 January 1945 to the end of the war. Though no test mission was flown, photographs taken on combat missions and included in the report show the formation and spacing achieved. Careful analysis of strike photographs on a sample mission showed that six squadrons of the wing—the other group was materially off course due to cloud obscuration along the bomb run and misidentification of the target—bombed within a total time of forty-five seconds or less. Thus, they flew within a total space of about three miles or less. Moreover, there was a very real indication that the maneuver had both improved bombing accuracy and reduced flak damage and loss. The wing, beginning in February 1945, consistently led the division in bombing accuracy and ranked among the highest in the air force. Its losses were approximately half those of the other Second Division wings attacking the same targets.

While damage figures did not show the same trend, the subsection believed this was due to incomplete reporting by other Second Division wings. This formation did not increase vulnerability to fighters. The wing never sustained enemy fighter attacks, although other wings attacking the same targets did. [23]

Cooperation with other air forces to reduce flak risk. As part of its campaign to make the Eighth Air Force more aware of the importance of flak loss and damage, Major Marietta of the Flak Intelligence Section, Dr. Kuiper of the RCM Subsection, and Pilat of the Loss and Battle Damage Subsection made a trip to the continent 24 October–9 November 1944 to plan a better interchange of information between the Eighth and Ninth Air Forces on flak matters. Among topics discussed with Ninth Air Force flak officers and OAS personnel were available tactics for reducing flak risk, as well as the extent and manner in which they were applied by the Eighth and Ninth Air Forces. They agreed to hold joint flak conferences each month and exchange monthly summaries of flak information.

Accordingly, on 11 and 12 January a flak officers' conference was held at Eighth Air Force headquarters. Lieutenant Colonel Gregory of the Flak Intelligence Section served as chairman. The conference was attended by flak officers and OAS personnel of the Eighth, Ninth, and Fifteenth Air Forces, flak officers of Headquarters Mediterranean Allied Air Force and the Eighth Air Force fighter wings, and officers of the Ninth Air Defense Command, Troop Carrier Command, and Electronics Intelligence Section USSTAF.

General O. A. Anderson, deputy commander for operations at Eighth Air Force, was present for part of the session. ORS Battle Damage and the RCM subsection presented most of the topics for discussion. Among the subjects covered were the Ninety-third Bomb Wing's maneuver at the target and a reconstruction of the courses and spacings flown on the 30 November Leuna mission in which the Eighth Air Force lost thirty planes to flak.

Pilat and Major Marietta originally prepared a preliminary analysis of possible causes for the unusually high losses on the 30 November mission. Pilat then decided instead to attempt a more comprehensive analysis. With a map of the target area, courses flown were plotted and the bomb release point located. By going forward or backward from that point, on the basis of the lead bombardier's and navigator's reported times of bombs away, the location of each squadron at a particular instant could be shown. Their relative position could be graphically illustrated. Into that picture was fitted the location of flak positions as plotted by the Flak Intelligence Section. Thus, it was possible to see not only how many guns each squadron had flown within range of, but also to identify instances in which we had or had not successfully forced division of fire between two or more squadrons flying within range of the same guns at the same time.

A chart produced by the analysts indicating possible causes for high losses and revealing defects in the general manner of flying provided the basis for an extended exposition of the mission at the January 1945 flak officers' conference. [24]

Body armor. Pilat writes,

> The Flak suit to be worn by crews, was developed by the Surgeon's office and saved many lives. ORS had little to do with its development; we did point out, however, the extent to which our interrogations of crew members of lost aircraft disclosed that crew members were not wearing their flak suits. We also supported strongly the program for installing flak curtains and rugs in aircraft, pointing out that most hits and most casualties were, during 1944 and 1945 caused by flak fragments, and that consequently a greater area could be given adequate protection by lightweight flak pads designed to stop low velocity missiles than by armor plate designed to stop machine gun shells. [25]

The flak suit consisted of a special helmet, a vest, an apron, and later groin armor and neck armor. This armor was made from nylon cloth, incorporating two-inch square overlapping Hadfield manganese steel plates. All body armor was worn over flight suits. In case of emergency the armor could be jettisoned by a single pull on a cord attached to all the fasteners.

A unit of the U.S. Army Surgeon General decided to carry out a comprehensive survey of casualties in bomber crews and to study the effects of the use of body armor. The three-month period 1 June to 31 August 1944, when all forty groups used body armor, was compared with earlier periods when body armor was not available.

Medical studies indicated that body armor prevented at least half of the expected casualties and reduced the fatality rate for wounded personnel.

The statistics show an interesting distribution of casualties. The percent of casualties for each crew position was: pilot 7.4, copilot 6.6, navigator 12.2, bombardier 17.6, radio operator 8.5, waist gunner 20.9 for the two gunners (10.45 for each waist gunner), ball turret gunner 5.9, top turret gunner 8.5, and tail gunner 12.5. [26]

Fortunately, the crew knew nothing of these statistics. The bombardier's morale would have suffered had he known that his chances of dying were nearly three times that of the copilot. The bombardier's position in the B-17 was called "greenhouse" because it was in the part of the nose made of Plexiglas.

THE LAST BIG REPORT ON BOMBING ACCURACY

The bombing accuracy subsection, in addition to issuing monthly visual bombing reports, also prepared a few major studies on bombing accuracy covering certain time periods. The last major study of the subsection, for the period September–December 1944, was titled "Report on Bombing Accuracy, Eighth Air Force, 1 September 1944 to 31 December 1944" and was dated 20 April 1945. [27]

The report covers a key period of the air war. Seventy-two percent of the Allied bombs dropped on Germany were dropped between July 1944 and April 1945, [28] a period of crucial importance in the strategic bombing of Germany. It was prepared in the final months of the war in Europe.

Unlike earlier reports, this dealt with all types of Eighth Air Force bombing—visual, Gee-H, Micro-H, and H2X. It reports on these various types of bombing and compares their accuracy.

Writing such a report was a large job. Thus, it was divided into parts. Colonel Scott, head of the Bombing Accuracy Subsection, wrote about visual bombing. The mathematician Frank Stewart wrote the part on Gee-H and Micro-H bombing; Baley Price wrote the section in H2X bombing. [29] Dr. J. W. T. Youngs, an expert on the Norden bombsight, helped by writing the last part dealing with the use of the bombsight in blind bombing which came at the end. The credit line reads, "Report prepared by Dr. G. B. Price, Dr. J. W. T. Youngs, Mr. F. M. Stewart, Lt. Col. P. C. Scott, OAS consultants, and it was approved for release by Leslie H. Arps, Lt. Colonel, A. C., Director, Operational Analysis." [30]

At the time the report was written the Bombing Accuracy Subsection faced a most pressing problem regarding bombing accuracy. Techniques for bombing in poor visibility needed to be developed and improved. The air force made substantial progress in developing techniques for achieving reasonably good accuracy in clear weather. Several factors, however, severely limited the volume of bombing which could be done under conditions of good visibility.

Poor visibility during daylight bombing was caused by cloudiness and haze, smoke screens put up by the enemy, and smoke and fire from our own preceding bombfalls. The three forms of radar bombing listed earlier were developed and used to overcome poor visibility.

The purpose of this report by the Bombing Accuracy Subsection was

> ... to give as complete an analysis as possible of all our bombing during an essentially bad weather period, namely, 1 September 1944 through 31 December 1944, with the following ends in view: (1) to indicate the extent to which our accuracy is presently affected by the various conditions of visibility; (2) to give some evaluation of the success achieved with the various forms of radar bombing; and (3) suggest, where possible, lines along which improvement may be expected. [31]

From 1 September 1944 to 31 December 1944, the Eighth Air Force conducted heavy bombardment operations on seventy-three days, an average of slightly over eighteen days per month. In these operations, between 60,000 and 65,000 sorties of heavy bombers were flown for an average of approximately 900 sorties per operation. The Eighth Air Force in this period was at its maximum strength of forty heavy bomb groups.

On twenty-six of the seventy-three days of operations some or all of the bombing was done visually. On the remaining forty-seven days (64 percent of the days) all the bombing was done with some form of radar under varying conditions of cloud cover. Table 11.1 gives the total bombing effort of the Eighth Air Force in this period by categories. In terms of bombing accuracy, the results vary significantly according to each type of bombing.

Table 11.1. Distribution of Total Effort by Categories of Bombing
1 September 1944–1 December 1944

Category of bombing	Percent of total effort
H2X—10/10 cloud	35
H2X—8/10–9/10 cloud	15
H2X—6/10–7/10 cloud	5
H2X—4/10–5/10 cloud	3
Micro-H	3
Gee-H	15
Visual—poor visibility	10
Visual—good to fair visibility	14

Only 14 percent of the bombing was done in good visibility; only 24 percent was done visually.

Bombing accuracy under conditions of good visibility. The study found that even under conditions of good visibility, the bombing accuracy of the Eighth Air Force fell off in the period under study. For June, July, and August an estimated 40 percent of all bombs dropped under conditions of good visibility fell within 1,000 feet of preassigned aiming points. For the period 1 September through 31 December 1944 the figure dropped to approximately 30 percent. It dropped even lower, to 22.6 percent, in the three-month period 1 October to 31 December 1944.

The study identified two causes for this decrease. First, bombs were dropped from much higher altitudes than before. In the first quarter of 1944 only 37 percent of the bombing with good visibility was done above 21,000 feet. In the second quarter 50 percent was done above 21,000 feet. This rose to 75 percent in the third quarter. Finally, in the fourth quarter of 1944, 97 percent of all bombing was done at altitudes of 21,000 feet or higher. The bombers had been driven up by the heavy defenses at German industrial targets. Furthermore, by the fourth quarter almost all targets were in Germany.

The second cause for the decrease in accuracy had to do with the size of the air force and, more specifically, the size of the attacking force. The study showed that as an attack progressed, bombing accuracy decreased. Though the level of accuracy was reasonably high for the first three groups (nine to twelve combat boxes) in a formation, bombing accuracy for subsequent groups dropped by approximately half.

In the last quarter of 1944 the number of visual bombing missions done in large forces of more than nine combat boxes was more than double that of either of the two preceding quarters. Thus, larger attacking forces decreased bombing accuracy during the period.

Larger attacking forces did serve a purpose. A force requirement example illustrates their importance. Assume that to achieve a given bomb density on a single target, 500 aircraft and five attacks are required. To achieve the same density on a single mission, just 900 aircraft would be needed. Because flying weather and visibility were scarce, the air force wisely opted to mount a few large attacks rather than several small attacks despite the resulting decrease in accuracy.

The Bombing Accuracy Subsection recommended techniques to help compensate for the obscuration of the target by previous bombing, such as grid bombing and offset bombing. These recommendations, however, were never thoroughly explored by the air force.

Visual bombing accuracy under conditions of poor visibility. In the last four months of 1944 the amount of visual bombing done in poor visibility was much greater than in preceding months. This was due to the dominance of poor weather during the period, and the extensive use of smoke screens by the enemy over oil targets.

Of the total visual bombing done under conditions of poor visibility, slightly over 25 percent was due to the use of smoke screens by the enemy. The smoke screens were effective. The analysts found that four to five times the force was required to achieve the required density of bombs on a target protected by smoke screens than would be necessary otherwise. No effective countermeasure was devised.

The remaining 75 percent of the total visual bombing done under conditions of poor visibility was caused by cloud cover and haze. Whereas 30.2 percent of the bombs dropped under conditions of good visibility fell within 1,000 feet of the preassigned aiming point, only 9.4 percent of the bombs dropped visually but with cloud cover and haze fell within 1,000 feet of the aiming point. The recommendation of the section here was to use radar aids.

H2X bombing.   H2S and H2X were types of high altitude blind bombing radar equipment that used the echoes of radar waves to show the target on a scope inside the bomber. They differ from Gee-H and Micro-H, which operated from beacons.

H2S was introduced in the RAF in 1942 as an aid to navigation. Special aircraft equipped with H2S dropped illuminating flares in the neighborhood of the target. Bombing then proceeded visually. H2X, similar to H2S, was introduced in the Eighth Air Force in 1943 as an instrument for bombing through cloud. It was first used as an instrument for blind bombing without the aid of the bombsight or any other equipment. A procedure was needed to enable the bombardier to bomb visually when a break in the clouds permitted. The result was a synchronous procedure in which the H2X operator sets up the course of the aircraft and supplies information to the bombardier for positioning the cross hairs and setting up rate in the bombsight. This became standard operating procedure in the Eighth Air Force.

The analysts viewed H2X as an aid to visual bombing and as a last-resort means of bombing through heavy clouds. However, the air force wanted to keep up its strategic bombing and needed to frequently rebomb its strategic targets, especially oil. Consequently, 58 percent of all Eighth Air Force bombing from 1 September to 31 December 1944 was done with the aid of H2X, and 35 percent was done through 10/10 cloud cover. Thus, in practice, H2X had become the dominant mode of bombing.

The problem of locating H2X bombfall. The biggest problem of all blind bombing for the analysts was ascertaining its accuracy. Four sources of information helped locate the bombfall of H2X bombing: photographs of the H2X scope made during the course of the mission; PRU (Photo Reconnaissance Unit) photographs taken after the mission; the strike photographs of the falling bombs; and mission reports made by crew members and others involved in the mission.

The report explains in detail why the scope photographs and the PRU photographs were biased. For example, the PRU photographs were of the target area and never included bombfalls five or more miles from the aiming point. Alone, these photographs supplied a misleading sample of H2X bombfalls.

The analysis of H2X bombing contained in the report was based on information obtained from strike photographs and mission reports. In many cases—even when the cloud cover on the bombing run was reported as 10/10—small breaks in the cloud enabled the strike photographs to show either the bombfall or sufficient ground detail to calculate the position of the bombfall. In many cases it was possible to check the calculated position of the bombfall with PRU photographs. These checks indicated that, on the average, the pattern center was within a quarter of a mile of the calculated position.

In the period 1 September 1944 to 31 December 1944, 3,025 squadrons (combat boxes) attempted to bomb with H2X and reported cloud cover at the target of from 4/10 to 10/10. Of these, 2,933 dropped their bombs.

The bombfalls of 1,589 combat boxes were not identified—that is, the study of H2X bombing was based on the knowledge of approximately half of the bombfalls. The accuracy of the half not identified was reasonably assumed to be the same as the half identified.

Cloud cover—the main factor in H2X bombing accuracy. The degree of cloud cover in the target area affected the accuracy of the H2X missions more than any other factor. For example, the percent of the pattern centers of bombfalls which fell more than five miles from the aiming point was 42 percent for 10/10 cover, 18 percent for 8/10 to 9/10 cover, 9 percent for 6/10 to 7/10 cover, and 5 percent for 4/10 to 5/10 cover. Table 11.2 gives a more complete picture.

Table 11.2. The Relation of H2X Bombing to the Percent of Bombs Landing within Standard Distances from the Assigned Aiming Point Based on Reported Cloud Cover, 1 September 1944–31 December 1944

Reported cloud cover	Estimated percent of bombs dropped that fell within				
	$1,000'$	$\frac{1}{2}$ mile	1 mile	3 miles	5 miles
10/10	0.2	1.2	5.6	39.8	58.5
8/10–9/10	1.0	7.3	22.5	67.4	82.0
6/10–7/10	2.0	12.5	36.5	84.0	90.5
4/10–5/10	4.4	22.8	48.5	89.1	96.0

The table shows, for example, that in order to put a given density of bombs on a target approximating in size circles with diameters of one mile or less, twenty times the force would be required, on average, if the attack were made by H2X under 10/10 cloud rather than by H2X under 4/10 to 5/10 cloud cover.

We see that visibility was all-important for H2X bombing accuracy. Also, no sharp line of demarcation between visual bombing and H2X bombing existed. Instead, there was a gradation of bombing, according to a scale of visibility, with pure visual bombing at one extreme and pure H2X at the other.

The following example illustrates the two extremes. For targets of the order of one mile in diameter, visual bombing under good visibility was, on the average, approximately fifty times more effective than H2X with 10/10 cloud cover. For targets two miles in diameter, the ratio was approximately 15 to 1, while for targets of the order of six miles in diameter, the ratio was approximately 2.5 to 1.

As an instrument for precision bombing with 10/10 cloud cover, H2X was ineffective. It was, however, a reasonable instrument for area bombing of large targets.

Other reasons for inaccuracy. Throughout the period 1 September to 31 December 1944 there were not enough H2X-equipped planes for each combat box (squadron). A typical practice was for the lead squadron to have two H2X planes—the lead crew and a deputy crew. The second H2X plane served as a backup in case the first plane was lost or its equipment was damaged—not infrequent occurrences. The high squadron would have its own H2X plane. The third squadron would drop its bombs on a smoke marker dropped by the lead squadron. Thus, H2X was used to drop bombs four ways: an H2X plane could drop bombs; an H2X plane could drop smoke markers, upon which other planes released bombs; an H2X plane could drop bombs with the visual assistance (VA) of the bombardier; and bombs could be released on smoke markers dropped with visual help.

The most accurate was the VA sighting. Of course, bombs on smoke markers, H2X marker, or VA marker, were less accurate then those dropped by H2X and VA. Bombs were also dropped accidentally during equipment failure or enemy combat.

An interesting fact revealed in the study was that the H2X bombing of targets in small cities was more accurate than H2X bombing of targets in large cities. This part of the report concludes with the statement,

> If the objective is merely to drop bombs in built up areas, the efficiency of [H2X] attacks on cities of various sizes will probably vary little. The RAF has found that it can place 50 percent of its bombs in built-up areas regardless of the size of the city. On the other hand, if the objective is to place bombs on a target that can be represented by a circle from 2,000 feet to one mile in diameter, it is clear [from the data of the report] that the efficiency of attacks on such targets will be greater when they are located in small cities than when they are located in large cities.

The analysts felt that this was caused by "an inherent inability of the equipment to locate the target with precision and certainty."

The report deals with other causes of error. H2X-aimed bombs, for example, systematically fell short of the aiming point (.53 miles on the average). Furthermore, larger H2X attacks were slightly less accurate—especially with less than 10/10 cloud cover.

H2X bombing accuracy did not improve. A great handicap to progress in H2X bombing was the difficulty in getting quick and thorough information about past operations. Each visual attack was another piece of data in an ongoing experiment. The results, recorded on strike photographs, were analyzed and reported periodically to the operating units. No such complete analysis for H2X missions was possible. Half of the H2X bombfalls were never identified. The studies that were made became available only weeks or even months after the mission. It had not been possible to praise good performance or call attention to poor performance on H2X missions as on visual missions.

The part of the report on H2X bombing ends with the following pessimistic summary:

> The accuracy achieved on our H2X missions has been substantially lower than that achieved with the beacon type radar systems as well as with visual bombing. Indeed, except for extremely large area targets, it has been less effective than our visual bombing by factors ranging from about 45 times for targets of the order of one half mile in diameter to six times for targets of the order of two miles in diameter. Similarly, it has been less effective than the beacon type radar systems thus far employed by this Air Force by factors ranging from about seven times for targets of the order of one half mile in diameter to about four times for targets of the order of two miles in diameter.

> With the employment of the synchronous procedure the discrepancy between the results obtained under conditions of solid cloud and under conditions of partial cloud is extremely large. Any system of planning, therefore, which would result in increasing the proportion under partial cloud would greatly increase the effectiveness of the overall effort.

> From the standpoint of possible improvement, nothing in our experience to date has given a basis for expecting any substantial improvement with our present equipment on our present type of targets.

In its first report of 31 January 1944 on the accuracy of H2X missions, the Bombing Accuracy Subsection had estimated that 5 percent of all bombs had fallen within one mile of the assigned aiming point.[32] For the four-month period 1 September 1944 to 31 December 1944, 5.6 percent of all H2X bombs dropped with 10/10 cloud cover fell within one mile of the assigned aiming point. After a year of operations there had been no improvement in accuracy with this equipment.

Gee-H and Micro-H accuracy.   Only two types of radar bombing which depended on beacons were used to any great extent by the Eighth Air Force. They were Gee-H and Micro-H.

The Gee-H equipment had a transmitter that sent out pulses which triggered ground beacons. The pulses of the beacons were picked up by a receiver in the aircraft, and the initial pulse together with the responding pulses from the two beacons were shown on a cathode ray oscilloscope in the plane. By manipulating the oscilloscope controls, the Gee-H navigator could determine his distance from the ground beacons.

Two techniques for Gee-H bombing, the warning point procedure and the synchronous procedure, were used by the Eighth Air Force. In the warn-ing point procedure the Gee-H navigator determined both the track and the release point. In the synchronous procedure, the navigator determined the track and furnished the bombardier with information enabling him to set up the bombsight which dropped the bombs automatically when the indices of the sight met.

In Micro-H bombing the H2X equipment was used to trigger ground bea-cons, and the pulses from the beacons were shown on the H2X scope. A synchronous procedure using the bombsight to determine when to drop the bombs was used with Micro-H, but two techniques were used to establish track. In the first of these the difference in the distances of the aircraft from the two beacons was kept constant. The plane approached the target along a hyperbolic curve. In the second technique its distance from one of the beacons was fixed.

Since Micro-H was operational for only about the last six weeks of the time period covered by the report, the number of bombfalls that could be analyzed was too small to draw reliable conclusions. However, the indications were that its accuracy was about the same as that of Gee-H.

Gee-H accuracy. Exclusive of the ground support missions of 9 November (Metz and Thionville) and 16 November (Duren) on which Gee-H was used, there were, during the period 1 October to 31 December 1944, eighty-one at-tacks made primarily with Gee-H. A total of 794 squadron formations were dispatched. Of these, twenty-six did not bomb, while ninety-seven bombed targets other than their Gee-H primary. The bombfalls of 185 of the re-maining 671 squadrons were located. Six of the bombfalls were located by mission reports, fifty-five were located from photographic reconnaissance pic-tures, and 124 were located by strike photographs. Two of the six bombfalls found by mission reports were excluded from the study; one was treated as a PRU-located bombfall, and the other three were regarded as strike photo-graph bombfalls. Since the study showed that the fifty-six PRU-located sam-ple bombfalls showed a slight, though optimistic bias, they were not used. Thus, the Gee-H accuracy study was made using a sample of 127 bombfalls out of 671 bombfalls in all. This underscores the great difference in assessing the bombing accuracy of blind bombing as compared with visual bombing where virtually all bombfalls were located by strike photographs.

It was found that something of the order of 25 percent to 40 percent of the effort on Gee-H missions resulted in errors of over one and a half miles. The remaining 60 percent to 75 percent approximated a normal distribution with an average error of approximately 0.7 miles or 3,700 feet. Comparable figures were available for visual bombing under conditions of good visibility at the higher altitudes. They show that 20 percent to 25 percent of the bombing resulted in errors of over 3,000 feet. The remaining 75 percent to 80 percent approximated a normal distribution with an average error of about 1,000 feet. H2X bombing, on the other hand, with 10/10 cloud would result in 35 percent to 45 percent over five miles. The remaining 55 percent to 65 percent would have average errors of approximately two and a half miles.

Table 11.3. Comparison of Expected Percents of Bombs
within Standard Distances in Gee-H Bombing,
Visual Bombing under Conditions of Good Visibility,
and H2X Bombing under Conditions of Total Cloud

	Estimated percent of all bombs dropped that fell within				
	$1000'$	$\frac{1}{2}$ mile	1 mile	3 miles	5 miles
Visual bombing, good visibility	30	64	82	91	92
Gee-H	5	26	56	90	94
H2X, 10/10 cloud	0.2	1.2	6	40	59

Table 11.3 compares the three modes of bombing.

The table shows that for targets of 2,000 feet in diameter Gee-H was approximately 1/6 as effective as visual bombing with good visibility, and it was twenty-five times as effective as H2X under total cloud. For targets of the order of one mile in diameter Gee-H was approximately 2/5 as effective as visual and twenty times as effective as H2X under conditions of total cloud.

Interestingly, but not unexpectedly, the study showed that little relationship existed between cloud cover of target and Gee-H accuracy. The report concluded

> It does not seem improbable that the accuracy does decrease somewhat as the amount of cloud increases but the effect is not very marked in this data and may safely be ignored, at least for the purpose of comparing techniques of units.

Summary statement on Gee-H and Micro-H. The Gee-H, Micro-H portion of the report concludes with the following summary.

> Gee-H and Micro-H bombing, while far behind visual bombing, have nevertheless achieved a significant measure of success. Several different techniques have been used but none shows a clear advantage over the others. This problem of the choice of the best technique will continue to be of importance certainly until the introduction of a radar bombing device with an automatic computing system as an integral part .... .
>
> The fundamental limitation of all beacon bombing is its range, and in view of the large errors in H2X bombing, it would appear

desirable to make every effort to extend substantially the range of
our beacon bombing.

A note on the American bombing of German cities. It was not an avowed
policy of the Eighth Air Force to bomb German cities as a target system.
Nevertheless, the Eighth Air Force was responsible for a large part of the
devastation of German cities.

While air force mission planners and the bomber crews had been much
concerned about the civilians in occupied countries, such as France and the
Low Countries, their concern for the civilians in Germany was markedly less.
Bomb groups were less inhibited in selecting targets of opportunity when they
were unable to drop their bombs on assigned primary or secondary targets
in Germany. The American bombing of German towns and cities as targets
of opportunity was a relatively minor factor. Nevertheless, for whatever
reasons, in the stress of combat there were many times the Eighth Air Force
did not know with certainty what it had bombed. For example, the 7 October
1944 entry for the Eighth Air Force in "Combat Chronology" states, "Over
1,300 heavy bombers, in 4 forces, bomb 5 synthetic oil plants, an armament,
a tank, and an aero engine works in central and northeast Germany, plus 16
identified and 19 other unidentified targets in the area." [33]

The major explanation for bombing German cities was "spillage"—bombs
aimed at military targets that fell in nearby areas. American bomber crews
were seldom assigned city areas as aiming points. However, the majority of
their targets in Germany were in cities or their outskirts. The aiming points
given the bomber crews were almost invariably military targets such as oil
plants, rail centers, marshalling yards, factories, etc. within the metropolitan
area of some city. The large number of H2X bombs aimed at such targets
in the period 1 September to 31 December 1944—58 percent of all bombs
dropped by the Eighth Air Force in the period—constituted a major attack
on German cities.

As mentioned earlier, one of the studies of the Bombing Accuracy Subsection had shown that H2X bombing was more accurate when bombing targets
in small cities than when bombing targets in large cities. The sample of small
cities selected for the study was: Bielefeld, Hamm, Kassel, Mainz, Münster,
Neumünster, and Saarbrücken. The sample of large cities was: Berlin, Bremen, Cologne, Dusseldorf, Frankfurt, Hamburg, Ludwigshafen, Magdeburg,
Nürnberg, and Stuttgart. [34]

Unwittingly, I was part of the study. During this time I bombed targets at three of the small cities and five of the large ones. I bombed Ludwigshafen three times. Though not all were H2X missions, I remember one
that certainly was, the first USAAF mission to Nürnberg on 3 October 1944.
Nürnberg, as a center of Nazi activity, served as a symbol of what we were
fighting against. Aiming points were airfields west of the city and the city
itself. [35] We were told at our briefing that the mission was an important sym-

bolic paying of our respects to the führer. In the target area, the dark clouds underneath us came almost to the level at which we bombed, which was over 22,000 feet. We dropped our bombs into the clouds. I must confess that my main concern at the time was not for the citizens of the city but whether we hit the target or not. During this period our mission was the only one to Nürnberg. The bombfalls studied by the Bombing Accuracy Subsection were ours.

Why the section was unable to improve H2X bombing. The OAS was successful in helping the air force improve accuracy with visual bombing. It was not, however, able to do the same with H2X bombing. Dr. G. Baley Price gives two reasons.

> 1. We were never able to assess the results of blind bombing missions with sufficient speed and especially accuracy so that we could put out reports that compared the performance of the various Groups. We could never 'rate the Groups' in blind bombing. As one Commander put it, 'the Groups were not charged for the bombs they dropped blind'. It is a considered opinion that the competition by the monthly reports of Bombing Accuracy for visual bombing was the most important factor that contributed to improvement in accuracy with the Norden bombsight. There was no similar competition in blind bombing.
>
> 2. We had no access to Headquarters, Eighth Air Force. Dr. Murrell, with allegiance to the technical men who built and promoted the equipment but without the knowledge of missions and results that could be gained only from our studies, was always called upon to advise Command on matters pertaining to H2X. The experience of Bombing Accuracy was never fully utilized. [36]

In his discussion of H2X research, Leslie Arps, the director of the section, mentions a mismanagement of personnel.

> With regard to H2X the [Bombing Accuracy] Subsection never was quite able to function as effectively as was originally hoped. The reason for this was quite simple. The Radiation Laboratory never was willing to release radar personnel to the ORS and instead installed at the Eighth Air Force its own radar adviser. This seemed most unfortunate for it resulted in some duplication of effort and it slowed up the effective employment of the results of the H2X blind bombing analysis. One thing seems clear; if there is an ORS at a Command and it is charged with furnishing the Commanding General with scientific advice then to have a separate scientific adviser leads to confusion. [37]

REFERENCES

1. "Eighth Air Force, History of Operations Analysis Section, October 1942–June 1945," Leslie H. Arps, 520.303-3, Archives, Simpson Historical Research Center, Maxwell Air Force Base, Alabama, 136.

2. Wesley Frank Craven and James Lea Cate of the USAF Historical Division, eds., *Europe: From Argument to V-E Day, January 1944 to May 1945*, vol. 3 of *The Army Air Forces in World War II* (Chicago: University of Chicago Press, 1951) 539.

3. "Report for Colonel W. B. Leach on the History and Development of the Bombs and Fuzes Subsection of the Operational Analysis Section, Headquarters Eighth Air Force," 10 April 1945, Bissell Alderman, 520.303-3, Archives, Simpson Historical Research Center, Maxwell Air Force Base, Alabama, 21.

4. *Europe: From Argument to V-E Day*, 525.

5. Ibid., 106.

6. Ibid., 540.

7. Ibid., 541.

8. Ibid., 541–42.

9. "The Army Air Forces in World War II, Combat Chronology 1941–1945," 1973, Office of Air Force History, Simpson Historical Research Center, Maxwell Air Force Base, Alabama, 979.

10. "Report for Colonel W. B. Leach," 40.

11. Roger A. Freeman, *Mighty Eighth War Manual* (London: Janes, 1984), 228.

12. "Report for Colonel W. B. Leach," 44.

13. *Mighty Eighth War Manual*, 228.

14. "Report for Colonel W. B. Leach," 27.

15. Ibid., 39.

16. Ibid., 40–41.

17. Leroy A. Brothers, *Operations Analysis in World War II, United States Army Air Forces* (Philadelphia: Stephenson-Brothers, 1948), 36.

18. George W. Ball, *The Past Has Another Pattern* (New York: Norton, 1982), 41–44.

19. "Report for Colonel W. B. Leach," 41–42.

20. "History of the Battle Damage Subsection, Operational Analysis Section, Eighth Air Force, December 1943–May 1945," 520.303-1, Archives, Simpson Historical Research Center, Maxwell Air Force Base, Alabama, 33.

21. Ibid., 39–41.

22. Ibid., 41–42.

23. Ibid., 43.

24. Ibid., 46, 49.

25. Ibid., 18.

26. Martin J. Miller, "The Armored Airmen: World War II, U.S. Army Air Force Body Armor Program." *Aerospace Historian* **32** (Spring/March 1985): 27–32.

27. "Report on Bombing Accuracy, Eighth Air Force, 1 September 1944–31 December 1944," 20 April 1945, Archives, Simpson Historical Research Center, Maxwell Air Force Base, Alabama.

28. "Overall Report, European War," United States Strategic Bombing Survey, 30 September 1945, 10.

29. G. Baley Price, *Gremlin Hunting in the Eighth Air Force, European Theater of Operations, 1943–1945*, 95–96.

30. "Report on Bombing Accuracy," 65.

31. For the statement of purpose, see "Report on Bombing Accuracy," 1.
32. "Eighth Air Force, History of Operations Analysis Section," 125.
33. "Combat Chronology," entry for 7 October 1944, Eighth Air Force.
34. "Report on Bombing Accuracy," 27.
35. "Combat Chronology," entry for 3 October 1944, Eighth Air Force.
36. *Gremlin Hunting*, 100, 101.
37. "Eighth Air Force, History of Operations Analysis Section," 99, 100.

12

Operations Analysis in the Eighth Air Force
The Last Four Months of Combat Operations

JANUARY

The reassessment of bombing priorities. By the end of December 1944 it was clear that the Germans, in their great gamble, the Ardennes Counteroffensive or Battle of the Bulge, were losing. However, it had been a very sobering experience for the American generals. Spaatz, Eaker, and Doolittle, as well as the British, reexamined their bombing priorities. On 12 January General Spaatz and Air Marshal Bottomley issued a directive listing these priorities:

1. Oil [Spaatz also sent out instructions for the American heavies to regard jet production as a "parallel obligation."]
2. Communications [railways, marshalling yards, bridges]
3. Blind bombing attacks on industrial areas whenever weather or tactical conditions prevented attacks on higher priority targets.
4. Counter air force action.
5. Support of land and naval operations. [This always superseded the others upon request by General Eisenhower.] [1]

On 30 and 31 January 1945 these priorities were modified somewhat at the Malta Conference, held by the Allied leaders as a preliminary to the Yalta Conference of American, British, and Russian leaders on 4 February 1945. At the Malta Conference it was decided that

as second priority after synthetic oil came "Berlin, Leipzig, Dresden, and associated cities where heavy attack will cause great confusion in civilian evacuation from the east and hamper reinforcements". As a third priority the heavy bombers would direct their efforts on communications in the Ruhr-Cologne-Kassel area to keep the Germans from withdrawing forces in the west to bolster the east. [2]

Regarding the setting of priorities, the record shows that

> On 1 January 1945, General Eaker had advised Spaatz against sending heavy bombers to attack transportation targets in small German towns, for there would be many civilian casualties and the German people might be convinced the Americans were barbarians, just as Nazi propaganda charged. Eaker concluded that "you and Bob Lovett are right and we should never allow the history of this war to convict us of throwing the strategic bomber at the man in the street." [3]

In January the Eighth Air Force completed heavy bomber missions on twenty days. On every one of these days marshalling yards and communications centers were bombed. On seven days oil targets were bombed. On six days "city areas" were bombed. [4]

In January 1945 the Eighth Air Force spent very much time supporting the land battle.

> Approximately three-fourths of the USSTAF effort went on tactical targets, and RAF Bomber Command was similarly taxed. Eighth Air Force mission reports for most of January show enormous numbers of heavy bombers, sometimes as many as 1,500 going out day after day to bomb targets whose neutralization would benefit Allied ground forces but would not directly accelerate the dislocation of Germany's industries. The preponderant weight of such air effort went on what was officially a secondary objective, enemy communications. [5]

The GAF and the gunnery subsection.   The Eighth Air Force celebrated New Year's Day 1945 by sending over 700 bombers to attack three oil targets, five Rhine river bridges and rail junctions, three marshalling yards, and various other targets in ten German cities. Their escorting fighter groups encountered over 120 German fighters in the Frankfurt/Main and Hannover areas. Our fighters claimed seventeen kills, including one jet.

The GAF had a nasty surprise of its own planned for New Year's Day. It launched an attack of about 800 airplanes against Allied airfields in the Brussels, Eindhoven, and Metz areas. One hundred twenty-seven Allied aircraft were destroyed. Allied fighters claimed 160 air victories against the German attackers. Allied antiaircraft claimed more kills than the Allied fighters did. [6] For the GAF it was a very costly raid.

There was one other air battle in January. On 14 January over 650 bombers attacked four oil targets, two steel mills, a benzoil plant west of Berlin, and one marshalling yard. The fifteen escorting fighter groups engaged about 250 German fighters and claimed 100 kills. Four other fighter groups on fighter sweeps engaged 150 fighters and claimed over forty destroyed. [7]

Just about this time Dr. Ayres and Lieutenant Jillson left the Gunnery Subsection to return to the States. This left Porter Henry and Dr. John Odle to carry the work of the section. Odle states:

> Starting in January I began to take an increasingly active part in getting out the tactics posters started a few months previously by Porter Henry...I did a large part of the work preparing the poster for January 14. [8]

Back in October in *Short Bursts* Porter Henry had written an article "Cohen's Cameras—They Never Lie" about an emerging gun camera training program. The article begins:

> Over in the 4th Combat Wing, you won't hear many gunners beating their gums about what redhot shots they are. The reason for this modesty is that each group in the Wing—the 94th, 385th and 447th—has one B-17 completely equipped with British Mark IC gyro-computing sights and GSAP gun cameras to check up on a gunner's accuracy. [9]

By October all bomb divisions were getting gyro sights and cameras to set up their own training programs. They were trying to catch up with the gunnery program instituted by the acting gunnery officer of the Fourth Combat Wing, Major Ralph Cohen, who had a three-month head start. The Fourth Combat Wing was commanded by the legendary Colonel Castle.

Porter Henry tells of how Castle backed Cohen in instituting the program:

> Last July, by going through channels, across channels, and under channels, Maj. Cohen succeeded in scraping together the necessary equipment and installing it in the Forts. The Wing commanding Officer, Col. Frederick W. Castle, claims Maj. Cohen uses "second story supply channels". Col. Castle, incidentally, is a firm believer in keeping up gunnery training in the combat theater, and has backed up the camera program from the start. [10]

On Christmas Eve 1944 General Castle was killed when his B-17 was shot down by the GAF. [11]

By January 1945 the Eighth Air Force had started to set up provisions for regular gun camera practice missions for its gunners. Porter Henry and Dr. Odle, as a result of requests for information, began to become experts on gun camera work. They read the air force manuals on the subject, traveled around to the several groups which had made experimental installations, and conferred with RAF gun camera specialists on their work.

As a result of their findings and other information brought out during the gunnery conference, Henry and Odle worked out a complete set of instructions for assessing gun camera film. These were written up and sent to the groups for their use. [12]

Bombing accuracy.   Bombing accuracy of the Eighth Air Force in January 1945 was no different than for the period 1 September to 31 December 1944. Thus, the statement in the official U.S. Air Force history of WWII, namely: "...radar-bombing methods continued to prove disappointing. The Eighth Air Force had an average circular probable error of about two miles on its blind missions..." [13] is interesting. According to that statement, on the average half of the bombs dropped by radar fell within a two-mile radius of the aiming point. The reference for the above statement given in the air force history is correspondence between Lieutenant General Barney Giles of AAF Washington and General Doolittle, the Eighth Air Force commander. [14] What is interesting about the alleged average CPE (circular probable error: the radius of the circle around the aiming point within which half the bombs fell) for Eighth Air Force blind bombing is how good it is.

Bombs and fuzes

Ground surveys can be misleading. Alderman in his memoir [15] describes a sensitive situation that developed within the operations analysis family. It resulted in a report, "Summary of the Effectiveness of Bombs and Fuzes on Concrete Hangars and Hangar-type Buildings," which was released on 10 January 1945.

An ORS consultant at one of the division headquarters had made a number of field trips to the continent to survey damage to a few targets that had been hit by his division. He had gone with the division bombardier and photo-interpreter. They submitted a report to their commanding officer upon return. Alderman says, "Their report contained many boners."

The report claimed that 500-pound GPs had been ineffective on the concrete hangars at Rheims-Champagne Airfield and that 1,000-pound GPs would have been better. At Orleans-Bricy Airfield it was claimed that effective damage to concrete hangars had been caused by 1,000-pound GPs whereas Alderman was sure that some of the damage had been done by 500-pound GPs. Alderman then says:

> Since there was a growing tendency in that Division to request heavier bombs on certain targets and since their report falsely supported their beliefs in the heavier weapons, we decided that the amount of data we had on concrete hangars would prove or disprove their contentions of the superior effectiveness of the larger bomb, at least on these targets. Hence an intensive study was undertaken. [16]

The Bombs and Fuzes Subsection, visiting several airfields, carefully inspected bomb damage to concrete hangars and hangar-type buildings and took good photographs. On some of the targets, the only ones included in the study, there had been as many as five attacks. Studying old strike photographs enabled the subsection to isolate individual attacks and study the effectiveness of each weapon use. Of the eighteen concrete hangars and hangar-type buildings, fifteen had been completely destroyed by 500-pound GP bombs at the Rheims-Champagne Airfield. At Orleans-Bricy the damage by the 500-pound GPs was greater than that done by the 1,000-pound GPs which had been used on one attack.

The study covered the attacks on the hangars and hangar-type buildings at the following airfields: Rheims-Champagne, Villacoublay, Le Bourget, Orly, Orleans-Bricy, Chartres, and Chateaudun.

Alderman concludes, "From a very large sample, the 500-pound GP bomb, fuzed .01, proved to be the most effective weapon."[17]

Flak and the Loss and Battle Damage Subsection.   On 10 January 1945 the Eighth Air Force lost twenty heavy bombers to flak.[18] Thus, the flak officers' conference held on 11 and 12 January at Eighth Air Force headquarters was certainly timely. It was attended by flak officers and OAS personnel of the Eighth, Ninth, and Fifteenth Air Forces and by flak officers of the Mediterranean Allied Air Forces, the Eighth Air Force fighter wings, the Ninth Air Defense Command, and Troop Carrier Command. The Loss and Battle Damage members were prominent in setting up and presenting parts of the program of interchange of information.[19] At this meeting the subsection presented its analysis of the 30 November attack on Leuna when Eighth Air Force lost 5 percent of the attacking force to flak. In January the subsection actively promoted and studied precision flying maneuvers at the target to reduce flak risk and damage.

FEBRUARY

Despite a great deal of bad weather the Eighth Air Force managed to complete missions on twenty days in February. The target priorities were really the same as for January, except that attacks on targets in cities like Berlin, Leipzig, and Dresden were emphasized with the goal of "causing confusion in civilian evacuation from the east" as the Russian army closed in on these cities and also to "hamper reinforcements" to the resisting German forces.

The Eighth Air Force bombed oil targets on nine of the twenty days and communications targets on virtually all twenty days. Towns and city areas are also mentioned as having been targets *per se*, sometimes as targets of opportunity.[20]

The Berlin and Dresden bombings give the bombing accuracy subsection a special assignment.   The February bombings of Berlin and Dresden, with their unusually lethal effect on civilian populations, caused a special assignment for the Bombing Accuracy Subsection.

On 3 February 1945 nearly 1,000 B-17s flew to Berlin while 400 B-24s attacked rail and oil targets at nearby Magdeburg. "Combat Chronology" gives marshalling yards as the Berlin target. The Americans had expected the Berlin attack would have to be by radar. Instead they found most of Berlin exposed to visual bombing. Hence, accuracy was high even though the bombs were dropped from altitudes ranging from 24,000 to 27,000 feet. German flak brought down twenty-one of the Berlin bombers. The bombers inflicted

> severe damage on marshalling yards and railway stations throughout the Berlin area. Furthermore, the bomb-pattern was heavy in the government district. The Reichs-chancellery, Air Ministry, Foreign Office, Ministry of Propaganda, and Gestapo Headquarters all sustained many hits... .Civilian casualties were exceedingly high, the number of fatalities reaching perhaps 25,000, and Swedish newspaper accounts were full of lurid details about the horror of Berlin. [21]

This particular Berlin raid and its publicity turned much attention to what the German radio called "terror bombing."

> The leaders of the AAF had long been on record in opposition to indiscriminate attacks on civilians. If bombardiers were sometimes less circumspect in this matter, or if Germans found it hard to differentiate between spillage and terror bombing, it nevertheless seemed important during those pre-Hiroshima months not to deviate from the stated policy of attacking stated military objectives. [22]

General Kuter, who represented General Arnold at the Yalta Conference during Arnold's convalescence from an illness, asked Spaatz whether the revised priority list of 31 January 1945 authorized indiscriminate attacks on cities. From Washington, Lieutenant General Barney M. Giles cabled his support. Spaatz's reply was that "the Americans were not bombing cities indiscriminately but attacking transportation facilities inside cities in missions which the Russians had requested and seemed to appreciate. [23]

Then came the Allied THUNDERCLAP bombings of Dresden on 13–15 February. On the night of 13 February Dresden was bombed by the RAF and on 14 February and 15 February by the Eighth Air Force. The USAAF history states,

> The Eighth Air Force devoted two days' effort beginning with 14 February to the central German railway centers which were believed to serve armies opposing the Russians in the east. Three hundred and eleven Fortresses dropped 771 tons on Dresden, 249 dropped 718 tons on Chemnitz and 340 Liberators unloaded 811 tons on Magdeburg, while small forces struck targets of opportunity in this general area. Dresden, which the heavy bombers had left alone until 1945, had received a terrible bombing from the RAF on the previous night. Smoke was still rising to 15,000 feet

by the time the Americans arrived to make their attack by instrument. It was this blow which helped set off the flurry about terror bombing.

The next day 210 B-17s of the Eighth Air Force bombed again, dropping 461 tons by instrument on Dresden as a secondary target.[24]

The extent of the casualties of the Dresden attacks is really unknown. However,

> an estimated 35,000 of the million or so townspeople and refugees perished in the February bombings alone. These attacks, along with Thunderclap [type] poundings of Berlin, Chemnitz, and Cottbus, inspired press reports of 'deliberate terror bombing' as a 'ruthless expedient' to hasten victory. Actually Harris [RAF Bomber Command] was merely continuing his policy of area bombing, which had originated as an attempt to reduce production by attacking German workers in their homes rather than bombing their factories. In the United States, General George C. Marshall tried to reconcile the conflict between newspaper reports of terror bombing and official statements calling it precision bombardment.[25]

At this time a news story widely printed in the United States claims that the senior American air commanders had determined to terrorize the German people into submission. This account grew out of a SHAEF (Eisenhower's headquarters) press conference in which an RAF officer described how the air forces planned to bomb large population centers and then attempt to prevent relief supplies from reaching them.

General Arnold, understandably disturbed by this publicity, cabled Spaatz asking which bombing directive he was using and

> ... implying that he would like to know whether there was any significant distinction between morale bombing and radar attacks on transportation targets in urban areas. Spaatz hastened to reply that he had not departed from the historic American policy in Europe, even in the case of Berlin, and Arnold expressed himself as entirely satisfied with the explanation.[26]

The Bombing Accuracy Subsection wrote a report, "Analysis of Attack on Berlin 3 February 1945," which was dated 24 February 1945.[27] However, this mission and the Dresden mission resulted in a special request of Bombing Accuracy from General Anderson. Baley Price tells of it:

> It [the February 3 mission to Berlin] was a highly successful operation, but apparently the newspaper reports that 25,000 people were killed attracted a lot of attention. We were told that General Anderson had been called to Washington to explain the wanton

bombing of civilian population, and we were asked to prepare a memorandum showing the accuracy of the Eighth Air Force. [28]

The subsection had to work night and day in order to meet the time limit. Price says,

If the big report for the period 1 September–31 December 1944 had been ready, a copy of it would have filled the bill. Fortunately, however, enough results could be extracted from the data quickly to serve the purpose. We spent considerable time working out simple and vivid tabular and graphical presentations of the result, had them expertly drafted, and then reproduced. Finally, we bound this material in a large book with copies of all bomb plots on the night target maps that were available.

General Anderson took this to Washington. Price then says,

The only comment that I have ever heard on our memorandum was one made by Col. Ramsey Potts after the General had returned: "That was a hell of a memorandum to prove that the Eighth Air Force is accurate."

Price concludes with these observations:

Our accuracy on visual missions was good, but the memorandum stated that during the last four months of 1944 our H2X bombing under conditions of 10/10 cloud had placed only 58% of the bombs within 5 miles of the assigned aiming point! If the public knew the facts about our blind bombing in Europe, perhaps the outcry over the *indiscriminate* destruction caused by the atomic bomb would not have arisen. [29]

Operation CLARION. On 8 March 1945 the Bombing Accuracy Subsection released a report, "Report on Attacks against Enemy Rail Communications— 22 February 1945." These were no ordinary attacks but were part of a huge coordinated Allied attack on German communications given the code name CLARION. By the middle of February 1945 the Allied land armies were prepared to resume the offensive toward the Rhine which the German counteroffensive in the Ardennes had interrupted in December 1944. Eisenhower's headquarters [30] requested the air forces to mount CLARION, a long-standing plan designed to utilize all available Anglo-American air power in a blow at German communications which would affect both economic life and the tactical situation.

CLARION called for British-American bombers and fighters to range over most of the Reich simultaneously on a clear day to attack all sorts of transportation targets: grade crossings, stations, barges, docks, signals, tracks, bridges and marshalling yards. Most of the objectives were located in small towns that had never been bombed before." [It was hoped that the bombings would] "produce a stupefying effect on morale on the eve of the land offensive." [31]

The opportunity for the attack came on 22 February when most of Germany was expected to be vulnerable to visual bombing attacks. The RAF struck targets in the Ruhr, and the Eighth Air Force with 1,359 bombers attacked forty targets, including over twenty marshalling yards in northern and central Germany. Over 800 Eighth Air Force fighters participated. The Fifteenth Air Force attacked twenty-five marshalling yards and a number of railroad lines and bridges in Germany and Austria. Over 300 of its fighters participated. The U.S. Ninth Air Force attacked forty-six rail bridges, twelve marshalling yards, eleven stations and other rail targets with 450 of its medium bombers, B-26s, A-20s, and A-26s. Over 1,000 Ninth Air Force fighters were also involved. [32]

The Eighth Air Force was able to depart from its usual operating tactics on the CLARION missions. The heavy bombers attacked from about 10,000 feet or lower instead of the customary 20,000 feet or higher. The bombers also formed small attacking units instead of the usual large formations. The Eighth's fighters went along, mainly for independent strafing and bombing operations. The GAF had not attempted a serious interception since New Year's Day. Bombing was generally accurate. Only seven of the Eighth's bombers were lost, all to flak.

The 22 February missions seemed so successful that another CLARION-type mission of similar size was flown the next day. After two days of CLARION operations the Allied air forces resumed their normal operations.

Micro-H bombing in February.   All of the Micro-H bombing of the Eighth Air Force was done by the Third Air Division. A study of the February activity was made by its operations analyst, the mathematician Angus E. Taylor, in "A Report on the Micro-H Bombing Missions during February, 1945," [33] which was released on 9 March 1945.

In February the Third Air Division dispatched ninety-nine squadrons with instructions to bomb by Micro-H technique or visually if possible. The ninety-nine Micro-H squadrons had been sent out in ten task forces. Bridges were targets of five of the task forces. Underground oil storage depots were targets of two of the task forces, and marshalling yards were targets of the remaining three task forces.

Of the ninety-nine squadrons, eleven were able to attack the primary target visually; forty-seven bombed their target by independent Micro-H sightings. Eleven more squadrons bombed on the smoke markers of other squadrons' Micro-H sightings. The remaining thirty squadrons either made H2X sightings on the assigned target, attacked another target, or failed to bomb.

Twenty-seven squadrons, 27 percent of the ninety-nine squadrons, failed to bomb either visually or by independent Micro-H sighting. In each case, either the Micro-H equipment failed or was unsatisfactory, or the plane could not receive the beacon signal. The corresponding figure for January was 30 percent.

Seventeen of the Micro-H sightings were identified. Ten of these had received some visual assistance. The distribution of the pattern centers in terms of distance in miles from the assigned aiming point was: none within 0.2 mile (or 1,000 feet); 24 percent within 0.5 mile; 47 percent within 1.0 mile; 71 percent within 2.0 miles; 94 percent within 3.0 miles; 100 percent within 5.0 miles.

The report concludes:

> There were five instances in February in which Micro-H squadrons failed to bomb the primary target because the bombardiers took over from the radar navigators for visual runs, but found subsequently that visual runs were impossible. These instances serve to underline the importance of good judgement in such circumstances. The demonstrated accuracy of Micro-H bombing with a certain amount of visual assistance should be remembered when debating whether to attempt to bomb entirely by visual means under conditions of uncertain visibility. [34]

The Paris conference on bombing and gunnery effectiveness in February. On 1 and 2 February, a conference on bombing and gunnery effectiveness was held in Paris at the headquarters of the United States Strategic Air Forces in Europe. In addition to the appropriate military representatives there were OAS delegations from the Eighth, Ninth, and Fifteenth Air Forces. From the Eighth Air Force were Dr. J. W. T. Youngs of Bombing Accuracy, Mr. Porter Henry of Gunnery, and Mr. Bissell Alderman of Bombs and Fuzes. From the Ninth Air Force were Dr. F. L. Mohler of Bombing Accuracy, Dr. D. W. Armstrong of Blind Bombing, Dr. A. E. Brandt of Gunnery, Dr. H. O. Wyckoff of Rockets, Dr. H. L. Reinke of Damage Assessment, Dr. M. Eudy of Fighter Bombers, Dr. L. S. Taylor, the chief of the section, and Dr. D. West of Bombs and Fuzes. From the Fifteenth Air Force was Dr. L. Tarshis. Among several other civilian consultants at the conference was the mathematician and ballistics expert Dr. E. J. McShane.

Alderman describes the conference in his memoir. [35] It was called together in Paris by Col. P. Schwartz, ordnance officer of USSTAF. Brief lectures were given by each delegate on current problems and practice in the field. The talks were followed by general discussion. The intent was to get the sections together to exchange ideas. After the last formal session of the conference the analysts were invited to meet General Spaatz at his chateau. Alderman recalls that General Spaatz had numerous questions and comments.

One of General Spaatz's comments was especially interesting to the Eighth

Air Force representatives. Since obscuration of the target by smoke was a problem, especially at oil targets, General Spaatz had the idea that all bombs dropped on the oil plants should have long delay fuzes. This way the bombs could not contribute to the obscuration of the target. Alderman writes, "He [General Spaatz] informed us that the experts were opposed to using long delay fuzes in all bombs in attacks on Synthetic Oil Targets." Alderman then told General Spaatz that the effectiveness of each bomb might be reduced as much as 50 percent or more by a long delay fuze. Furthermore, long delays would not solve the problem, since German-generated smoke screens were chiefly responsible for obscuring the target. Dr. Youngs supported Alderman's position in this exchange with General Spaatz.

Nevertheless, the matter was only temporarily closed. General Spaatz said that on the next mission to a synthetic oil target his plan to use all long-delay fuzes would be tested.

Sure enough, back at Eighth Air Force headquarters, the next time synthetic oil targets were the order of the day, USSTAF proposed that all the bombs be fuzed long delay. At the OPS conference the Bombs and Fuzes men objected to this proposal. Alderman says,

> We did of course approve the use of a few long delays for hindering firefighting and delaying reconstruction, but since it was so costly to deliver what few bombs were scored on these targets, and since obscuration by bomb bursts was not the critical factor, it seemed to us that any device which seriously reduced the effectiveness of the bombs that did get on the target should not be used.

The advice of the Bombs and Fuzes men was followed. [36]

The February conference in Paris brought together the two mathematicians, Dr. Youngs of Bombing Accuracy and Dr. E. J. McShane. By this time Dr. Youngs had become the section's acknowledged expert on the Norden bombsight. Dr. McShane was serving as head mathematician, Ballistic Research Laboratory, Aberdeen Proving Grounds. The two mathematicians put their heads together and came up with an extraordinarily simple method for using the Norden bombsight to determine ground speed. The method involved the use of a special table giving tangents of dropping angles and trail for specified altitudes. Using this table the bombardier preset the tangent of the dropping angle and the trail in the bombsight for the appropriate altitude. He then synchronized by using the disc drum, rather than the rate knob. After synchronizing by use of the disc speed drum, the bombardier took a disc speed reading. The disc speed reading, for typical bombing altitudes of the B-17s and B-24s, was the ground speed. This technique did not require the bombardier to perform a single calculation at operational altitudes. It replaced a more complicated technique using the bombsight which required one addition and three multiplications. Mathematical calculations at 22,000 feet by men wearing oxygen masks and heated suits were best avoided if possible.

Youngs and McShane reported their procedure in "A Method for Determining Ground Speed by Using Norden Bomb Sight and Ground Speed Tables," dated 12 February 1945.[37]

Bissell Alderman's return to the States in February for two months of temporary duty and leave was a significant event. Though he attended conferences on bombing effectiveness in Washington, D.C., and Orlando, Florida, his primary task was to write a "Report for Colonel W. B. Leach on the History and Development of the Bombs and Fuzes Subsection, Headquarters Eighth Air Force."[38]

Also in February the Gunnery Subsection obtained the services of Dr. Ralph D. James, professor of mathematics at the University of British Columbia, Vancouver, Canada. Dr. James's Ph.D. was from the University of Chicago, 1932.[39] James arrived in time to help Odle prepare a set of firing tables for the .50 caliber machine gun. The tables were requested by Mr. Lupton, the chief instructor of the American Power Turret School at Kirkham. Odle was fortunate to have James to help him, because, as he says, 'It was a long computing job, and was not completed until March."[40]

MARCH

No new air force target directives were issued for March. British and American armies were moving eastward into Germany, and the Russians were moving in from the east. The area defended by the Germans was getting smaller. By the beginning of March the Allied troops had reached the Rhine. By the end of March major bridgeheads across the Rhine were established in a number of places.

German oil supplies in March were adequate only for a fitful defense against the Allied advance. The Eighth and Fifteenth Air Forces and the RAF dropped 36,000 tons against oil targets alone in March, making this the second largest amount against oil in the whole oil campaign.[41]

The Eighth Air Force completed missions on twenty-six days in March. On twenty of these days communications targets were bombed. On twelve days oil targets were bombed. On eleven days city areas were targets. In addition, numerous other targets received attention, such as jet plane factories, tank factories, and U-boat pens and facilities.[42]

The jets attack. Except for 1 January the GAF had made no really serious challenge to the Allied air forces in January and February 1945. Nevertheless it remained enough of a threat that the Eighth Air Force fighters still escorted the bombers on missions. In March the wisdom of this precaution was demonstrated. Upwards of thirty bombers were lost to German jet fighters in March alone.[43]

On 1 March several jets attacked a lead bomber box without success. On 2 March about seventy-five conventional German fighters attacked the bombers of the Third Division in the vicinity of Dresden and shot down six B-17s. German fighter losses were reported as heavy. On one of the missions of 3 March the jets came out in force.

> More than fifty Me-262's and Me-163's playfully encircled the slower P-51's, making a few attacks and eluding the Mustangs without apparent difficulty. Finally, the jets shot down six American fighters and three bombers before allowing themselves to be driven off by the P-51's. [44]

The Berlin mission of 18 March. The 18 March mission to Berlin was noteworthy for several reasons. It was the biggest daylight raid ever made on Berlin. The Eighth Air Force received orders from USSTAF to mount a 1,200-plane assault on Berlin, which by now was also the goal of the Russian armies. The Eighth Air Force, in fact, sent 1,250 heavy bombers and fourteen fighter groups to Berlin on 18 March. [45] The Bombing Accuracy Subsection wrote a special report on the mission, "Report on Bombing Accuracy on Berlin Operation of 18 March 1945," which was dated 1 April 1945. [46]

The planes dropped over 3,000 tons by H2X sightings with two rail centers, two tank and armament plants, two marshalling yards, three town areas, and an industrial area near Berlin as aiming points. [47] Damage was widespread throughout the city.

On the Berlin mission twenty-four bombers and five fighters were lost, mainly to jet fighters that attacked in formations as large as thirty-six aircraft. These fighters displayed a range of interception greater than the Americans had expected. The aggressive German attack on the bombers promised a new phase of the air war. Moreover, flak had been heavy and accurate enough to damage more than half the bombers. Sixteen were so badly damaged that they crash-landed behind Russian lines instead of trying to reach England. [48]

On the mission of 19 March the Eighth Air Force lost three bombers to jets. On the mission of 20 March two more bombers were lost to jets. However, just as the superior German jet fighter, the Me-262, began to make an impact on the air war, the war in Europe began its final weeks.

Ground support—crossing the Rhine. By the third week of March Russian armies were closing in on Berlin and Vienna in the east, and the American and British armies were preparing to cross the lower Rhine river on a broad front. Just before the great airborne and land assault over the Rhine, the air forces undertook a gigantic operation lasting four days to complete the isolation of the Ruhr and to paralyze German defenses. The combined strength of the Eighth Air Force, RAF Bomber Command, and the tactical air forces was turned over to this project. The Bombing Accuracy Subsection wrote a report, "Use of Eighth Air Force in Tactical Air Operations," dated 31 March on the Eighth's bombing in support of the Rhine crossings. [49]

On the first day, 21 March, the Eighth Air Force sent 1,254 bombers to bomb ten airfields. This was followed on the next day with attacks by 1,284 heavy bombers on five more airfields, military encampments, defended villages, and store areas near the intended crossing site. On 23 March the Eighth Air Force sent 1,240 heavies to bomb marshalling yards in and around the Ruhr. On D day, 24 March, the first day of the ground assault, more than 1,000 bombers of the Eighth Air Force attacked German airfields again. Eighth Air Force Liberators (B-24s) dropped supplies to airborne troops that had jumped earlier in the day.

The crossing of the Rhine was an outstanding success. The bombing had been accurate and effective. The enemy was isolated and battered. Although the GAF was able to fly 200 sorties that day, none reached the battle area. [50]

Gunnery activities. The regular appearances of the German jets in March kept the Gunnery Subsection busy with its air battle posters and the monthly *Short Bursts*. These things, of course, came on top of other time-consuming duties. In March Captain Roger Russell of the Central School for Flexible Gunnery came to the Eighth Air Force on temporary duty. At his suggestion the Gunnery Subsection conducted some special firing and training experiments at one of the groups. Dr. Odle was put in charge of this in its beginning stages. Later Porter Henry was in charge of writing up the results.

The arrival of Dr. James made it possible for the subsection to turn its attention to the problems of fighter gunnery in the Eighth Air Force. The Eighth Fighter Command had had its own small but energetic operations analysis section consisting of the physicist Dr. Ralph P. Johnson and the lawyer Theodore Tannenwald, Jr. However, in September and October 1944, after the Eighth Fighter Command was absorbed into the divisions, these men returned to the States to assume other duties. [51]

In March Colonel Arps recommended that the Gunnery Subsection become acquainted with some of the Eighth Air Force fighter groups to see if there were problems that OAS could help with. Dr. James made a number of trips to the fighter groups and found that the biggest problems concerned rockets. Odle and James discussed these problems with Major E. Miller, Eighth Air Force fighter gunnery officer, and made one trip with him to the RAF Central Fighter Establishment at Tangmere to attend a conference on rockets. Odle and James made another trip to the Royal Aircraft Establishment at Farnborough to discuss rocket sighting developments with Mr. A. A. Hall. Dr. James worked on several technical questions connected with the use of rockets by Eighth Air Force fighter bombers until the end of the war. [52]

Loss and battle damage and radio countermeasures. On 6 March 1945 William J. Pilat of the Loss and Battle Damage Subsection returned to the States.

After a little over two months' stay in the States he was reassigned as an analyst with the Far Eastern Air Forces in the Pacific Theater. On 10 March 1945 Helmer L. Webb joined the OAS of the Eighth Air Force. Webb, an experienced, professional librarian from Union College in Schenectady, New York, was assigned the now formidable task of being in charge of keeping the bombing accuracy records. [53]

By March 1945 a division of Flak Intelligence had been established at USSTAF headquarters in Paris with Lieutenant Colonel Devereux at its head. Colonel Devereux called the flak officers' conference in St. Germain, a town on the Seine west of Paris, for 14–16 March. All the air forces in the European and Mediterranean theaters were represented. A representative of the OAS Eighth Air Force was also present. This conference, and the two flak conferences that had preceded it, resulted in much exchange of information. The Loss and Battle Damage Subsection was visited on various occasions by OAS representatives. Flak officers of the Ninth Air Force, the Fifteenth Air Force, and the MAAF were shown the major activities and techniques used by the section.

David Park, an analyst who had joined the section in November, worked both with the Radio Countermeasures and Battle Damage Subsections. In the last six months of the war the RCM subsection reconstructed courses flown to demonstrate the effectiveness of RCM protection. This was part of an attempt to promote an understanding of the principles of flak risk reduction throughout the air force. In particular, determining which formations had flown within 4,000 feet of chaff trails left by previous formations was important. Hence, it was necessary to determine course quite accurately.

Park developed a technique of plotting courses in the target area by carefully studying strike photographs and using all available data from navigators' logs and other reports. Earlier, Pilat, using Park's techniques, analyzed and charted the Merseburg-Leuna mission of 30 November in which 5 percent of the attacking force was lost to flak. This poster was presented at the first flak officers' conference in January. Because it was so instructive, five subsequent posters were made of major missions. These posters included a detailed analysis of the mission from all points of view—weather, navigation, bombing accuracy, and flak and fighter loss and damage. They were distributed to the commands at Eighth Air Force, divisions, and wings.

> We felt that they [the posters] gave a reasonably accurate picture of the general character of a mission—the closeness to which briefed courses were adhered to, the speed of axes of attack, and the kind of spacing in trail achieved. As such they could validly be used both to indicate some of the possible reasons why a particular mission did or did not suffer heavily from flak, and also to illustrate the effect on our flak exposure of various types of spacing and of deviation from the course. [54]

Baley Price recalls two conferences. In March Colonel Scott and Baley Price of Bombing Accuracy were called to the Second Bomb Division to defend the policies of the OAS on assessing bombing accuracy. Price recalls

> The meeting with General Johnson and his Group Commanders was very depressing to Col. Scott. It seemed that [some of] the professional Army men were afraid of what our figures might do to their records. [55]

Baley Price got a chance to go to Paris in March. A conference on bombing had been called by Colonel Schwartz, director of armament at USSTAF. For such travel on the Continent it was deemed wise for the civilian analysts to wear uniforms without rank designation. Price tells how he obtained a uniform to go to the Paris conference:

> The atmosphere in our outfit was somewhat like that of a university...informal friendly, trying to get the job done. In March 1945 I was sent to a Bombing Conference in Paris. I was advised to wear a uniform for identification. I did not own one, and we all knew that it was too late to buy woolen uniforms for England because we would be heading for the Pacific soon. Les Arps lent me his uniform. He was a Lt. Col. and about my build, so I took the insignia off of Arps' uniform and wore it to Paris. [56]

Price and Gilman represented the Bombing Accuracy Subsection at the conference. Price recalls,

> The trip over on March 21 involved a pleasant flight from Bovingdon in an AT-7 plane [United States navigation plane, with twin engines and twin tail]. The meeting filled three busy days. And why wouldn't Colonel Schwartz let someone else preside? There were representatives present from all the air forces in Europe, and there was great interest in the problems that were being considered, but Col. Schwartz stifled all discussion. On Saturday we were free to look around Paris. Like everyone else, I bought some perfume; but different from most, I bought three of the four volumes of Bourbaki [a famous collection of French mathematics books]. Dr. Youngs later got a complete set for me. The push across the Rhine began on this day. I still remember the headlines: "C'est l'offensive." On Sunday March 25, we flew from Villacoublay (how our bombing had wrecked that field!) back to England in a C-47 [cargo plane]. [57]

THE END OF THE WAR IN EUROPE

By the end of April, German resistance had collapsed. On 7 April the RAF ceased its area attacks on German cities. [58] On 16 April the Russians began their final offensive on Berlin. On 18 April United States forces completed operations against German defenses in the Ruhr, taking 300,000 prisoners. On the same day the U.S. Third Army entered Czechoslovakia, and the U.S. Seventh Army captured Nürnburg. [59] On 20 April the U.S. Eighth Air Force bombed Berlin for the twenty-first and last time. On 25 April the Eighth Air Force flew its last mission against an industrial target in Germany. [60] Also on 25 April the American and Russian forces met near Torgau on the Elbe river, splitting Germany in two. On 30 April Hitler committed suicide in his bunker in the Berlin chancellory. (Ironically, President Roosevelt had died about two weeks earlier, on 12 April.) All German forces surrendered unconditionally on 7 May and V-E (Victory in Europe) day was declared on 8 May 1945. [61]

The last gasp of the GAF. In January 1945 Adolf Galland, former commander of the German fighter forces in the West, was put in command of a squadron of jet fighters—Me-262s. He collected and attracted a "Squadron of Experts." This included German aces Lutzow from Italy and Barkhorn, with over 300 kills in the East. Some of the men were just out of hospitals.

> Most of them had been in action since the first day of the war and all of them had been wounded. All of them bore the scars of war and displayed the highest medals. The Knight's Cross was, so to speak, the badge of our unit. Now, after a long period of technical and numerical inferiority, they wanted once more to experience the feeling of air superiority. They wanted to be known as the first jet boys of the last fighter pilots of the Luftwaffe.

On the morning of 31 March 1945 Galland's squadron arrived in close formation at Munich and began operating from Munich-Riem. Galland describes some of the difficulties of the GAF at this point in the war:

> We not only battled against technical, tactical and supply difficulties, we also lacked a clear picture of the air situation of the floods coming from the west—a picture absolutely necessary for the success of an operation. Every day the fronts moved in closer from three sides. But worst of all our field was under continuous observation by an overwhelming majority of American fighters. During one raid we were hit three times very heavily. Thousands of workers had to be mobilized to keep open a landing strip between the bomb craters.
>
> Four weeks before the collapse of the armed forces the fighter arm was still in a position to represent a factor that could not be overlooked. Operations from Riem started despite all resistance and difficulties. Naturally we were able to send up only small

units. On landing, the aircraft had to be towed immediately off
the field. They were dispersed over the countryside and had to
be completely camouflaged. Bringing the aircraft onto the field
and taking off became more and more difficult: eventually it was
a matter of luck. [62]

The operations of the jets kept the Gunnery Subsection of the OAS at
Eighth Air Force busy in April. Odle writes:

In April I spent two weeks computing the correct deflections for
support fire against Me-262 jet aircraft, which had been giving our
bombers their chief opposition. The deflections required against
the most prevalent tactics of these jets turned out to give a nice
simple set of rules for the gunners to learn. I wrote up a complete
report and sent copies to all the groups after discussing the situation with Capt. Allen D. Brown, the new 8th Air Force gunnery
officer. [63]

The air battles with the jets in April kept the subsection busy with its air
battle posters. Odle did the posters for 4 April and 7 April.

On 4 April nearly 900 heavy bombers bombed in the Hamburg area, striking airfields which jets might use and U-boat yards inside the city. During
this attack about fifty jet fighters shot down five American bombers. Had
it not been for an overwhelming fighter escort the mission might have been
disastrous for the bombers. [64]

On 7 April over 1,200 Eighth Air Force bombers attacked six airfields,
five marshalling yards, two explosive plants, two oil storage depots, and an
ordnance depot in central and northern Germany. The fifteen supporting
fighter groups met well over 100 conventional fighters and over fifty jets. In
the resulting air battles fifteen bombers were downed. The American fighters
and bombers claimed 100 German fighters destroyed. [65]

On 10 April, 1,224 Eighth Air Force bombers attacked eight airfields, two
marshalling yards, a factory airfield, an ordnance depot, and some German
headquarters buildings—all in north Germany. About sixty jets and a few
conventional fighters were encountered. The jets downed ten bombers, and
flak accounted for six more. The U.S. fighters claimed twenty aerial victories
and 335 parked airplanes destroyed.

On 16 April Eighth Air Force bombers attacked marshalling yards at Plat-
tling, Regensburg, and Landshut. The fifteen supporting fighter groups then
strafed over forty landing grounds in Czechoslovakia and Germany, claim-
ing a record 747 parked German fighters destroyed. Antiaircraft fire downed
thirty-four U.S. fighters.

On 17 April Eighth Air Force bombers again attacked targets in eastern
Germany and Czechoslovakia. The fifteen supporting fighter groups encountered over fifty fighters, mostly jets, and claimed thirteen destroyed. The U.S.

fighters claimed over 250 parked German aircraft destroyed.[66]

Right up to the end German fighters forced the Eighth Air Force to continue the fighter escort of its bombers. Adolf Galland flew his last mission on 26 April. His squadron shot down five B-26 bombers that day—Galland claimed two of them—with no Me-262 losses. However, Galland's plane was damaged, and as he landed his base was attacked by U.S. P-47 dive bombers. Although Galland managed to jump out of his plane and into a foxhole, he was wounded in the knee. The command of Galland's squadron was then taken over by Heinz Bar. The squadron, JV-44, then flew about sixty jets to Salzburg.

Galland writes:

> On May 3 the aircraft of the JV-44 were standing on the aerodrome of Salzburg without any camouflage. American fighters circled overhead. They did not shoot, they did not drop any bombs; they obviously hoped soon to be flying the German jet fighters that had given them so much trouble. Salzburg prepared for the capitulation. The advanced units of Devers' army approached the town. As the rattle of the first tank was heard on the airfield, there was no other possibility left: our jet fighters went up in flames.[67]

Colonel Heinz Bar, while serving in Galland's Me-262 squadron, downed sixteen Allied planes, becoming history's first jet ace.[68]

Bombs and fuzes.   The increased operations of the Allied air forces in the last months of the war caused an old problem to resurface—bomb shortages. Hedefine writes:

> The bomb supply became somewhat acute toward the last phases of the war and considerable effort was put forth to alleviate the situation and the Bombs and Fuzes Subsection came in for a large share of the work involved.[69]

Conferences on bomb shortages were held at USSTAF in Paris with all air forces represented. Along with ordnance and operations officers, Hedefine of OAS represented the Eighth Air Force. As a result of these conferences and studies, a considerable tonnage of bombs was shifted to the Ninth Air Force. Hedefine writes:

> In conjunction with the above efforts a bombardiers' conference was held at headquarters, attended by division bombardiers and Messrs. Hedefine and Kring, and one phase of this meeting was devoted to the problem of bomb shortages. An attempt was made to smooth out some of the operational problems that had been created on the bases by having to resort to bombs other than the most effective ones due to the existing shortage.[70]

Until April 1945 German garrisons denied the Allies use of the port of Bordeaux, France, situated about sixty miles from the Bay of Biscay on the Garonne river about fifteen miles from where it joins Dordogne to form the Gironde estuary. On the bank of the Gironde river is the town of Royan. The Eighth Air Force devoted two and a half days in April to air-ground attacks in support of French troops in the operation VENERABLE.

At the Eighth Air Force headquarters, days before the attacks, Hedefine and Kring of Bombs and Fuzes helped plan bomb loads to soften the Royan defenses. Hedefine says:

> On a large portion of the air attack a new weapon was to be used for the first time by our air force—a 'napalm fire bomb' and Major General O. A. Anderson was desirous of obtaining first-hand information concerning the effectiveness of this fire bomb as well as the high explosive bombs.

Arrangements were made to have a team of observers in the field during the entire operation. Mr. Hedefine along with Captain Chipley of OAS were assigned to the team. Upon arrival at the headquarters of the Western French Air Force, Hedefine and Chipley arranged to be assigned to a French infantry and tank regiment. A French officer familiarized them with the battle plan. [71]

D day was 15 April. The day before, 1,161 heavy bombers of the Eighth Air Force attacked twenty-two defensive installations consisting of antiaircraft and artillery positions and strong points on the Gironde estuary. Other Allied air forces and French naval units attacked similar targets.

On 15 April the first and last operational use of napalm bombs was made by the Eighth Air Force when 850 bombers dropped the bombs against pill boxes, gunpits, tank trenches, and heavy gun emplacements in the Royan pocket. A total of 1,280 heavy bomber sorties were made that day in support of the assault by French ground troops. The next morning 487 B-17s bombed a tank ditch defense line at Point de Grave on the south side of the Gironde estuary, across from Royan, in support of a ground assault there. [72]

Hedefine and Chipley observed the bombing from a vantage point. Advances were made by the ground troops, under artillery barrage, into the enemy-occupied strong points. Hedefine and Chipley observed at close hand the tank and infantry battles. During this time they were subjected to enemy counter barrage and attack.

Hedefine and Chipley spent five days with the ground troops, observing air attacks and ground attacks, interviewing French officers, and interrogating captured German troops. Some strong points could not be examined due to enemy occupation or restrictions imposed because of mines.

Upon return to Eighth Air Force headquarters Hedefine made his report to Generals O. A. Anderson, E. L. Eubanks, and W. E. Todd as well as Colonel James and Colonel Potts. As a result, headquarters recommended against napalm for this type of target. [73]

On 2 May Hedefine wrote another report, "Ground Survey on the Effect of Napalm Fire Bombs and HE Bombs on the Royan Area Tactical Targets in the Operation 'VENERABLE'." [74]

On 6 May Alderman and Kring made their final bomb damage assessment trip. They visited targets at Munich, Leipzig, Nürnburg, Prague, Merseburg, and Innsbruck.

The Eighth Air Force alone had bombed targets at Munich eleven times, at Leipzig seven times, at Nürnberg four times, and at Merseburg thirteen times. The Fifteenth Air Force had bombed targets at Munich thirty-one times, at Prague four times, and at Innsbruck twenty-one times. [75]

There was plenty of bomb damage to inspect. Alderman and Kring had recommended the bombs and fuzes for a great deal of it. It must have been a sobering experience.

The section closes. On 19 April Dr. Eugene G. Fubini, head of the RCM Subsection, left the section. He was replaced by Mr. John G. Stephenson, who served as head until 20 May. [76]

On 25 April the Eighth Air Force flew its last bombing mission. Its remaining missions, to Holland on 1 May, 2 May, 3 May, 5 May, and 6 May, were food drop missions to civilians. [77]

On 26 April, the day after the last bombing mission, Frank Stewart of the Bombing Accuracy Subsection left. Ironically, on the same day, Robert M. Whitmer, a physicist from the Radiation Laboratory at Cambridge, Massachusetts, became head of the Micro-H bombing group. [78]

On 20 April Bombing Accuracy's last big report, "Report on Bombing Accuracy, Eighth Air Force, 1 September 1944 to 31 December 1944," went to the printer.

About 1 May, Colonel Scott and Dr. G. Baley Price of the Bombing Accuracy Subsection presented the results at Second Division headquarters. As guests of the general, they occupied a room overlooking the formal gardens and ate in the general's mess. Baley Price writes:

> I was elected to do the talking on this occasion. The audience that gathered for the meeting was an impressive one: there were four generals present in spite of the fact that General Kepner was away. The audience of fifteen or twenty included the four Wing Commanders and the key personnel from 2nd Division Headquarters. I somewhat feared the outcome of the meeting because I intended to give the figures which indicated poor performance in blind bombing, and to say that our studies showed no evidence that there had been any improvement in the accuracy of H2X bombing under conditions of 10/10 cloud since the Eighth Air Force first began using the equipment.

The outcome was more fortunate than I could have anticipated. The Wing Commanders split into two groups of two each. Both groups accepted without question our figures: they agreed that the blind bombing had been as bad as we said it was. One group insisted, however, that it had been a great mistake to expend so much effort on bombing that had been so inaccurate; the other group, admitting the inaccuracy, insisted nevertheless that the Air Force had followed a wise policy in conducting these operations. The question posed by the two groups was the ultimate one; and Col. Scott and I made no claims to knowledge sufficient to answer it. We merely insisted that the accuracy figures which we had gathered were pertinent and relevant data that must be considered in trying to answer the ultimate question. [79]

The meeting of Colonel Scott and Dr. Price with the wing commanders of the Second Division was the last appearance of the Bombing Accuracy Subsection. Price recalls, "It was completely successful from our point of view, and in addition, the meeting had involved completely satisfying relationships with the Air Force." [80]

When Price returned to the States he was called to a meeting in Orlando, Florida, by Dr. William B. Shockley to discuss bombing accuracy figures. Dr. Shockley, the distinguished physicist, was serving as a consultant of the Office of the Secretary of War. [81] Price recalls that Colonel Geerlings, Shockley, and several others were present at the meeting. [82] Despite the Bombing Accuracy Subsection's extensive work on all types of Eighth Air Force bombing, Colonel Geerlings, director of Radar Bombing, had remained aloof and critical of its reports on H2X blind bombing accuracy.

Finally, Dr. Shockley forced a confrontation between Colonel Geerlings and Dr. G. Baley Price. At Dr. Shockley's request, Price presented the section's figures on H2X bombing accuracy. Baley Price gives the following account:

"Those figures are all wrong" said Col. Geerlings bluntly; "we did much better than that."

"Well, Col. Geerlings, tell us what the figures ought to be; how should Price's figures be changed?" said Dr. Shockley.

"How do you expect me to know what the figures ought to be?" Col. Geerlings was not even trying to be pleasant.

"Then why do you say Price's figures are wrong?" asked Dr. Shockley.

"Well, didn't we break the Minden Canal twice? And furthermore, I saw a K-report that showed we did a lot of damage to Leuna!" shot back Col. Geerlings with an air of triumph.

"Col. Geerlings, the figures I have quoted do not deny damage of the extent you have indicated," I said, "ORS Bombing Accuracy was charged with the responsibility of knowing the accuracy of the Eighth Air Force, and it carried on its studies for approximately two and one half years. It is our expert opinion that the figures I have given are accurate." [83]

Thus ended the confrontation between the two men, the one responsible for radar bombing in the Eighth Air Force, the other responsible for assessing its accuracy.

If the OAS had indeed been unsuccessful in helping the Eighth Air Force improve accuracy with one of the three forms of blind bombing, it was eminently successful in helping it improve in every other kind of bombing—visual with the Norden bombsight, Gee-H, and Micro-H.

The section officially closed on 1 June 1945. In its entry that day for the Eighth Air Force, "Combat Chronology" has the single sentence,

> The Operational Analysis Section ceases to function as a unit after a successful career of statistical research which assisted materially in improving the effectiveness of U.S. strategic bombing. [84]

The air force expresses its appreciation.   That the work of the operations analysts was important to the USAAF is indicated in a memorandum from General H. H. Arnold, commanding general of the army air forces, to the chief of the Operations Analysis Division in Washington. Dated 14 October 1944, it dealt with the subject of services of the operations analysts. General Arnold says:

> 1. It has been called to my attention that several Operations Analysts have already completed their assignments and that others will shortly do so. Most of these men have served in a civilian capacity. Official acknowledgement of their service equivalent to an honorable discharge should be furnished.
>
> 2. Operations Analysts, comprising some of the ablest analytical minds of the country, have served in all Air Forces at the request of the respective commanding generals. They have made a significant contribution to the impact of American air power upon the enemy and the excellence of their work has been commended in official communications. The nature of the work must remain largely secret.
>
> 3. Civilian analysts have been willing to forego the distinction and recognition that go with commissioned status. They have been subject to the same risks as other staff officers when in combat zones. As was to be expected, casualties have been suffered.
>
> 4. It is desired that, when exemplary service of an Operations Analyst terminates, you make appropriate acknowledgment

in writing on behalf of the Army Air Forces. You are authorized to transmit with such acknowledgement a photostat of this memorandum.

A copy of Colonel Arnold's memorandum was placed in Bissell Alderman's records by Colonel W. B. Leach, chief, Operations Analysis Division at AAF headquarters, the Pentagon, along with a letter of commendation from Colonel Leach. [85]

In 1948 General Carl Spaatz expressed his appreciation for operations analysts when he wrote a foreword to Leroy Brothers' *Operations Analysis in World War II, United States Army Air Forces*. General Spaatz wrote:

I welcome this opportunity to express to the Operations Analysts the appreciation of the Army Air Forces for their efforts during World War II. I do this with some personal pride, since the pioneer of the analysis groups was the Operational Research Section established in the Eighth Air Force under my command and at my request.

The Operations Analysis Sections were essentially field units. They devoted their varied scientific and analytical talents to the problems of the particular command which they served—to the mission it had to accomplish, to the conditions it had to face, and to the enemy it had to beat. They stayed on the job, mastering the hard realities of combat operations and acquiring the confidence of the officers by whose side they worked. [86]

We all hope that no similar national crisis will arise in the future. But we must be ready for it if it does. If that time ever comes we shall call on you again as we called on you before. Meanwhile we hope that you, and many like you, will keep in touch with our progress and our problems to the greatest possible extent. For the Air Force considers you as part of itself.

Lieutenant General J. H. Doolittle, commander of the Eighth Air Force, issued a statement of appreciation on 11 May 1945 to Bissell Alderman. It says:

Dear Mr. Alderman:

Now that the air warfare in this theater has been brought to a successful conclusion, I take this opportunity to express my appreciation to you and your associates in the Operational Analysis Section of the Eighth Air Force. Through the careful and painstaking scientific investigation and analysis of operations, the Operational Analysis Section has made a substantial contribution toward the success of the Eighth Air Force. Many of the improvements in air operations have resulted from the work of the Section and the importance of its accomplishments cannot be overemphasized. [87]

Members of each of the subsections of the OAS of the Eighth Air Force received recognition from the air force in the form of awards. In the Bombing Accuracy Subsection Lt. Col. Philip Scott received the Legion of Merit, and Dr. James A. Clarkson and Dr. W. J. Youden received the Medal of Freedom.

In the Bombs and Fuzes Subsection Bissell Alderman and Charles U. Kring received the Medal of Freedom. In the Gunnery Subsection J. Porter Henry, Jr., received the Medal of Freedom, and Dr. Edwin Hewitt was awarded the Air Medal.

In the radar bombing department Major Warren E. Bales was awarded the Legion of Merit and Dr. Norris W. Tuttle the Medal of Freedom.

In the Loss and Battle Damage Subsection Dr. Richard G. Gettell was awarded the Emblem for Exceptional Civilian Service.

Finally, the first chief of the section, Col. John M. Harlan, was awarded the Legion of Merit.

The Air Medal was established by executive order in 1942 and may be awarded to any person serving with the armed forces after 8 September 1939 who distinguishes himself by meritorious achievement in aerial warfare. Edwin Hewitt appears to have been the only civilian operations analyst in the USAAF to have received this award. He flew seven combat missions, two to Berlin and one on D day.

The above list of awards, though probably incomplete, is based primarily on the service roster of the OAS of the Eighth Air Force as given by Leroy Brothers. [88]

We know from Alderman's records that he and Dr. James A. Clarkson were formally awarded the Medal of Freedom at Westover Air Force Base on 26 June 1948.

The value of operations analysts. In April 1942, Brigadier General Ira C. Eaker, commander of the Eighth Bomber Command, had recommended to General Spaatz that an Operational Research Section be established at his headquarters at Wycombe Abbey. General Spaatz had in turn requested of General Arnold that an operational research section be established in the Eighth Air Force. Spaatz's request was granted, and in October 1942 the OAS began as a section of General Eaker's staff. On V-E Day 1945 the section had some twenty-six civilian analysts, twenty-two officers, and forty-five enlisted personnel. [89] General Eaker, chief of staff of the AAF in Washington at the time, was now moving to make operations research a permanent part of the air force structure. He requested comments from each of the air force generals who had an Operations Analysis Section. We give only those who had a close connection with the Eighth Air Force.

Major General W. E. Kepner, former commander of the Eighth Fighter

Command and Second Air Division, was now commander of the Eighth Air Force. He had taken over on 10 May when General Doolittle was reassigned to Washington. Kepner, in a letter to General Eaker, dated 29 May 1945 says:

> I was glad to learn from your letter of May 4th that an Operations Analysis Section may be a permanent addition to the Air Staff. We feel that our OAS contributed heavily to the success of our mission. As a group of scientifically trained civilian specialists, they brought capable and enquiring minds to bear on a host of operational problems. The freedom which they enjoyed from military regimentation enabled them to deal directly with all ranks and echelons in the Air Force with no lost motion. They tackled with avidity any and all problems thrown at them and, in the majority of cases, came up with the right answer.
>
> The Bombing Accuracy Subsection of OAS instilled a healthy competitive spirit into the bomber units.... It resulted in changes in the bomber formations (when enemy fighters were no longer a problem), which made for better concentrations.
>
> The Bomb and Fuze Subsection, composed of structural engineers, did a first-rate job in the selection of the proper weapon for each type of target.
>
> Our losses to flak were reduced by the changes in formations suggested by the Battle Damage Subsection...
>
> The Radar Subsection was of great help in the development of PFF bombing.... As a result, the Operations Section was enabled to use the equipment to constantly better advantage....
>
> The success of our RCM program was due in large degree to the RCM Subsection of OAS.[90]

The next evaluation is by Major General Curtis E. LeMay, commanding general of the Twenty-first Bomber Command in a letter to General Eaker, dated 14 June 1945. LeMay had served under Eaker in the Eighth Bomber Command, first as a group commander and then as commander of the Third Bomb Division. General LeMay writes:

> I feel that the greatest value of the operations analysis program accrues from the fact that the analysts are able to approach military problems from a strictly unbiased point of view.... Furthermore, the program gives the military service access to technical specialists that would otherwise be unavailable. Further, I feel that the program has made a substantial contribution to Army Air Force accomplishments to date and can be further improved in the postwar program. It should be continued.[91]

Finally, a letter of General F. L. Anderson to General Eaker, dated 2 June 1945 states:

> The Operations Analysis Section was invaluable to me when I had the VIII Bomber Command. It increased our efficiency; gave me the necessary information to make command decisions; and was extremely valuable in preparing reports required by higher authority for over-all program requirements. [92]

The Operations Analysis Section had a very high reputation within the Eighth Air Force and beyond. The section, with its civilian specialists, had established for itself an important place in the inner councils of the Eighth Air Force.

Final comments.   By the end of the war in Europe a number of the section's members had left to serve in Operations Analysis Sections in other air forces where they could share their experience:

Dr. Richard Gettell	Twentieth Air Force and Twenty-first Bomber Command
Dr. Edwin Hewitt	Twentieth Air Force
Kenneth Norton	Twentieth Air Force
William J. Pilat	Far Eastern Air Forces
Lt. Col. Philip Scott	Twenty-first Bomber Command
Dr. W. Norris Tuttle	Twentieth Air Force
Dr. W. J. Youden	Army Air Force, India-Burma Theater Twentieth Air Force, and Twenty-first Bomber Command

Twenty-two members of the Eighth Air Force OAS served for over one year. Of these, ten served two years or more. Of the original six members of the section who arrived on 22 October 1942, only Leslie Arps served until the section's end in June 1945. He was its director (chief) at the end.

Eighteen of the analysts to serve with the section were university professors when they joined. Fifteen of the eighteen professors were mathematicians, one of them a department head. Of the other three former professors, one was a physicist, one an economist, and one an architect. Two additional analysts were mathematicians but not university professors. Dr. W. J. Youden was a chemist and statistical analyst.

Nine analysts were lawyers.   There were also more physicists, a newspaperman, business analysts, engineers, a librarian, and a few unclassified individuals. [93]

Most of these men made career and family sacrifices to be in the section. All had volunteered. When Colonel Leach contacted them and explained the need for their particular expertise in the Operations Analysis Section of the

Eighth Air Force, they joined. On the other hand, many others elected not to join. Those who accepted the sacrifices and risks of service overseas in an enterprise they had never heard of before saw an opportunity to make a direct contribution to the war effort. They accepted the call to be with the young men and women of the armed forces who had been their students or friends.

The Operations Analysis Section at the Eighth Air Force had organized itself into subsections, each contributing to the overall objective of improving bombing accuracy and damage to the targets, while reducing damage, loss, and risk to the aircrews and planes.

The most distinct contribution of the Eighth Air Force OAS was its work in measuring the accuracy of visual formation bombing. In an early decisive act, the section used strike photographs rather than reconnaissance photographs in determining bombfalls. Using the strike photographs as the fundamental data for bombing accuracy studies, the Bombing Accuracy Subsection quickly identified two variables in formation bombing accuracy, distance of center of bombfall from aiming point (aiming error) and pattern size. By preaching the doctrine of smaller aiming errors and smaller bomb patterns as the key to greater accuracy, and by keeping a monthly score of the bombing accuracy of each group, wing, and division, the section helped the Eighth Air Force more than triple the number of bombs it put within 1,000 feet of the aiming point in visual bombing.

The results of the section's work in this field were eventually written up in Air Forces Manual No. 67, "How to Improve Formation Bombing," which was published by the Training Aids Division of the Headquarters, Army Air Forces, on 2 April 1945. The manual was written by W. J. Youden.

The manual includes the introductory statement:

> It is intended to present here a simple statement of the inter-relation of pattern size and aiming error and how they affect the percentage of bombs dropped by a formation which actually strike the target. If the commanding officers of bombardment units understand the relationships between pattern size and aiming error, they will find them of material assistance in evaluating the performance of their commands and taking the necessary steps to improve their bombing accuracy. Moreover, an understanding of these relationships is indispensable for the estimation of force requirements and for the preparation of a time schedule for a strategic bombardment program. [94]

The pioneering work of Youden, Scott, and Clarkson of the Bombing Accuracy Subsection of the Eighth Air Force OAS became official bombing doctrine for the entire United States Army Air Force.

REFERENCES

1. Wesley Frank Craven and James Lea Cate of the USAF Historical Division, eds., *Europe: From Argument to V-E Day, January 1944 to May 1945*, vol. 3 of *The Army Air Forces in World War II* (Chicago: University of Chicago Press, 1951), 658.

2. Ibid., 75.

3. Ibid., 733.

4. "The Army Air Forces in World War II, Combat Chronology 1941–1945," 1973, Office of Air Force History, Simpson Historical Research Center, Maxwell Air Force Base, Alabama. See January 1945, Eighth Air Force.

5. *Europe: From Argument to V-E Day*, 722.

6. "Combat Chronology," 1 January 1945.

7. Ibid., 14 January 1945, Eighth Air Force.

8. Eighth Air Force, "Activities Report of Dr. John W. Odle, Operations Analyst," Simpson Historical Research Center, Maxwell Air Force Base, Alabama, 7.

9. *Short Bursts*, October 1944, Headquarters, Eighth Air Force, Simpson Historical Research Center, Maxwell Air Force Base, Alabama.

10. Ibid.

11. Roger Freeman, *The Mighty Eighth, A History of the U.S. 8th Army Air Force*, (London: Macdonald, 1970), 201.

12. "Activities Report of Dr. John W. Odle," 4–5.

13. *Europe: From Argument to V-E Day*, 723.

14. Ibid., 903, item 48.

15. "Report for Colonel W. B. Leach on the History and Development of the Bombs and Fuzes Subsection of the Operational Analysis Section, Headquarters Eighth Air Force," 10 April 1945, Bissell Alderman, 520.303-3, Archives, Simpson Historical Research Center, Maxwell Air Force Base, Alabama, 41.

16. Ibid.

17. Ibid.

18. "Combat Chronology," 10 January 1945, Eighth Air Force.

19. "History of the Battle Damage Subsection, Operational Analysis Section, Eighth Air Force, December 1943–May 1945," 520.303-1 Archives, Simpson Historical Research Center, Maxwell Air Force Base, Alabama, 45–46.

20. "Combat Chronology," February 1945, Eighth Air Force.

21. *Europe: From Argument to V-E Day*, 725–26.

22. Ibid., 726.

23. Ibid.

24. Ibid., 731–32.

25. Thomas Parrish and S. L. A. Marshall, eds., *The Simon and Schuster Encyclopedia of World War II* (New York, 1978), 163.

26. *Europe: From Argument to V-E Day*, 727.

27. "Eighth Air Force, History of Operations Analysis Section, October 1942–June 1945," Leslie H. Arps, 520.303-3, Archives, Simpson Historical Research Center, Maxwell Air Force Base, Alabama, 126.

28. G. Baley Price, *Gremlin Hunting in the Eighth Air Force, European Theater of Operations, 1943–1945*, 96.

29. Ibid., 96–97.

30. *Europe: From Argument to V-E Day*, 732.

31. Ibid.

32. "Combat Chronology," 22 and 23 February 1945.

33. Headquarters, Third Air Division, "A Report on the Micro-H Bombing Missions During February 1945," 9 March 1945, Angus E. Taylor, 527.310-4 (November 1944), Simpson Historical Research Center, Maxwell Air Force Base, Alabama.

34. Ibid.

35. "Report for Colonel W. B. Leach," 45.

36. Ibid.

37. Headquarters Eighth Air Force, Operations Analysis Section, "A Method for Determining Ground Speed by Using Norden Bomb Sight and Ground Speed Tables," 12 February 1945, E. J. McShane and J. W. T. Youngs, Simpson Historical Research Center, Maxwell Air Force Base, Alabama.

38. Travel orders of Bissell Alderman, 13 February 1945.

39. Leroy A. Brothers, *Operations Analysis in World War II*, *United States Army Air Forces* (Philadelphia: Stephenson-Brothers, 1948), 10.

40. "Activities Report of Dr. John W. Odle," 4.

41. *Europe: From Argument to V-E Day*, 739.

42. "Combat Chronology," March 1945.

43. *Europe: From Argument to V-E Day*, 745.

44. Ibid., 740.

45. Ibid., 744.

46. "Eighth Air Force, History," 126.

47. "Combat Chronology," 18 March 1945.

48. *Europe: From Argument to V-E Day*, 744.

49. "Eighth Air Force, History," 126.

50. *Europe: From Argument to V-E Day*, 747.

51. *Operations Analysis in World War II*, 13.

52. "Activities Report of Dr. John W. Odle," 6.

53. *Operations Analysis in World War II*, 12.

54. "History of the Battle Damage Subsection," 51.

55. *Gremlin Hunting*, 97.

56. Letter from G. Baley Price to Charles W. McArthur, 21 May 1982.

57. *Gremlin Hunting*, 98.

58. *Europe: From Argument to V-E Day*, 752.

59. *Encyclopedia of World War II*, 715.

60. "Combat Chronology," 25 April 1945, Eighth Air Force.

61. *Encyclopedia of World War II*, 715.

62. Adolf Galland, *The First and the Last* (Harrisburg, VA: Bantam, 1979), 294.

63. "Activities Report of Dr. John W. Odle," 6.

64. *Europe: From Argument to V-E Day*, 752.

65. "Combat Chronology," 7 April 1945, Eighth Air Force.

66. Ibid., 17 April 1945.

67. *The First and the Last*, 302.

68. "History of the Battle Damage Subsection," 49.

69. "Report for Colonel W. B. Leach," appendix 1 on Hedefine's work.

70. Ibid.

71. Ibid.

72. "Combat Chronology," 14–16 April 1945, Eighth Air Force.

73. "Report for Colonel W. B. Leach."

74. "Eighth Air Force, History," 137.

75. "Combat Chronology." See cities listed in index.

76. *Operations Analysis in World War II*, 10–11.

77. "Combat Chronology," 25 April 1945 and 1–3 and 5–6 May 1945.

78. *Operations Analysis in World War II*, 12.

79. *Gremlin Hunting*, 98–99.

80. Ibid., 99.

81. Jacques Cattell Press, ed., *American Men and Women of Science, Physics, Astronomy, Mathematics, Statistics, and Computer Science 1977* (New York and London: R. R. Bowker, 1977), 889.

82. *Gremlin Hunting*, 99.

83. Ibid., 100.

84. "Combat Chronology," 1 June 1945, Eighth Air Force.

85. From the records of Bissell Alderman.

86. *Operations Analysis in World War II*, foreword.

87. From the records of Bissell Alderman.

88. *Operations Analysis in World War II*, 9–12.

89. "Operations Analysis, Headquarters AAF, December 1942–June 1950," Simpson Historical Research Center, Maxwell Air Force Base, Alabama.

90. Ibid., TAB B, General Officers' Evaluation of Wartime Operations Analysis Sections.

91. "Operations Analysis, Headquarters,"

92. Ibid.

93. *Operations Analysis in World War II*, 9–12.

94. Air Forces Training Manual No. 67, Training Aids Division, Headquarters, Army Air Forces, "How to Improve Formation Bombing," 2 April 1945, Simpson Historical Research Center, Maxwell Air Force Base, Alabama.

Appendix

AIR FORCE ORGANIZATION

The Eighth Air Force was composed of three divisions. The First Division was composed of B-17s. The Second Division was composed of B-24s. At first the Third Division was composed of half B-17s and half B-24s, but it was finally converted to a B-17 division entirely.

Each bombardment division was composed of two or more wings. Each wing was composed of several groups. Each group had its own air base. There were twenty fighter groups, forty-seven bombardment groups, two photographic groups, three troop carrier groups, one reconnaissance group, and two fighter training groups. Each group was composed of three or four squadrons.

In addition, there were four independent squadrons: the Fifth Emergency Rescue Squadron (commonly known as the Air-Sea Rescue Squadron), the Fifteenth Bombardment Squadron (H), the Radio Countermeasures Squadron, and the Night Leaflet Squadron.

On each base the administrative personnel were divided into five or more sections: A-1 (personnel), A-2 (intelligence), A-3 (training), A-4 (materiel) and A-5 (operations).

STATESIDE BOMBING TRAINING

Bombardiers received excellent training in using the Norden bombsight in the States. Advanced bombardier school, where the cadet bombardier became an expert in the use of the bombsight, was a three-month course where the bombardier cadet learned the theory and practice of bombing. The cadet bombing was from relatively small bi-planes from altitudes of less than 15,000 feet and with practice low-power bombs. Then, in the States, when the bombardier became part of a heavy bomber crew, there was more practice bombing—now at high altitude with real bombs, some of it at night.

However, all practice bombing in the States was visual. It was mostly done in daylight, in good weather, and by single planes. Although there was a little practice in formation flying, there was no practice in formation bombing, and there was no practice at bombing through overcast.

THE BOMB RUN (VISUAL BOMBING)

On the bomb run the bombardier of the lead crew became, for about eight minutes, the leader of his thirty-six-plane group. The bombardiers of the Eighth Air Force aimed their bombs using the Norden bombsight. To reduce the danger of enemy antiaircraft, the bombers normally flew at 25,000 feet on the bomb run. The location of the target and the planned bombing route to the target were, of course, studied, mapped, and revealed to the crews at a briefing just before the mission. The beginning of the planned bomb run was marked on the map as the IP—the initial point. It was selected about eighteen or twenty miles from the target.

At or before the IP the bombardier began to feed numerical data into the bombsight. The numerical data consisted of the altitude, which determined the time of bombfall; forward speed, which determined the distance the bombs would travel forward from their initial point of release to their point of impact (the bombs would trail some distance behind the aircraft); wind strength and direction, which caused bomb deflection; and bomb ballistics, which affected dropping time and trajectory.

Although altitude and airspeed were planned before, they had to be checked about five minutes before the IP. The wind conditions were also checked at this time, and drift was determined. In readying the sight for bombing, the bombardier would first set in the figures for drift and dropping angle, taking into account bomb ballistics, trail, altitude, and speed. As soon as the target was identified, the bombardier asked the pilot for control of the plane with the autopilot.

The remarkable Norden bombsight was mounted on a unit called the stabilizer, which housed gyroscopic stabilizing equipment and electronic components for bombsight directional control. The bombardier's desired directional changes were conveyed to the automatic pilot (or if desired to the pilot's directional indicator on the pilot's instrument panel). When the bombsight was connected to the autopilot, the bombardier was in control of the directional flight of the airplane by means of signals (right or left) through the bombsight. Thus, from the IP to the target, the pilot kept the plane at constant altitude and constant speed, and the bombardier controlled the direction of the plane through the bombsight.

The bombardier's job was to pick up the target in the telescope of the bombsight and to align the cross hairs on the target. The vertical cross hair established course and the horizontal cross hair the rate of closure. By means of a control on the left of the sight, the bombardier centered the vertical cross hair on the aiming point (AP), and by means of a control on the right he brought the horizontal hair across the aiming point. The bombardier then checked the gyroscopic stabilization of the bombsight and clutched in the electrical drive motor. The sight then computed the time for the point of release of the bombs. On the right of the sight were two indices, one indicating the bombing angle set in by the bombardier, the other the factor established by alignment of the cross hair. The rate indicator synchronized with the forward speed of the aircraft and moved toward the other indicator. When they met the bombs released automatically. The bombardier and the rest of the crew could tell if the bombs actually fell at the moment he called bombs away because the plane would surge upwards. However, it was the bombardier's job to go to the bomb bay, wearing his portable oxygen bottle, to make sure all the bombs fell out and to take appropriate action if they had not.

In a way the lead bombardier was lucky to be fully occupied on the bomb run. His sighting duties directed his attention to the ground, so he had little or no time to look at the black cloud of flak bursts over the target that he was leading his group into. In the vicinity of the IP the bombers began to experience antiaircraft fire. Although one consideration in selecting the IP was to avoid as much flak as possible, heavy flak could nevertheless be expected on the bomb run. The lead bombardier tried to throw the German gunners off by taking gentle evasive action at the beginning of the bomb run. However, in the last four minutes or so of the bomb run, evasive action was not compatible with accurate bombing. The bombers became "sitting ducks." The eyes of the thirty-six or so bombardiers of the individual planes in the group were glued on the lead plane so that each plane in the group (or squadron) could hit the toggle switch and drop his bombs when the leader did. Virtually all Eighth Air Force bombing was formation bombing, with the bombardier of the lead crew of the formation doing the sighting. Thus, the lead bombardier was aiming a large pattern of bombs at the target. His aiming point was chosen accordingly and would be different from the aiming point that would have been chosen had a single plane been bombing the target.

THE BOMB RUN (RADAR)

Throughout 1944 and until the end of hostilities, most of the Eighth Air Force bombing was radar assisted through the overcast—so-called blind bombing. The groups were led to their targets by Pathfinder (PFF) airplanes. These were specially equipped B-17s or B-24s whose crews were intensively trained in the use of their H2X radar equipment.

In the first PFF missions there were only enough Pathfinder planes to lead the leading combat wings of each of the three bomb divisions. Succeeding wings had to bomb on smoke trails left by the groups ahead. These trails were often dissipated by wind. More smoke bombs were dropped by succeeding group leaders in an attempt to replenish the smoke at the marked spots, but this was not accurate and resulted in widely scattered bombfalls.

By August 1944, when more aircraft were available, an H2X Pathfinder was placed to lead each combat wing. It was not until December 1944 that enough H2X Pathfinder airplanes were available so that each bomb group had its own Pathfinder planes. By June 1944, the capabilities of H2X bombing under combat conditions had been ascertained. It was not accurate enough for pinpoint bombing. However, the H2X radar scope was capable of presenting types of large isolated targets with sufficient clarity to be identified and bombed through the overcast. In particular H2X radar was reasonably successful in the bombing of large isolated built-up areas such as large industrial complexes or factories in small cities. It was the American equivalent of British area bombing.

BOMBING TERMINOLOGY

The *intervalometer* was a timing device triggered by the bombsight, which released the bombs from their racks at predetermined intervals. Thus, the bombs from each plane could be dropped in short or long "strings" as desired. The bombs could also be *salvoed*. That is, the entire bomb load of a plane could be dropped at once. Virtually all Eighth Air Force bombing was formation bombing, which by its nature caused large bomb patterns. Thus, in order to make for smaller bomb patterns and thereby increase the concentration of bombs on the target, it became the practice to *bomb on the leader* (that is, on the Pathfinder plane) and to bomb by salvo. The intervalometer was seldom used. The CEP (or CPE), circular probable error, is the radius of a circle, centered at the aiming point, within which half the bombs of a bombfall fell.

STRIKE PHOTOGRAPHS

In each combat box (squadron, group) several aircraft carried automatic cameras. These cameras began shooting shortly after bombs were released and continued at short intervals until after the bombs hit the ground. These *strike photographs* showed on their face the name of the target, the date of the attack, the unit attacking, the number of the photograph in the series, and the altitude of attack. By assembling these photographs the bomb fall of each attacking unit could be identified and plotted individually with respect to the aiming point. Circles of 500, 1,000, and 2,000 feet were drawn around the aiming point, and the bomb craters were marked within these circles. Also, the picture indicated the track of the airplane. The finished products were called bomb plots, and separate plots of the results of each unit's attacks were made whenever possible.

THE BOMBING PAYOFF

The results that could be expected from strategic bombing had to be learned. As one analyst has said, "Before the war, in the US, the general idea was to make a run on a target, drop a bomb on it, observe its destruction, and then go home singing." For example, although the strategic bombing planners were correct in wanting to paralyze the railroad systems in northern France before the invasion, they soon learned that destroying marshalling yards was not enough. The Germans didn't bother to repair marshalling yards, but laid tracks around or through them. Ruined bridges over rivers like the Seine and the Loire were replaced by pontoon bridges or ferries whenever the Germans needed to cross. Synthetic oil plants were very quickly patched together by German technicians so that they might continue producing the precious fuel they so desperately needed. Craters in airplane runways were filled by emergency repair crews to keep them operational. In short, the analysts discovered that if a target of vital importance was bombed, the Germans repaired it quickly. Thus, targets had to be bombed and rebombed on a regular schedule monitored by Allied air reconnaissance. By the end of the war, tons of bombs per acre had become a relevant measure for the neutralization of many targets.

NATURAL HAZARDS OF HIGH ALTITUDE FLYING
ANOXIA AND FROSTBITE

Each B-17 and B-24 crew member had his own oxygen face mask, which he put on at around 12,000 or 13,000 feet. Extra masks were carried in case breath moisture froze and obstructed a mask. A continuous supply of oxygen was crucial. Each plane had several independent oxygen systems to reduce the possibility of complete oxygen supply failure in combat. In addition, numerous walk-around oxygen bottles in the bombers enabled crew members to move about the plane at high altitudes and perform their duties.

In order to provide escort for the bombers to and from their targets, the P-38s, P-47s, and P-51s had to fly even higher than the bombers, so their pilots, like the bomber crewmen, all wore oxygen masks.

Temperatures between −45 and −30 degrees Fahrenheit were normal over northern Europe at 25,000 feet, the typical altitude for the Eighth Air Force heavy bombers at their German targets. Frostbite was a constant hazard. In 1942 and 1943 the air force tried, with only partial success, to provide crewmen with adequate cold weather clothing. It was not until 1944 that the air force developed a reasonably reliable, electrically heated suit. The two-piece olive drab suit had two parallel circuits in the jacket and three in the trousers. If one circuit failed the others provided partial heating. The suits were cumbersome, especially because they had to be plugged into an electrical outlet in the plane to work. Electrically heated boots and gloves were also supplied.

Glossary

ANVIL (also ANVIL-DRAGOON) Code name for the Allied southern France invasion. During planning stages, DRAGOON was added as a second code name for security reasons.

Bendix chin Nose gun turret on the B-17.

Benito An enemy communication and navigational control system.

Bergias hydrogenation Process used in German synthetic oil plants.

BIGOT, BIGOTED A special top-secret clearance for those working on plans for D day.

black box (IFF) A radar warning device located in each plane to detect whether a plane was friend or foe.

Boozer A small receiver in an aircraft to detect whether the plane was under observation from the ground.

Bourbaki The name of a famous group of French mathematicians.

breakout The breakthrough at St-Lô and Caen, 25 July 1944.

breakthrough The Allied breaking of the German defensive line at St-Lô and Caen, 25 July 1944.

breakthrough missions (Carpet bombing). Bombing of enemy troop positions by large numbers of planes, as at Caen and St-Lô.

buzz bomb (V-1). A pulse-jet-powered flying bomb used by the Germans against Great Britain and the Allied lines on the continent. This was the V-1, also called pilotless aircraft, Doodle Bug, Robot, Junebug, or Jitterbug.

Carpet Airborne radar jammer used by Eighth Air Force bombers.

Carpet I A jamming transmitter for use against German ground radars.

Carpet III An improvement on Carpet I.

carpet bombing (breakthrough missions). Bombing of enemy troop positions by large numbers of planes, as at St-Lô and Caen.

Category A strike Neutralization of target for three months.

Chaff (Window) The simplest of radio countermeasures—strips of metal foil dropped from airplanes to produce clutter on radar scopes.

CLARION Code name for widespread attacks by Allied Air Forces to disrupt German transportation systems.

COBRA Code name for the Allied Normandy breakout on 25 July 1944.

Combined Bomber Offensive The Allied strategic bombardment of German military and industrial targets.

company front attack A German fighter formation for attacking bombers.

CROSSBOW Code name for Allied operations against the German "vengeance" weapons—V-1 flying bombs and V-2 rockets.

Disney rocket bomb An American 4,500-pound bomb developed for use against submarine pens.

Droop Snoot Bomber A P-38 converted to carry a bombsight and bombardier in the nose.

Eagle RAF fighter squadron composed of American pilots.

E-boat Abbreviation (nickname) for enemy motor torpedo boats.

Fisher-Tropsch Process used in German synthetic oil plants.

Focke-Wulf (FW-190) A German fighter bomber.

frags Fragmentation bombs.

FRANTIC Code name for shuttle bombing missions between the United Kingdom and bases in Russia.

Gee A British navigation aid.

Gee-H A refinement of Gee, used for blind bombing.

glide (or glider) bombs Miniature aircraft equipped with radio-controllable control surfaces, designed to be towed or carried to within striking range of their targets.

Great Blow Plan of Germany's General Galland to stop the strategic bombing of the Eighth Air Force by use of his fighters in a major attack.

Ground Mandrel Radar jamming device. See Mandrel.

gun climb Tendency of a gun to rise as a result of recoil when fired.

heavy sites Part of the German V-weapon complex along the French coast.

Jackal An American airborne device for jamming the radio transmissions of enemy armored fighting vehicles on the ground.

Jerries Nickname for Germans.

Kommando Nowotny An Me-262 fighter unit named for its commander, a German ace.

Luftwaffe German Air Force.

Madison Code name of operation planned to allow Patton's Third Army to cross the Moselle River in two places with air force heavy and medium bombers near Metz and Thionville.

Mandrel U.S. development of a British airborne device designed to jam certain early warning German radars.

MARKET-GARDEN An unsuccessful two-phase airborne (MARKET) and armored (GARDEN) operation intended to capture bridges at Arnhem and Nijmegen.

Micro-H A form of American radar.

mission failure A mission where bombing accuracy was negligible by visual bombing standards.

Moonshine Radar jamming device.

Mustang (P-51) An American fighter plane.

Noball (NOBALL) Code name for operations against V-weapons launching sites.

oboe A form of Allied radar.

OMAHA Code name for an American landing area on the Normandy beaches assigned for D day landings. (6 June 1944)

Ops conference (Also OPS) Operations conference.

Overlord (OVERLORD) The code name of the Allied cross-channel invasion, spring 1944.

Oxford Experiment Experiment designed to determine and measure factors affecting the accuracy of H2X bombing.

Panzer German tank.

Panzer Lehr A crack German Panzer tank division.

Pathfinder (PFF) A bomber especially equipped to lead other bombers on radar missions.

Pointblank campaign Code name for the strategic bombing campaign of the German aircraft industry in early 1944.

Purple Heart American military medal given to those wounded or killed.

Purple Heart corner High casualty area.

QUEEN Code name for WWII's heaviest aerial bombardment operation in direct support of ground troops, east of Aachen, 16 November 1944.

radar　A contraction of *ra*dio *d*etection *a*nd *r*anging. It detects distant objects by analyzing very high frequency radio waves.

Rug　Experimental jammer similar to Carpet.

Rug (Carpet)　Experimental radar jammer.

Section 8　Army section for mental patients.

Siegfried Line　Name used by Allied troops for German frontier fortifications, the West Wall.

ski site　Site for launching V-1 flying bombs.

skip-and-run bombers　German bombers that came in low, bombed, and got away.

Spitfire　A British fighter plane.

spoof electronics　Use of RCM B-24s to simulate an assembling bomber force and confuse the enemy.

Sturmgruppe　A German air group of thirty planes (FW-190s) specially trained and equipped to storm US-AAF bomber boxes.

submarine pens　German concrete-covered ports in the water along the French coast.

U-boat　Submarine.

VENERABLE　Code name of the operation by French forces to open the port of Bordeaux, 14 April 1945.

Western Axis　German and Italian alliance.

Window (Chaff)　The simplest of radio countermeasures.

Acronyms

109 (ME-109)   German fighter plane. Also called simply 109.

190 (FW-190)   Focke-Wulf (German) fighter plane.

AA   Antiaircraft.

AAF   Army Air Force.

AAFSAT   Army Air Force School of Advanced Tactics.

ABL-15   An American-British Laboratory.

ACE   Average circular error.

AEAF   Allied Expeditionary Air Force.

AF   Air force.

AFCE   Automatic flight control equipment.

AMG-C   Applied Mathematics–Columbia University.

AP   Armor-piercing.

API   Armor-piercing incendiary.

AST   Army specialized training.

ASW   Anti-submarine warfare.

B-17 (Flying Fortress).   American four-engine bomber. This plane and the B-24 were the two main bombers used by the Americans in WWII.

B-17F   A particular model of the B-17.

B-24 (Liberator)   American four-engine bomber.

B-24D   A particular model of the B-24.

B-26 (Marauder)   Medium bomber used by the Americans in the European theater in WWII.

BBRL-MIT   British Branch of the MIT (Massachusetts Institute of Technology) Radiation Laboratory.

C-47   World War II general-purpose plane used for transporting cargo and troops. It also carried paratroopers, served as an ambulance, and towed gliders.

CBO   Combined Bomber Offensive.

COA   Committee of Operations Analysts.

CP   Command post.

D day (6 June 1944)   The day Allied armies invaded Normandy (Europe).

ETO   European Theater of Operations.

FC   Fighter Command.

FW-190   German Focke-Wulf fighter bomber, also called simply 190.

FW-190A-8   A model of the Focke-Wulf 190.

GAF   German Air Force.

GL   Gun-laying, the aiming of antiaircraft.

G-P bombs   General purpose bombs.

H2S   British airborne blind bombing radar.

H2X   American airborne improved blind bombing radar.

HE 111   German (Heinkel) bombers.

HE bombs   High explosive bombs.

IFF   Identification, Friend or Foe. Identification carried by American bombers and fighters.

IP   Initial point of the bomb run.

J.G. 3, J.G. 4   Fighter units of the

German Air Force.

K-13   Compensating bombsight.

LCTs   Landing-craft tank of the U.S. Navy.

M9   Part of the American radio countermeasures equipment.

M-47, M-50, M-69   American incendiary bombs.

MAAF   Mediterranean Allied Air Force.

Me-109   German fighter. Also called simply 109.

Me-163   German rocket-powered fighter interceptor (Komet).

Me-262   German twin-engine turbojet fighter plane that ran on diesel fuel.

MHS   (British) Ministry of Home Security.

MORG   Mine-Warfare Operational Research Group.

MPI   Mean point of impact of bombs.

NDRC   National Defense Research Council.

OPA   Office of Price Administration.

OPS   Operations.

ORG-ASN   Operational Research Group on Antisubmarine Warfare of the Navy.

ORG-ASW   Operational Research Group on Antisubmarine Warfare.

OSRD   Office of Scientific Research and Development.

OSS   Office of Strategic Services.

P-47 (Thunderbolt)   American fighter plane.

P-51 (Mustang)   American fighter plane.

PFF (Pathfinder)   A bomber especially equipped to lead other bombers on radar missions.

PRU   Photographic Reconnaissance Unit.

RAF   Royal Air Force.

RCM   Radio countermeasure.

SCR-297   A blind bombing device.

SCR-584   A form of radar used in radio countermeasures.

SHAEF   Strategic Headquarters of the Allied Expeditionary Forces. (Eisenhower's headquarters.)

SOP   Standard operating procedure.

SRG-C   Statistics Research Group–Columbia.

TAC   Tactical Allied Command.

TC-50   Army manual.

UHF   Ultra high frequency.

UK   United Kingdom.

USSAFE   United States Strategic Air Force in England.

USSAFUK   United States Strategic Air Force in the United Kingdom.

USSBRH   United States Strategic Bombing Mission Research.

USSBS   United States Strategic Bombing Survey.

USSTAF   United States Strategic Air Forces

V-1   German pulse-jet powered flying bomb directed against Great Britain from the coast of France, then Holland.

V-2   A liquid-fueled rocket bomb launched by the Germans against Great Britain from France, then Holland.

VA   Visual assistance (in bombing).

V-E day (8 May 1945)   The day Germany surrendered (Victory in Europe day).

VH (VHF)   Very high frequency (radio).

VHF   Very high frequency.

V-J day (15 August 1945)   Victory in Japan day—the day fighting officially ended in Japan in WWII.

V-mail   Mail to or from the armed forces in WWII, reduced to microfilm to conserve shipping space, and enlarged and printed for delivery.

WAAF   Women's Auxiliary Air Force.

WAC   Women's Army Corps.

WWI   World War I.

WWII   World War II.

Index